HOLT
ENVIRONMENTAL SCIENCE

Karen Arms

This book was printed with soy-based ink on acid-free recycled content paper containing 10% POSTCONSUMER WASTE.

HOLT, RINEHART AND WINSTON
Harcourt Brace & Company
Austin • New York • Orlando • Atlanta • San Francisco • Boston • Dallas • Toronto • London

STAFF CREDITS

EDITORIAL

Robert W. Todd
Executive Editor

David F. Bowman
Managing Editor

Jennifer Childers
Senior Project Editor

William Burnside
Associate Project Editor

COPYEDITORS

Steve Oelenberger
Copyediting Supervisor

Suzanne Brooks
Denise Haney
Tania Hannan

EDITORIAL STAFF

Christy Bear
Gail Coupland
Bernadine Gonsalez
Jeanne Graham
Monique Mayer
Rose Munsch
Tanu'e White

EDITORIAL PERMISSIONS

Amy Minor

ART, DESIGN, AND PHOTO

BOOK DESIGN

Diane Motz
Art Director

Robin Bouvette
Designer II

Teresa Carrera-Paprota
Design Assistant

IMAGE SERVICES

Deb Schorn
Director

Elaine Tate
Art Buyer Supervisor

Sherry France
Art Buyer

Linda Richey
Art Buyer

PHOTO RESEARCH

Peggy Cooper
Photo Research Manager

Jeannie Taylor
Senior Photo Researcher

Mike Gobbi
Photo Researcher

DESIGN IMPLEMENTATION AND PRODUCTION

Preface, Inc.

COVER DESIGN

Preface, Inc.

NEW MEDIA

Linda K. Miller
Project Manager

PRODUCTION

Mimi Stockdell
Senior Production Manager

Beth Sample
Production Coordinator

Sara Carroll-Downs
Senior Secretary

TRAINING AND TECHNICAL SUPPORT

Armin Gutzmer
Manager

Cathy Kuhles
Technical Assistant

ACKNOWLEDGMENTS

CURRICULUM CONSULTANTS

John F. Disinger, Ph.D.
School of Natural Resources
Ohio State University
Columbus, Ohio

Harold R. Hungerford, Ph.D.
Department of Curriculum
and Instruction
Southern Illinois University
Carbondale, Illinois

John Padalino
National Science Teacher's
Association
Task Force on Environmental
Education
Pocono Environmental Center
Dingmans Ferry, Pennsylvania

FIELD-TEST TEACHERS

Karolyn Adams
San Marcos High School
San Marcos, Texas

Jim Cramer
Brookfield East High School
Brookfield, Wisconsin

Cheryl Frazier
Madison High School
San Antonio, Texas

Donna Kerlin
Altoona Area School District
Altoona, Pennsylvania

Sheila Lightbourne
Choctawhatchee High School
Ft. Walton Beach, Florida

Betty Neitzke
Minnetonka High School
Minnetonka, Minnesota

George Newberry
Sparrows Point High School
Baltimore, Maryland

Tracy Patsch
Nyack High School
Nyack, New York

Marie E. Rediess
Algonac High School
Algonac, Michigan

Barbara Rothstein, Ph.D.
North Miami Beach High School
Miami, Florida

Diane Savage
Nashua High School
Nashua, New Hampshire

Shirley Schoenberger
Santa Rita High School
Tucson, Arizona

Anne Tweed
Eaglecrest High School
Aurora, Colorado

Carol Wagner
Pflugerville High School
Pflugerville, Texas

Douglas Young
Coronado High School
Lubbock, Texas

CONTRIBUTING WRITERS

Letitia Blalock
Marshall Frech
Natalie Goldstein
Ann Hoffman Harris
Maureen Jablinske
Jacquelyn Jarzem, Ph.D.
Mitchell Leslie
J. Ed de Steiguer

CONTRIBUTING EDITORS

Amy Daniewicz
Anna Graybeal

TEACHER REVIEWERS

Pedro Alaniz
South San Antonio High School
San Antonio, Texas

Robert Avakian
Trinity School
Midland, Texas

Lyn Bayer
Horticulture Department
West County Technical School
Chesterfield, Missouri

Kimberly Berg
Salado High School
Salado, Texas

For permission to reprint copyrighted material, grateful acknowledgment is made to the following sources:

*sci*Links is owned and provided by the National Science Teachers Association. All rights reserved.

The Nature Conservancy®: From "Protecting Biodiversity" by Bruce Babbitt from *Nature Conservancy*, vol. 44, no. 1, January/February, 1994, pp. 17-18. Copyright © 1994 by The Nature Conservancy. All rights reserved.

Printed in the United States of America

ISBN 0-03-052019-3

3 4 5 6 7 032 03 02 01 00

ACKNOWLEDGMENTS (CONT'D)

Elke Bergholz
United Nations International
    School
New York, New York

Richard P. Filson
Edison High School
Stockton, California

Aulikki Flagan
Ramona Convent Secondary
    School
Alhambra, California

Claudia Fowler
Science Coordinator/
    Educational Services
Louisiana Public Broadcasting
Baton Rouge, Louisiana

William Glover
Austin High School
Austin, Texas

Marguerite A. Graham
Gulliver Preparatory School
Miami, Florida

Gordon Hahn
Glasgow High School
Glasgow, Montana

James Kraft
Green Bay East High School
Green Bay, Wisconsin

Janis Lariviere
Westlake High School
Alternative Learning Center
Austin, Texas

Clifford Lerner
Keene High School
Keene, New Hampshire

Sheila Lightbourne
Choctawhatchee High School
Ft. Walton Beach, Florida

Michael W. Lubich
Mapletown High School
Greensboro, Pennsylvania

Elizabeth A. Moore
Oak Ridge High School
Orlando, Florida

Richard Myers
Cleveland High School
Portland, Oregon

Barbara R. Pietrucha
Neptune Middle School
Neptune, New Jersey

Jeb Schenck
Hot Springs County School
    District Number 1
Thermopolis, Wyoming

Sandra Seim Tauer
Derby Middle School
Derby, Kansas

John Michael Trimble
Corona Del Sol High School
Tempe, Arizona

Patricia Lee Vaughan
Forks Alternative School
Forks, Washington

Celia Wesenberg
Ponderosa High School
Shingle Springs, California

UNIVERSITY AND GOVERNMENT REVIEWERS

Hugh C. Allen
Miami-Dade Community College
Miami, Florida

David M. Armstrong, Ph.D.
University of Colorado
Boulder, Colorado

Judith Banister, Ph.D.
Center for International
    Research
U.S. Bureau of the Census
Washington, D.C.

Bruce Briegleb
National Center for
    Atmospheric Research
Boulder, Colorado

Larry Canter, Ph.D.
Environmental and
    Groundwater Institute
University of Oklahoma
Norman, Oklahoma

Tim Clark, Ph.D.
School of Forestry and
    Environmental Studies
Yale University
New Haven, Connecticut

Peter Connell, Ph.D.
Lawrence Livermore
    National Laboratories
Livermore, California

Roger Del Moral, Ph.D.
Department of Botany
University of Washington
Seattle, Washington

William Ehmann, Ph.D.
Department of Biology and
    Environmental Science and
    Policy Program
Drake University
Des Moines, Iowa

Peggy Fong, Ph.D.
Department of Biology
University of California
Los Angeles, California

Thomas J. Givnish, Ph.D.
Environmental Studies
University of
    Wisconsin—Madison
Madison, Wisconsin

Robert Goodland, Ph.D.
Department of Environment
The World Bank
Washington, D.C.

Thomas H. Gorey
Bureau of Land Management
Office of Public Affairs
Washington, D.C.

Anna Graybeal, Ph.D.
Department of Zoology
University of Texas at Austin
Austin, Texas

David B. Green, Ph.D.
Natural Science Division
Pepperdine University
Malibu, California

John Haaga, Ph.D.
Committee on Population
National Research Council
National Academy of Sciences
Washington, D.C.

Susanna Hecht, Ph.D.
Department of Urban Planning
University of California
Los Angeles, California

Robert J. Heinsohn, Ph.D.
Department of
    Mechanical Engineering
Penn State University
University Park, Pennsylvania

Scott E. Hygnstrom, Ph.D.
Department of Forestry,
    Fisheries and Wildlife
University of Nebraska
Lincoln, Nebraska

Hugh Iltis, Ph.D.
Department of Botany
University of
    Wisconsin—Madison
Madison, Wisconsin

Harvey M. Jacobs, Ph.D.
Department of Urban
    and Regional Planning and
    Institute for Environmental
    Studies
University of
    Wisconsin—Madison
Madison, Wisconsin

John L. Kermond, Ph.D.
NOAA—Office of
    Global Programs
Silver Spring, Maryland

Mark Kirkpatrick, Ph.D.
Department of Zoology
University of Texas at Austin
Austin, Texas

Karen O. Levy
U.S. EPA—Office of Policy
    Analysis Review
Washington, D.C.

Ikubolajeh Logan, Ph.D.
Department of Geography
University of Georgia
Athens, Georgia

David Lombard, Ph.D.
U.S. Department of Energy
Washington, D.C.

Douglas MacCleery
U.S. Department of Agriculture
Timber Management
Washington, D.C.

Joe R. McBride, Ph.D.
Department of Forestry
University of
    California at Berkeley
Berkeley, California

Patrick McGovern, Ph.D.
Department of Urban and
    Regional Planning
University of Michigan
Ann Arbor, Michigan

Stephen F. Marshall
Department of
    Atmospheric Science
University of Washington
Seattle, Washington

Andrew Mason, Ph.D.
Program on Population
East-West Center
Honolulu, Hawaii

Leonard R. Massie, Ph.D.
Department of Agricultural
    Engineering
University of
    Wisconsin—Madison
Madison, Wisconsin

Gilbert Masters, Ph.D.
Department of Civil and
    Environmental Engineering
Stanford University
Stanford, California

Laurence Meissner
Department of Biology and
    Environmental Science
Concordia University
Austin, Texas

Molly Harriss Olsen
President's Council on
    Sustainable Development
Washington, D.C.

Nestor R. Ortiz, Ph.D.
Nuclear Energy Technology Center
Sandia National Laboratories
Albuquerque, New Mexico

Kavita Pandit, Ph.D.
Department of Geography
University of Georgia
Athens, Georgia

Georgia Parham
U.S. Fish and Wildlife Service
Washington, D.C.

Wayne Pferdehirt
Solid and Hazardous
    Waste Education Center
University of
    Wisconsin—Madison
Madison, Wisconsin

David Pimentel, Ph.D.
Department of Entomology
Cornell University
Ithaca, New York

Kenneth Potter, Ph.D.
Department of Civil and
    Environmental Engineering
University of
    Wisconsin—Madison
Madison, Wisconsin

Bobby E. Price, Ph.D., P.E.
Department of Civil Engineering
Louisiana Tech University
Ruston, Louisiana

G. Allen Rasmussen, Ph.D.
Department of Range Science
Utah State University
Logan, Utah

Jimmy Richardson, Ph.D.
Department of Soil Science
North Dakota State University
Fargo, North Dakota

Armin Rosencranz, Ph.D.
Pacific Environment and
    Resources Center
Sausalito, California

Norman Rostocker, Ph.D.
Department of Physics
University of California, Irvine
Irvine, California

Daniel Sivek, Ph.D.
Wisconsin Center of
    Environmental Education
Learning Resources Center
University of
    Wisconsin—Stevens Point
Stevens Point, Wisconsin

Wayne B. Solly
Chief: Branch of
    Water-Use Information
U.S. Department
    of the Interior
Geological Survey
Atlanta, Georgia

William Thwaites, Ph.D.
Department of Biology
College of Sciences
San Diego State University
San Diego, California

Kurt Usowski
U.S. Department of Housing
    and Urban Development
Office of Policy and
    Development Research
Washington, D.C.

William Vencill, Ph.D.
Crop and Soil Sciences
University of Georgia
Athens, Georgia

Dennis Yockers, Ph.D.
Wisconsin Center of
    Environmental Education
Learning Resources Center
University of
    Wisconsin—Stevens Point
Stevens Point, Wisconsin

Ali Azimi-Zonooz, Ph.D.
Department of Civil and
    Materials Engineering
University of Illinois at Chicago
Chicago, Illinois

CONTENTS

▲ To learn how mussels have been useful in studying river pollutants, turn to page 3.

CHAPTER 3

HOW ECOSYSTEMS WORK 54

▲ To find out why jack pines
depend on forest fires for
survival, see page 68.

CHAPTER 4

KINDS OF ECOSYSTEMS 78

▲ This plant is close to
stardom. Curious?
Turn to page 94.

▲ These macaws are part of the most diverse ecosystem on Earth. Read more on page 80.

▲ The water you drink may have quenched the thirst of a dinosaur. Find out more on page 121.

C H A P T E R 5

WATER **120**

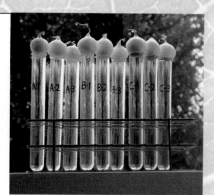

▲ **Don't cry for these onions. They've found a solution!** Learn why on page 28.

▲ **How can working together to plant trees help the Earth's atmosphere?** Find out on page 185.

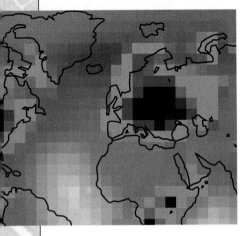

▲ Turn to page 182 **to find out how computers are being used to study global warming.**

▲ **Who owns this beautiful area? You do!** Discover why on page 213.

C H A P T E R **8**

▲ **These students are mining for peanuts. Sound like a challenge?** Turn to page 222 for details.

▲ **What can be done to stop these rampaging beasts?** Turn to page 240 for details.

▼ **Chances are, an endangered species lives near you.** Learn more on page 262.

▲ **Imagine spending class in the grass.** Turn to page 274 to find your excuse!

▲ **Farms that harvest the wind?** See page 291.

▲ **Why doesn't the world contain more owls?** Find out what limits population growth on page 334.

CHAPTER 13

POPULATION GROWTH 330

▲ **What population-related problem does this picture illustrate?** Find out on page 342.

▲ **A house built of old tires and soda cans?** See page 370.

▲ **Play in the dirt and get paid for it!** James Bailey tells you how on page 376.

▲ **Why build a house for bats in your yard?** Find out on page 400.

▲ **Take a shot at revolutionizing the fast-food industry** on page 326.

▲ **This fish almost cost taxpayers 50 million dollars.** Find out how on page 264.

▲ **Wolves set free in your backyard?** You decide on page 76.

Like all other sciences, environmental science is a process of satisfying our curiosity about why things are the way they are and about how things happen the way they do. For example, in studying environmental science, you may discover the answers to the following questions.

How could the demise of this seemingly unimportant insect cause severe damage to the rain forest in which it lives?

How could the watering of this lawn affect the water quality of a nearby stream?

How could a population of iguanas help save a rain forest from destruction?

How could recycling an aluminum can help save fossil fuels and reduce both air and water pollution?

But environmental problems can be solved. For example, Seattle's Lake Washington is cleaner and healthier now than it was 25 years ago, as the Case Study on pages 6–7 describes. The bald eagle, shown in Figure 1-3, is now making a comeback from the brink of extinction. Thanks to emissions controls and catalytic converters, new automobiles discharge only a fraction of the air pollutants given off by older models.

Nevertheless, our environmental problems are huge, and they require careful attention and action. The twenty-first century will be a crucial time in human history, a time when we must find solutions that allow people on all parts of our planet to live in a clean, healthy environment and have the resources they need for a good life.

WHAT ARE OUR MAIN ENVIRONMENTAL PROBLEMS?

Your community may be facing several different environmental problems right now. Perhaps there is a debate about whether to ban septic tanks and hook everyone up to sewer lines. Or perhaps there is discussion about where the town is going to build a new landfill. The local news may mention from time to time that your city is under an ozone advisory and ask citizens to limit driving. Property owners may be arguing with environmentalists about the importance of a rare bird or insect. Even though there seems to be an unlimited number of environmental problems, almost all of them fall into one of three categories: resource depletion, pollution, and extinction.

Resource Depletion Any natural substance that living things use can be considered a **natural resource.** Natural resources include such things as sunlight, air, water, soil, minerals, plants, animals, forests, and fossil fuels. A resource is depleted when a large part of it has been used up.

Figure 1-3 The bald eagle was once on the brink of extinction. Today it is making a comeback, thanks to efforts to preserve its habitat and reduce pollution from the pesticide DDT. (The use of DDT has been banned in the United States since 1972.)

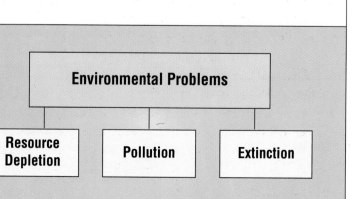

Figure 1-4 Environmental problems tend to fall into the three categories shown at left.

Some resources cannot be replaced. These are called **nonrenewable resources.** No more copper will be formed deep in the Earth after all of the copper ore has been removed from mines like the one shown in Figure 1-5. Similarly, fossil fuels like oil and natural gas are formed over millions of years. If we use up existing amounts in a few hundred years, there will be no more for our descendants to use. The more wasteful we are in our use of nonrenewable resources, the sooner they will be gone.

Other resources are continually being replaced, even as they are being used. These are called **renewable resources.** No matter how much solar energy we use, sunlight will continue to stream toward the Earth as long as the sun shines. Trees that are cut down to be used for furniture or firewood can be replaced by new trees

LAKE WASHINGTON:

AN ENVIRONMENTAL SUCCESS STORY

Oscillatoria rubescens, that had never been seen in the lake before.

This was not good news. The sewage was releasing large amounts of phosphates from human wastes and from detergents into the lake. Phosphate acts as "fertilizer" for bacteria and algae. These organisms can grow so rapidly when they are fertilized this way that they cloud the water and form dense mats of green scum. Bacteria that decompose algae when they die use up so much of the oxygen in the water that fish begin to die from suffocation.

Dr. Edmondson knew that in several lakes in Europe, pollution by sewage had been followed by the appearance of *Oscillatoria* and then severe deterioration of the lakes, which became cloudy, smelly, and unable to support fish. When they detected *Oscillatoria* in the lake, the scientists realized that they were seeing the beginning of this process.

About this same time, Seattle set up the Metropolitan Problems Advisory Committee, chaired by James Ellis. Dr. Edmondson wrote Ellis a letter explaining what was happening to

Seattle is located on a narrow strip of land between two large bodies of water. To the west is Puget Sound, which is part of the Pacific Ocean, and to the east is Lake Washington, a deep, 27-mile-long freshwater lake. During the 1940s and early 1950s, cities on the east side of Lake Washington completed 11 sewer systems that emptied into Lake Washington. Unlike raw sewage, this sewage was "clean" water that did not present a threat to human health. For this reason, both citizens and civic leaders were surprised by research in 1955 showing that the treated sewage was threatening their lake. Scientists working in Dr. W. T. Edmondson's lab at the University of Washington found a bacterium,

the lake and what could be expected in the future if action was not taken. The best solution to the problem seemed to be to quit dumping the sewage into Lake Washington. Instead, the sewage could be collected and carried around the lake to be emptied deep into Puget Sound. Although this may seem like saving one body of water by polluting another one, it was actually a good choice. The sewage had to go somewhere, and diluting it

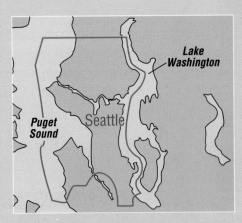

Today, treated sewage from the east side of Seattle is pumped across to Puget Sound, where phosphates and other chemicals become safely diluted in the marine waters.

that grow in their place. Fish, like the tuna pictured on the next page, supply an important source of protein. Fish reproduce and can be harvested each year.

However, even renewable resources can be depleted. For example, if trees are cut down faster than new ones can grow, we will run out of trees. The damage may be even worse than simply having to wait several decades for new trees. If all of the trees on a mountain are cut down, wind and rain will carry away the fertile topsoil. If this happens, new trees may not grow in this place for generations to come. We must be careful about how we use renewable resources, and we must learn to use them at a rate that allows them to renew themselves.

Figure 1-5 After all the copper has been removed from this mine, no more copper will be formed. To avoid running out of nonrenewable resources like copper, we must use them wisely and recycle whenever possible.

in the Pacific Ocean works much better than letting it build up in an enclosed lake.

All of the smaller cities around the lake had to work together to connect their sewage plants to large lines that would carry the treated sewage to Puget Sound. Since there was no legal way for cities to do this at the time, Ellis successfully worked for passage of a bill in the state legislature to set up boards to handle projects of this kind. Planners estimated that each household would have to pay about $2 per month extra on their wastewater bill to pay for the project. (In the end, the amount turned out to be slightly less.) Newspaper articles and letters to the editor addressed the issue. Public forums and discussion groups were held.

The first sewage plant was hooked up in 1963. Today, the lake is clearer than it has been since scientists began their studies of the lake in the 1930s.

The story of Lake Washington is a fine example of how environmental science and public action work together to solve environmental problems. Science was essential to understanding a healthy lake ecosystem, to documenting changes that were beginning to cause problems, and to making predictions about what would happen if changes were made or if nothing was done. Engineers could offer practical solutions to the problem of moving the sewage. Legislators and civic leaders addressed the legal problems. Volunteers, local media, and local activists provided public education and pressed to get the problem solved quickly. The clear blue waters of Lake Washington

Scientists measure the clarity of the lake water with a device called a Secchi disk.

Sailing is just one of the popular activities that Seattle residents can enjoy on Lake Washington.

stand as a monument to citizens' desires to live in a clean, healthy environment and their ability to work together to make it happen.

THINKING CRITICALLY

❶ *Analyzing Processes* Explain how each person and group played a crucial role in the cleanup of Lake Washington.

❷ *Analyzing Relationships* How was the scientists' work similar to the work of the Keene High School students you read about in this section?

Figure 1-6 **These tuna are a renewable resource. If we use renewable resources no faster than nature replaces them, there may be enough of these resources in the future.**

Chicken of the Trees

How can giant lizards help save a rain forest? Turn to pages 30–31 for the answer.

Figure 1-7 **These birds will never be seen on Earth again, because they are now extinct.**

a. passenger pigeon
b. dodo
c. great auk
d. Hawaiian o-o-a-a
e. dusky seaside sparrow
f. Atitlan giant pied-billed grebe

Pollution Pollution is the introduction of harmful levels of chemicals or waste material into the environment. Some pollutants, such as nitrous oxides and heat energy, are byproducts of processes such as fuel combustion. Other pollutants, such as pesticides, are intentionally created for a practical purpose, but can harm the environment when they enter air, water, and soil.

Pollutants may also be dangerous to human health. For example, mercury dumped into rivers may cause nerve damage in people who eat contaminated fish.

Extinction Scientists estimate that thousands of species, such as the birds shown in Figure 1-7, are becoming extinct every year—many without ever having been named or studied. Extinction means that the last individual member of a species has died and the species is gone forever. Although species have become extinct throughout the history of the Earth, they are probably disappearing faster today than at any other time in history.

The rapid disappearance of so many species from the Earth is considered to be one of the most significant environmental challenges we face today. Most species that are becoming extinct are dying because their natural homes are being destroyed.

Figure 1-8 The amount of carbon dioxide in our planet's atmosphere is increasing, which may cause the climate of the Earth to change. The burning rain forests in Brazil (left) and the cars in Atlanta, Georgia (below), both contribute to the problem.

A GLOBAL PERSPECTIVE

Many environmental problems are global problems. The sulfur dioxide released by coal-fired electric generators in the American Midwest comes back to Earth as acid rain falling on Canada. The millions of cars driven by people in America and Europe are increasing the amount of carbon dioxide in the atmosphere, which may cause the climate of the entire Earth to change. The destruction of tropical rain forests in South America and elsewhere is also contributing to the increase in carbon dioxide. Chemicals called chlorofluorocarbons, produced in many countries all over the world, are harming the ozone shield in the atmosphere, which helps to protect all of Earth's inhabitants from the sun's harmful rays.

When thinking about global environmental problems, it may help to visualize the **biosphere,** the thin layer of life around the Earth. The biosphere extends from the surface of the Earth to about

Figure 1-9 Trees and other plants remove carbon dioxide from the air.

9

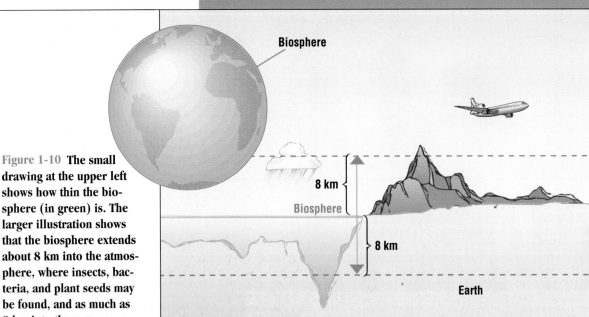

Figure 1-10 **The small drawing at the upper left shows how thin the biosphere (in green) is. The larger illustration shows that the biosphere extends about 8 km into the atmosphere, where insects, bacteria, and plant seeds may be found, and as much as 8 km into the ocean.**

Labels in figure: Biosphere · Biosphere · 8 km · 8 km · Earth

8 km (about 5 mi.) above the surface and to about 8 km into the deepest part of the ocean. Although this may seem like a large area, Figure 1-10 shows just how thin this layer of life is. Within the biosphere, all living things—including humans—exist in a close relationship with each other and with the nonliving things necessary for their survival.

Developed and Developing Countries

Although all humans live in the biosphere, people in different countries have different immediate needs and priorities. Most of the world's nations can be categorized into one of two groups: developed countries and

Figure 1-11 **People in developing countries, such as Guatemala (above), often have different priorities from people in developed countries, such as Japan (right). All people, however, will share the consequences of global environmental problems.**

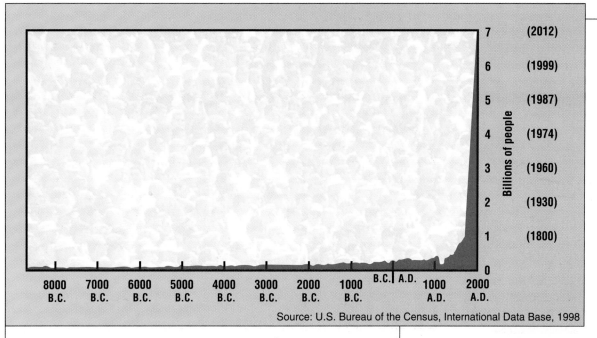

Source: U.S. Bureau of the Census, International Data Base, 1998

developing countries. The highly industrialized countries, whose citizens have high average incomes, are known as **developed countries.** The major developed countries are the United States, Canada, Japan, Australia, New Zealand, and the countries of western Europe.

The **developing countries** are less industrialized, and their citizens have a much lower average income. For example, the average farmer in India makes only $2,700 a year, and the typical city dweller in Kenya earns only $450 a year. However, some developing countries are not as desperately poor as others. The economies of countries such as Malaysia, Mexico, and Thailand are growing rapidly.

POPULATION AND CONSUMPTION

Many environmental problems can be linked to increasing human populations and increasing demand on natural resources. For example, in some regions on Earth the human populations are growing too quickly for the regions to support. This causes a **population crisis.** Furthermore, when people use up, waste, or pollute natural resources faster than those resources can be renewed, replaced, or cleaned up, the result is a **consumption crisis.**

The population crisis is most severe in the developing countries. Even though there are not enough resources for everyone now, the human population continues to grow most rapidly in the poorest countries. (See bottom graph in Figure 1-13.) When there are too many people, there are not enough natural resources for everyone to live a healthy, productive life. As people struggle for survival in severely overpopulated regions, forests are stripped bare, topsoil is exhausted, and animals are driven to extinction. Malnutrition, starvation, and disease are constant threats.

The consumption crisis is most severe in the developed nations. The population has stabilized or is growing slowly in

Figure 1-12 **The human population is increasing exponentially.**

Figure 1-13 **Developing nations account for most of the population growth, and developed nations account for most of the consumption of resources.**

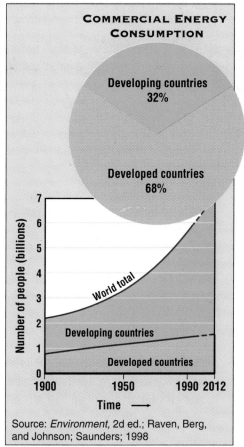

Source: *Environment*, 2d ed.; Raven, Berg, and Johnson; Saunders; 1998

11

Figure 1-14 **These photographs show a few of the ways we can work toward a sustainable future. Setting aside wildlife refuges helps preserve threatened species. Recycling makes our nonrenewable resources last longer. And finding replacements for polluting technology, such as a vehicle that runs on electricity instead of gasoline, should help keep our air cleaner.**

DRIVING
ELECTRIC
FOR CLEANER AIR

SECTION REVIEW

❶ Name the three categories into which most environmental problems fall. Give an example of an environmental problem that illustrates each of these categories.

❷ Explain the difference between the population crisis and the consumption crisis. Which countries are most affected by each of these crises?

❸ List three types of actions that can contribute to a sustainable world.

THINKING CRITICALLY

❹ *Applying Ideas* Give one example of a nonrenewable resource not mentioned in this chapter, and explain why it is a nonrenewable resource.

these countries, but the average citizen uses a disproportionately large share of the Earth's resources. Developed nations use up about 75 percent of the resources used every year, even though they make up only about 20 percent of the world's population.

A SUSTAINABLE WORLD

The goal of environmental problem solving is to achieve a **sustainable world,** a world in which human populations can continue to exist indefinitely with a high standard of living and health. In a sustainable world, habitats would be preserved and garbage would be turned into harmless substances. Nonrenewable resources would be used sparingly and efficiently. And renewable resources would be used no faster than they could be replaced, so there would always be enough for generations that follow.

USING SCIENCE TO SOLVE ENVIRONMENTAL PROBLEMS

AFTER READING THIS SECTION YOU SHOULD BE ABLE TO

❶ distinguish between pure and applied science.

❷ describe scientific methods.

❸ explain the uses of tables, line graphs, bar graphs, and pie charts.

In order to solve environmental problems, we must first understand our environment. The most effective tool that humans have developed for accurately understanding the natural world is science. There are two basic types of science: pure science and applied science.

Pure science seeks to answer questions about how the natural world works. Physics and biology are examples of pure sciences. These sciences try to answer questions like, "How does the sun produce light?" or "Why do insects and birds have different kinds of wings?" **Applied science** uses the information

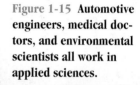

Figure 1-15 **Automotive engineers, medical doctors, and environmental scientists all work in applied sciences.**

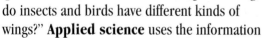

provided by pure science to solve problems. Engineering and medicine are examples of applied sciences. An engineer might use chemistry and physics to design a car that gets better gas mileage. A doctor uses the information provided by biologists, chemists, and other scientists to help a sick person get well.

Environmental science is an applied science. Many different sciences contribute to environmental science and are needed to solve environmental problems. Chemistry is used to understand the nature of pollutants. Botany and zoology provide information needed to protect species from extinction. Meteorology explains the air and atmosphere. An environmental scientist may use information provided by almost all of the pure sciences at one time or another. As you read this textbook, you will be studying the results of the many different sciences that contribute to solving environmental problems.

One of the most important foundations of environmental science is **ecology.** Ecologists study how living things interact with each other and with their nonliving environments. An ecologist might study, for example, the relationship between bees and the plants they pollinate, or how bacteria break down the bodies of dead animals and return the nutrients to the soil.

WHAT IS SCIENCE?

Science is really two things. On the one hand, it is something you *know.* It is all of the scientific information gathered by scientists throughout human history. This vast body of knowledge is passed down from generation to generation.

Science is also something you *do.* Figure 1-16 shows scientists at work "doing science." It is a way of getting the answers to questions about the natural world around us. In order to find these answers, scientists use methods—called *scientific methods*—that have been found to provide accurate, reliable answers to their questions.

Observing All science begins with observation. When we observe the natural world, we use our senses

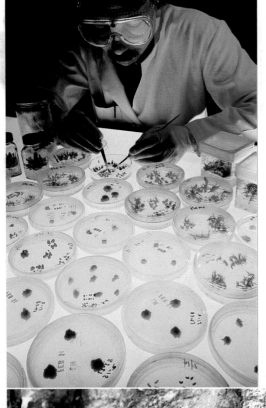

Figure 1-16 **Science is not just something you *know*. These working scientists are *doing* science to find out the answers to questions about how the natural world works.**

to discover what it is like. The sky is blue. Lemons have a sour taste. Rocks lying in the sunshine feel warm. Mockingbirds imitate the songs of other birds. Sulfur springs smell like rotten eggs. Scientists also use equipment that extends or enhances their senses. For example, a biologist might use underwater microphones to hear whale songs. Doctors routinely use X rays to view bones inside living bodies.

Science always begins with and rests on a solid foundation of observation. Good observations include accurate and detailed descriptions. How do ants find their food? What signals do male birds give to warn off intruders? What kinds of trees sprout after a fire? For information like this to be scientifically valuable, it must be carefully recorded so that it can be shared with others. Many scientists have answered important and fundamental scientific questions by simply observing an organism or a natural process very carefully for many years.

Remember the students at Keene High School? During a canoe trip they noticed that an area of riverbank was cleared of vegetation. They wondered if soil washing from this area into the river might be hurting the mussels, which live on the river bottom. These and other observations led to their involvement in the research project.

Hypothesizing and Predicting
Observations give us answers to questions about the natural world, but they almost always give rise to still more questions. When a scientist wants to know the answer to a very specific question, forming a hypothesis that can be tested is usually the best way to find the answer. A **hypothesis** is a testable explanation for an observation.

Consider the dwarf wedge mussel situation on the Ashuelot River. A biologist familiar with various mussel species might study the data collected by the students and recall that declines in mussel populations often occur when mussels do not reproduce successfully. The biologist might state the following hypothesis: *Reproductive failure is what is causing the reduction in the number of dwarf wedge mussels in the Ashuelot River.*

To test this hypothesis, the biologist might make the following prediction: *Over time, the proportion of older mussels will increase and the proportion of eggs, larvae, and young mussels will decrease.* This would indicate that the mussels are not reproducing successfully.

If the biologist finds fewer young mussels over time, the hypothesis has been supported. If, on the other hand, the biologist observes no changes in the age distribution of the mussels and finds instead the normal number of eggs and young, the hypothesis has not been supported.

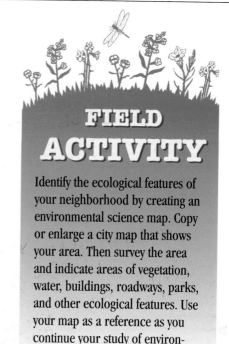

FIELD ACTIVITY

Identify the ecological features of your neighborhood by creating an environmental science map. Copy or enlarge a city map that shows your area. Then survey the area and indicate areas of vegetation, water, buildings, roadways, parks, and other ecological features. Use your map as a reference as you continue your study of environmental science.

Figure 1-17 **These students from Keene High School are conducting scientific research as they count the number of mussels at each site on the Ashuelot River.**

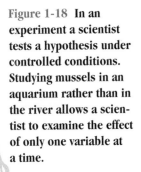

Experimenting Many times, the questions that arise from observations cannot be answered conclusively from general observations. In these cases scientists may do experiments to find answers. In an **experiment** a hypothesis is tested under controlled conditions. There are two essential ingredients to a good experiment: a single variable is tested, and a control is used.

In an experiment two groups or situations are studied. These two groups must be identical in every respect except one. For example, a biologist might wish to know if the level of cadmium (a potentially harmful heavy metal) detected by the Keene High School students in the river water is sufficient to harm mussels. Hypothesizing that the level of cadmium is in fact toxic to mussels, the biologist predicts that a significant number of mussels exposed to this level of cadmium will die. (This experiment could not be done with an endangered species!)

The biologist would then collect a number of common mussels and place equal numbers of them in two aquariums, like the one shown in Figure 1-18. First the biologist would ensure that the conditions in the two aquariums were identical in all respects—identical water temperature, food, plants, hours of light, natural substances present in the water, and so on.

Then just enough cadmium would be added to one aquarium to equal the concentration measured by the students in the river water. The amount of cadmium in the water is the variable. The

Figure 1-18 **In an experiment a scientist tests a hypothesis under controlled conditions. Studying mussels in an aquarium rather than in the river allows a scientist to examine the effect of only one variable at a time.**

group of mussels to which cadmium has been added is the experimental group, and the group of mussels to which cadmium has not been added is the control group. If the "no-cadmium" mussels thrive while most of the "cadmium" mussels die, then the biologist's hypothesis is supported by observations.

The key to the success of this experiment and all other experiments is changing only one variable and having a control group. What if the aquarium in which most of the mussels died had cadmium in the water *and* also happened to be 5°F warmer? The biologist would have no way of knowing if the cadmium or the higher temperature caused the mussels to die. What if the biologist had not used a healthy control group for comparison? The mussels in the cadmium tank could be dying from some other factor, such as being fed the wrong food.

Organizing and Interpreting Data

One of the most important parts of doing science is sharing what has been learned with others. This begins with keeping very careful and accurate records. Then the scientist must evaluate the data and decide if the hypothesis is supported. For example, what if the biologist observed that three mussels died in the control tank but five died in the experimental tank. Would that be a meaningful difference? What if 2 mussels died in the control tank and 10 died in the experimental tank? One factor that would affect the answer to this question is, "How many mussels were in each tank to start with?" In other words, what percentage of mussels died?

Scientists often use mathematics to determine whether their observations or experimental results are meaningful or are just the result of chance or coincidence. The mathematical discipline of statistics gives the scientist tools in the form of mathematical formulas to determine if the difference between the results in the control group and the experimental group is significant.

Using Graphics and Sharing Information

Organizing data into graphic illustrations helps scientists analyze the data and explain it clearly to others. Tables are a good way to summarize data. Figure 1-20 summarizes fecal coliform bacteria counts by the Keene High School students over a five-year period. The number of fecal coliform bacteria may indicate the amount of sewage present in water.

Figure 1-19 **Scientists often use mathematics to determine whether the results they get are meaningful or just the result of chance.**

Figure 1-20 **Tables organize and summarize information.**

Five-Year Fecal Coliform Averages					
	1992	**1993**	**1994**	**1995**	**1996**
Site 2a	18	20	7	17	46
Site 12	26	43	35	53	64
Site 13	16	42	9	72	87

Site 1	11
Site 2a	28
Site 2b	8
Site 3	2
Site 4	9
Site 5	6
Site 6	6
Site 7	3
Site 8	1
Site 9	2
Site 10	1
Site 11	0
Site 12	0
Site 13	0

Figure 1-21 This shows how the same data might look in a table (left) and in a line graph (right). Both show how the number of mussels decreased as the students moved downstream.

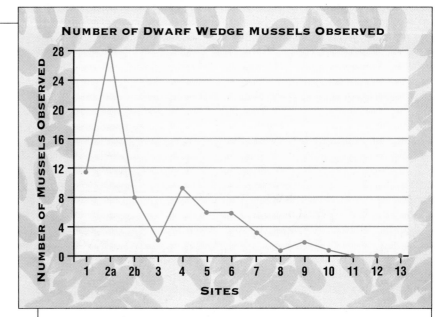

Graphs are often used by scientists to convey comparisons or trends that they have discovered. For this reason, graphs are especially useful when the scientist is discussing the conclusions that can be drawn from the research. The right side of Figure 1-21 is a line graph that shows the change in the number of mussels observed by the students as they moved downstream. Bar graphs using single bars are often used in the same way as line graphs, but bar graphs are especially effective at showing several comparisons at once. For example, Figure 1-22 allows you to see how the phosphate levels in the Ashuelot River varied at three different sites and on three different dates when samples were collected.

Pie charts show percentages, with the entire circle representing 100 percent. A single pie chart can show relative percentages of different factors, but two pie charts can convey even more

Figure 1-22 This bar graph allows you to compare the amount of phosphates measured by the Keene students at three different sites and on four different dates.

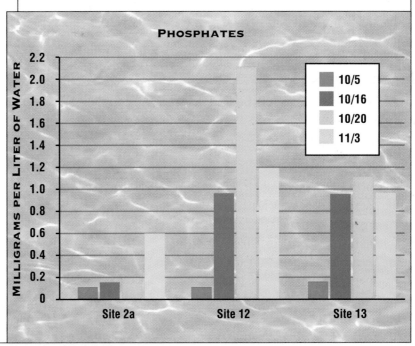

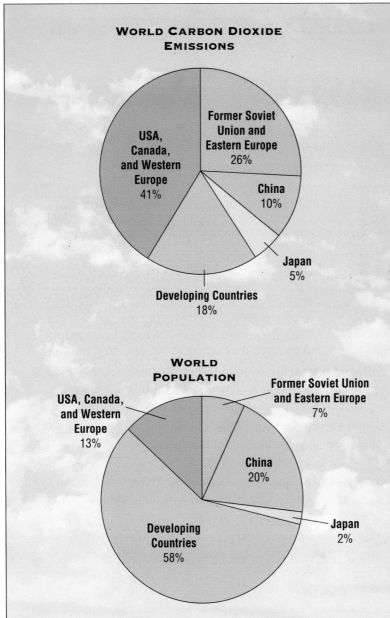

WORLD CARBON DIOXIDE EMISSIONS

- USA, Canada, and Western Europe 41%
- Former Soviet Union and Eastern Europe 26%
- China 10%
- Japan 5%
- Developing Countries 18%

WORLD POPULATION

- USA, Canada, and Western Europe 13%
- Former Soviet Union and Eastern Europe 7%
- China 20%
- Japan 2%
- Developing Countries 58%

Source: *Information Please: Environmental Almanac,* Houghton Mifflin, 1993

Figure 1-23 Pie charts show percentages, with the entire circle representing 100 percent.

information. For example, the pie charts in Figure 1-23 show the relative human populations in different parts of the world compared with the relative amounts of CO_2 produced in these regions. By studying the charts, you can see that the developed nations produce much more CO_2 per person than the developing nations.

Communicating Results

After the scientist has analyzed his or her data and has determined that what has been learned from the work is important enough to be of interest to other scientists, the results must be published. A scientific article must include the question to be answered, why the question is important or relevant, background information, a precise description of how the work was done, the data that were collected, and the scientist's evaluation of what the data mean.

SECTION REVIEW

❶ What is the difference between pure and applied science? What type of science is environmental science?

❷ Explain the relationship between ecology and environmental science. How are they different?

❸ Explain how scientists investigate questions about the natural world.

❹ What are the two essential components of an experiment? Explain why each is important.

THINKING CRITICALLY

❺ *Analyzing Processes* Science provides us with information to evaluate nonscientific issues. Generally, however, science only answers questions that can be tested. How can we use science to help think about this question: Should animals be kept in zoos?

MAKING ENVIRONMENTAL DECISIONS

AFTER READING THIS SECTION YOU SHOULD BE ABLE TO

❶ use a decision-making model to make a decision about an environmental issue.

❷ name values that are important in making decisions about the environment.

Scientific research is an essential first step in solving environmental problems. A sound scientific basis is necessary before any action should be taken. However, many other factors must also be considered. How will the proposed solution affect people's lives? How much will it cost? Is it ethically sound? Questions like these require an examination of values—what we consider important. What values should be considered when making decisions that affect the environment? Figure 1-24 lists some values that often affect environmental decisions. You can probably think of others as well.

Figure 1-24 Can you think of values not shown in this table?

Values That Affect Environmental Decision Making	
Value	**Definition**
Aesthetic	What is beautiful or pleasing
Economic	Gain or loss of money or jobs
Environmental	Protection of natural resources
Educational	Accumulation and use of knowledge
Ethical/Moral	What is right or wrong
Health	Maintenance of human health and prevention of sickness or disability
Recreational	Providing for human leisure activities
Scientific	Increasing understanding of the natural world
Social/Cultural	Maintaining human communities and respecting their values and traditions

AN ENVIRONMENTAL DECISION-MAKING MODEL

Making decisions about environmental issues is usually difficult and may even seem overwhelming. It helps to have a systematic way of analyzing the issues and figuring out what is important to you. Figure 1-26 shows a decision-making model that could prove helpful to you.

The first step in making an environmental decision is to gather all the available information. In addition to watching television reports and reading newspapers, magazines, and books about environmental issues, it helps to listen carefully to well-informed people on all sides of an issue. Then consider which values apply to the issue. Explore the consequences of each option. Finally, evaluate everything and make a decision.

Figure 1-25 Solutions to environmental problems begin with science, but other factors must also be considered. The value we give to the beauty of this view, for example, influences whether we want to keep our air free of smog that might obscure it.

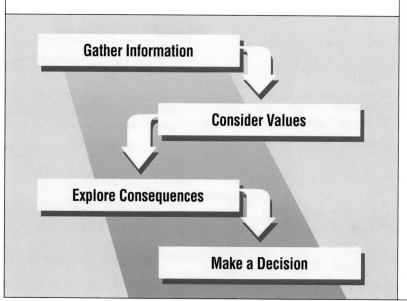

Figure 1-26 A decision-making model

A Hypothetical Situation

Consider the following hypothetical example. In the town of Pleasanton, in Valley County, biologists from the local college have been studying the spotted warbler (a bird). The warblers have already disappeared from several areas around the state, and their numbers are declining in Valley County. The biologists warn government officials in the county that if something is not done, the bird may be listed as an endangered species by the U.S. Fish and Wildlife Service.

Pleasanton is growing rapidly, and much of the new development, like that shown in Figure 1-27, is occurring outside the city limits. Valley County already has strict environmental controls on building, but these controls seem to be inadequate to protect the birds. Several environmental groups band together and propose that the county buy several hundred acres of land known to be critical habitat for the spotted warbler and place strict controls on development on several hundred acres immediately around the preserve. To encourage growth in less sensitive areas, they propose that environmental restrictions on building be made less stringent in those areas than they are currently.

The environmental groups obtain enough signatures to put the issue to a vote. Not surprisingly, many property owners in the area of the proposed preserve are opposed to the plan. They say that they will suffer serious financial losses if they have to sell their land to the county rather than develop it. On the other hand, local leaders warn that if the warbler population falls so low that it must

Figure 1-27 **Rapid growth often spills out of city limits and can destroy the habitats of rare species.**

Figure 1-28 **The map shows the imaginary plan to set aside protected habitat for the spotted warbler. The photograph shows a protected habitat in Austin, Texas.**

Pleasanton

Proposed preserve for spotted warbler

Rte. 280

Rte. 17

be listed as an endangered species, the recovery plan required by law may impose even stricter controls on development, threatening the economic health of the county. Many citizens of Pleasanton look forward to hiking and camping in the proposed nature preserve. Other residents are bothered by the idea of any government regulation of the use of private property.

HOW TO USE THE DECISION-MAKING MODEL

The hypothetical situation in Pleasanton can be used to illustrate how to use the decision-making model. Michael Price is a voter in Valley County. This is how he decided which way to vote on the referendum to make a nature preserve for the spotted warbler.

Figure 1-29 This is the table Michael made to help him decide how to vote on the referendum.

Should Valley County Set Aside a Nature Preserve?			
	Environmental	**Economic**	**Recreational**
Positive short-term consequences	Habitat destruction in the nature preserve area is slowed or stopped.	Landowners whose property was bought by the county receive a payment for their land. Property outside the preserve area can be developed with fewer restrictions.	Parts of the preserve are made available immediately for hiking and picnicking.
Negative short-term consequences	Environmental controls are made less stringent in parts of the county outside the preserve area.	Property owners inside the preserve area do not make as much money as if they had developed the land. Taxpayers must pay increased taxes to buy land for the preserve.	None
Positive long-term consequences	The population of spotted warblers increases, and the bird does not become endangered. Other species of plants, animals, fungi, and bacteria are also protected, even though it has not been possible to study them all. An entire ecosystem is preserved, rather than just a single species.	Property near the preserve increases in value because it is near the preserve. Businesses are attracted to Valley County because of its natural beauty and recreational opportunities, resulting in job growth. The spotted warbler is not listed as an endangered species, avoiding stricter federal controls on land use.	Large areas of the preserve are available for hiking and picnicking. Landowners near the preserve may develop campgrounds with swimming, fishing, and bike trails available on land adjacent to the preserve.
Negative long-term consequences	Other habitat outside the preserve may be damaged by overdevelopment.	Taxpayers must continue to pay for the maintenance and upkeep of the preserve.	None

23

FIELD ACTIVITY

When you go outside, look for a situation where human development is expanding into a natural area. Will any natural resources be affected? Do you see any evidence of pollution? How would you investigate any environmental effects? How would you make a decision about the value of the development?

SECTION REVIEW

❶ List three types of values, besides environmental values, that might be considered when making an environmental decision. Explain each one.

❷ Give two examples of situations in which environmental values could come into conflict with other values.

THINKING CRITICALLY

❸ *Making Decisions* Pick one of the situations you listed in question 2, and make a decision-making table showing the positive and negative consequences of taking a certain action. After reviewing the consequences, what decision would you make and why?

Gather Information Michael studied the warbler issue carefully—watching local news reports, reading the newspaper, and attending forums where the issue was discussed. Several of the arguments on both sides of the issue made sense to him.

Consider Values To help make up his mind about how he will vote on the referendum, he made the table shown in Figure 1-29 on page 23. There are many different values that he could have considered when making his table. Environmental values are key to the debate, of course, and economic values play an important role in these types of decisions. Since he loves the outdoors and likes the idea of having the nature preserve available for hiking and camping, he added recreational value to his table.

Explore Consequences As he studied his table, Michael decided that in the short term, positives and negatives seemed almost equally balanced. A few people would suffer economically, but others would gain financially from the plan. Taxpayers would have to pay for the plan, but all the citizens of the county would have access to land that was previously off-limits as private property. Finally, some parts of the county would have more environmental protection and some would have less.

It was looking at the long-term consequences, however, that enabled Michael to make up his mind about how he would vote. Michael decided that the long-term benefits of the plan outweighed the long-term negative consequences. The idea of a bird becoming extinct saddened him. And he thought it would be smarter and less costly to protect it now rather than later, when protection might be much more difficult. He also liked the idea of working toward a future for his community where natural beauty and recreational opportunities would be preserved. By ensuring that Valley County remained a pleasant place to live and work, he also thought that the plan would bring long-term economic gains for all of the county's citizens.

Make a Decision Michael chose to vote for the plan to set aside a nature preserve. Other people, looking at the same table listing pros and cons of the plan, might have voted differently. If you were a voter in Valley County, how would you have voted?

Throughout this book, you will be asked to use this decision-making model to make decisions about environmental issues. As you construct your tables to evaluate the issues, remember to include the values that you think apply to the issue and to consider both the short-term and long-term consequences of each option.

HIGHLIGHTS

SUMMARY

- Concerns about the environment have increased in the last few decades as problems of resource depletion, pollution, and extinction have become more common.

- Natural resources can be classified as renewable or nonrenewable. Care must be taken so that renewable resources are not depleted faster than they can be replaced and nonrenewable resources are conserved or recycled.

- Environmental problems have global scope. The activities of one area may affect other locations or the Earth as a whole.

- Many environmental problems can be linked to the population crisis and the consumption crisis.

- Environmental science is an applied science that incorporates many of the pure sciences, including ecology, to help understand and solve environmental problems.

- Science involves observing, hypothesizing, and experimenting. Results are organized, presented, and communicated to the scientific community at large.

- Making environmental decisions involves gathering information, considering consequences and weighing values.

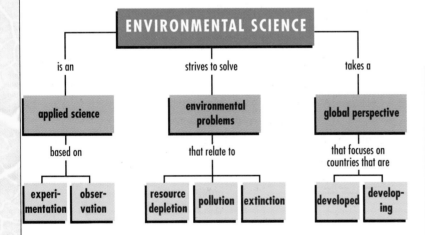

ENVIRONMENTAL SCIENCE

is an → **applied science**
based on → **experimentation** | **observation**

strives to solve → **environmental problems**
that relate to → **resource depletion** | **pollution** | **extinction**

takes a → **global perspective**
that focuses on countries that are → **developed** | **developing**

Vocabulary Terms

applied science (p. 13)
biosphere (p. 9)
consumption crisis (p. 11)
developed countries (p. 11)
developing countries (p. 11)
ecology (p. 14)
environment (p. 4)
environmental science (p. 4)
experiment (p. 16)
hypothesis (p. 15)
natural resource (p. 5)
nonrenewable resource (p. 6)
population crisis (p. 11)
pure science (p. 13)
renewable resource (p. 6)
sustainable world (p. 12)

Ecolog

Now that you've studied this chapter, revise your answers to the questions you answered at the beginning of the chapter, based on what you have learned.

❶ What do you consider to be our major environmental problems?

❷ How can science help solve environmental problems?

REVIEW

UNDERSTANDING VOCABULARY

1. For each pair of terms, explain the difference in their meanings.
   a. natural resource
      nonrenewable resource
   b. population crisis
      consumption crisis
   c. hypothesis
      observation
   d. ecology
      environmental science

RELATING CONCEPTS

2. Copy the unfinished concept map below onto a sheet of paper. Then complete the concept map by writing the correct word or phrase in each box containing a question mark.

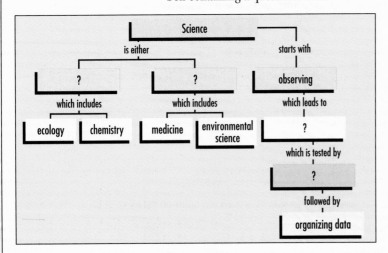

UNDERSTANDING CONCEPTS

Multiple Choice

3. When we talk about the environment, we are usually referring to
   a. people, plants, and animals.
   b. land, air, and water.
   c. streets, bridges, and buildings.
   d. all of the above

4. The environmental problems created late in the twentieth century are
   a. impossible to solve.
   b. partly a result of increased human population.
   c. not as bad as those created early in the twentieth century.
   d. both a and b above

5. All of the following would be considered resource depletion EXCEPT
   a. Texas petroleum running out.
   b. a rain forest in Brazil being burned.
   c. plants not growing in overused fields.
   d. solar energy not reaching the Earth's surface because of haze.

6. Though extinction is a natural process, it has become a problem because
   a. environmentalists have brought it to our attention.
   b. unknown organisms are now becoming extinct.
   c. the rate of extinction has increased drastically.
   d. the types of organisms becoming extinct are popular.

7. The consumption crisis is more severe in
   a. developing countries.
   b. developed countries.
   c. rural areas.
   d. complex ecosystems.

8. If the results of a scientist's experiment do not support the hypothesis, the scientist should
   a. publish the results of the experiment anyway.
   b. consider the results abnormal and continue working.
   c. find a way to rationalize the data.
   d. try another method.

ECOSYSTEMS: EVERYTHING IS CONNECTED

AFTER READING THIS SECTION YOU SHOULD BE ABLE TO

❶ distinguish between the biotic and abiotic factors in an ecosystem.

❷ explain the terms *population* and *community*.

❸ distinguish between habitat and niche.

The environment is so complex and interconnected that scientists don't yet completely understand how it works. This becomes clear to us when human actions have unexpected effects on the environment, as they did on the Southeast Asian island of Borneo. The events on Borneo are shown in Figure 2-1. In 1955 the World Health Organization used the pesticide DDT to kill the mosquitoes that carry the disease malaria. The DDT killed the mosquitoes and relieved the malaria

Figure 2-1 The use of DDT to control malaria in Borneo started a chain reaction that led to roofs collapsing and the decimation of the island's house-cat population.

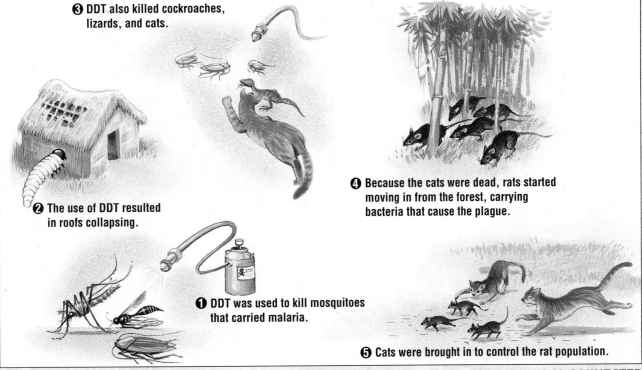

❸ DDT also killed cockroaches, lizards, and cats.

❷ The use of DDT resulted in roofs collapsing.

❶ DDT was used to kill mosquitoes that carried malaria.

❹ Because the cats were dead, rats started moving in from the forest, carrying bacteria that cause the plague.

❺ Cats were brought in to control the rat population.

problem on Borneo, but it also caused an undesirable chain reaction on the island.

First, the thatch roofs on the houses of Borneo started collapsing. What could this have to do with DDT? The DDT had killed the wasps that ate thatch-eating caterpillars. Without the wasps around, the caterpillars multiplied and devoured the thatch roofs.

Meanwhile, the DDT also landed on Borneo's cockroaches. The cockroaches were eaten by geckos (a kind of lizard). The geckos suffered nerve damage from the pesticide, causing their reflexes to become slower. Because the nerve-damaged geckos moved so slowly, most of them were caught and eaten by house cats. After the cats ate the geckos, they also suffered from the DDT and died in great numbers. Without the cats around, rats started moving in from Borneo's forests. On the rats came fleas, which carried the bacteria that cause the plague. Finally, officials resorted to bringing healthy cats into Borneo to control the rat population!

The unforeseen chain of events on Borneo occurred because the living things on the island were connected to each other in an ecological network called an ecosystem.

WHAT IS AN ECOSYSTEM?

An **ecosystem** includes all the different organisms living in a certain area, along with their physical environment. Figure 2-2 shows some of the inhabitants of a soil ecosystem. Other examples of

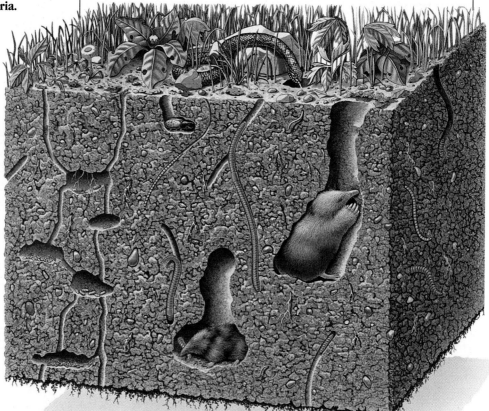

Figure 2-2 **This soil ecosystem includes a variety of organisms— earthworms, snakes, moles, insects, plants, fungi, and bacteria.**

ecosystems are shown in Figure 2-3. For convenience, ecologists often regard an ecosystem as an isolated unit, but ecosystems usually do not have clear boundaries. Things move from one ecosystem to another. Soil and leaves from a forest might wash into a lake, for instance, and birds might migrate from their winter homes in one ecosystem to their summer homes in another ecosystem.

An ecosystem is composed of both biotic and abiotic factors. **Biotic factors** are the living parts of an ecosystem—the animals, plants, and microorganisms. These biotic factors interact with each other in complex ways, and they also interact with the nonliving parts of the ecosystem—the **abiotic factors.** Some abiotic factors

TOPIC: ecosystem factors
GO TO: www.scilinks.org
KEYWORD: HE035

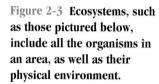

Figure 2-3 Ecosystems, such as those pictured below, include all the organisms in an area, as well as their physical environment.

a. Wetland in Texas
b. Desert in California
c. Mountains in Alaska
d. Polar region in Canada
e. Coral reef in Fiji

that influence living things are temperature, sunlight, humidity, water supply, soil type, and mineral nutrients such as nitrogen, phosphorus, and sulfur.

To appreciate how all the things in an ecosystem are connected, think about how an automobile works. The engine alone is made up of hundreds of individual parts, all working together to make the automobile run. If even one part breaks, the car might not run. Similarly, if one part of an ecosystem is destroyed—as it was in Borneo—the entire ecosystem can be affected. When thinking about ecosystems, remember that everything is connected.

If you look at Figure 2-4, you will see how an ecosystem fits into the organization of living things. The illustration shows the

Figure 2-4 **An individual organism is part of a population, a community, an ecosystem, and the biosphere.**

Biosphere

Ecosystem

Community

Population

Organism

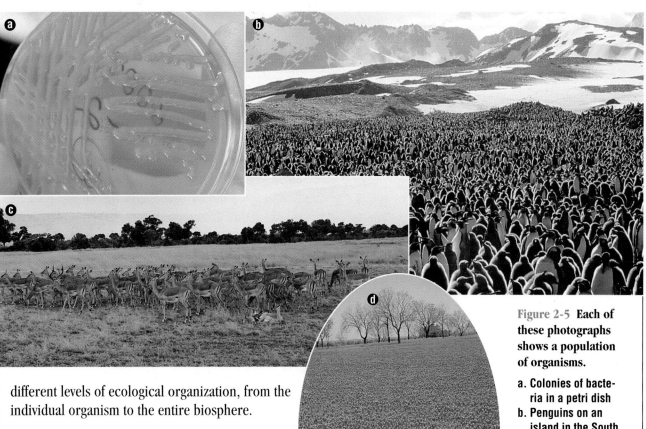

Figure 2-5 **Each of these photographs shows a population of organisms.**

a. Colonies of bacteria in a petri dish
b. Penguins on an island in the South Atlantic Ocean
c. Impala on a plain in Kenya
d. Bluebonnets in a Texas field

different levels of ecological organization, from the individual organism to the entire biosphere.

Organisms and Species An **organism** is one individual living thing. You are an organism. An ant crawling across the floor is an organism, an ivy plant on the window sill is an organism, a gorilla in the rain forest is an organism, and a bacterium living in your intestines is an organism.

A **species** is a group of organisms that are able to produce fertile offspring, and that share common genes and therefore resemble each other. All humans, for instance, are members of the species *Homo sapiens*. All domestic dogs belong to the species *Canis familiaris,* and all gorillas belong to the species *Gorilla gorilla.*

Populations A **population** is a group of individuals of the same species living in a particular place. Some examples of populations include the bullfrog population of a pond, the lion population of a savanna, the bluebonnet population of a field, and even the bacterium population of a petri dish. Examples of populations are shown in Figure 2-5. The factors that influence the growth of populations are discussed in Chapter 13.

Communities Just as an individual organism doesn't exist in isolation, neither does a population. Every population is part of a **community,** a group of interacting populations of different species. All of the living inhabitants of an ecosystem make up a community. A pond community, for example, includes the populations of all the different plants, fish, insects, amphibians, and microorganisms that live in and around the pond.

Butterfly Ecologist

Some monarch butterflies travel 3,200 km (2,000 mi.) to reach their wintering grounds in Mexico, only to find their habitat destroyed. Turn to pages 52–53 to see how one young man is helping to save the monarchs' habitat.

Figure 2-6 A lion's niche includes all of its relationships with its environment.

a. Tick on a lion's face
b. Lion fighting with hyenas
c. Lions feeding on kill
d. Lions drinking at water hole

SECTION REVIEW

❶ What are the biotic components of the soil ecosystem in Figure 2-2? What are the abiotic components?

❷ Give an example of a population that was not mentioned in this section.

❸ Choose an animal that was not mentioned in this section, and discuss the difference between that animal's habitat and its niche.

THINKING CRITICALLY

❹ *Analyzing Relationships* What part of an ecosystem is not part of a community? After you figure that out, write your own definition of the term *community,* using the terms *biotic factors* and *abiotic factors.* Your definition should be different from the one given in this textbook.

NICHE AND HABITAT

Consider a lion living on the savanna in eastern Africa. How does the lion fit into its ecosystem? Lions survive by killing and eating other animals, such as gazelles, zebras, and wildebeests. After the lions have killed an animal and eaten their fill, scavengers such as jackals, vultures, and hyenas devour what is left of the carcass. Bacteria, fungi, and insects in the soil also feed on the carcass, causing it to rot.

The lion itself is food for other organisms. Small animals, like ticks, fleas, biting flies, and mosquitoes, drink the lion's blood. The lion's dung serves as food for organisms that live in the soil. When the lion dies, it may be eaten by the same scavengers that once fed on the leftovers of its kills.

All of the lion's relationships with its environment—both the living and nonliving parts—make up its niche. An organism's **niche** is its way of life. The lion's niche includes the relationships already described as well as many others, such as when and how often it reproduces, how many offspring it has, what time of the day it is most active, and where it finds shelter. Think of an organism's niche as its "lifestyle," or how it contributes to and fits into its environment. Some parts of a lion's niche are shown in Figure 2-6.

The actual place an organism lives is called its **habitat.** The lion's habitat, for example, is a savanna. A howler monkey's habitat is a rain forest, a cactus's habitat is a desert, and a water lily's habitat is a pond. An organism's habitat may be thought of as its "address."

HOW SPECIES INTERACT WITH EACH OTHER

AFTER READING THIS SECTION YOU SHOULD BE ABLE TO

● explain the five major types of species interactions and give examples of each.

In Section 2.1 you saw that ecosystems are made up of biotic and abiotic components. In this section you will see ways in which organisms—the biotic components—affect each other. You will examine five major types of interactions: predation, competition, parasitism, mutualism, and commensalism.

PREDATION

In **predation,** one organism kills and eats another organism. The organism that is eaten is called the **prey,** and the one that does the eating is called the **predator.** Familiar examples of predation include lions feeding on zebras, cougars eating deer, snakes consuming mice, and birds eating insects. The blue whale, the largest animal on Earth, is also a predator because it feeds on tiny krill (shrimplike marine animals). Figure 2-7 shows various predators in action.

Figure 2-7 **When one organism kills and eats another, it is called predation.**

a. Chameleon catching a grasshopper
b. Starfish opening a clam
c. Golden eagle carrying away a prairie dog
d. Cougar attacking a mule deer
e. Red fox with a ground squirrel

Predators tend to feed on young and weak individuals and often limit the size of prey populations. As populations of prey decline, the predators either switch to other prey or begin to die off themselves.

COMPETITION

When hyenas fight with lions over the same animal carcass, they are competing for food. Such contests can turn into fierce battles in which hyenas or, more rarely, lions can be killed. The relationship between the lions and the hyenas is called competition. **Competition** occurs when two or more organisms of the same or different species attempt to use the same limited resource. Another example of competition is the relationship between two plants competing for the limited amount of sunlight that reaches the forest floor. Some examples of competition are shown in Figure 2-8.

Species can compete even if they never come into contact with each other. Suppose one insect species feeds on a certain plant during the day and another feeds on the same plant during the night. Because they use the same food source, the two species are competitors, even though they never come into direct contact with each other. Similarly, two plant species that flower at the same time and depend on the same pollinators are in competition for pollinators, even if they don't compete in any other way.

Figure 2-8 Competing species attempt to use the same limited resource.

a. Imported fire ants compete with native ants for territory.
b. Two young plants on a forest floor compete for sunlight.
c. Imported kudzu vines cover native plants.
d. Pandas compete with humans for bamboo.

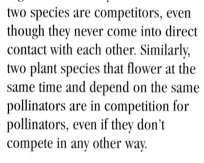

Wasp pupae
on tomato
hornworm

Ticks on hedgehog

Mistletoe on
poplar tree

Roundworms
from dog

Figure 2-9 These organisms
are parasites. The mistletoe is a
parasite because it grows into the
tissues of the tree and uses the tree
as a source of nutrients.

PARASITISM

What do ticks, fleas, tapeworms, viruses, blood-sucking leeches, and mistletoe have in common? They are all **parasites**—organisms that live in or on another organism and feed on it without immediately killing it. Figure 2-9 shows some examples of parasites. The organism the parasite takes its nourishment from is known as the **host.** The relationship between the parasite and its host is called **parasitism.**

How is parasitism different from predation? The main difference is that parasites, unlike predators, usually do not immediately kill their hosts. Another difference is that a parasite lives in or on the host for part of its life. Most organisms are negatively affected by parasites. Animals and plants may be weakened by parasites, making them more vulnerable to predators.

MUTUALISM

Although you are probably not aware of their existence, billions of bacteria live in your intestines. They do not make you sick. Instead, they are your partners in digesting food. They break down food that you would otherwise be unable to digest. They also produce necessary substances your body cannot make. For instance, they supply you with vitamin K, which is essential for proper blood clotting. And you give them something in return—a warm, dark, food-rich environment in which to live.

The relationship between you and your intestinal bacteria is known as mutualism. **Mutualism** is a cooperative partnership between two species in which both species benefit. Another example of mutualism can be found in Central America, where acacia trees are covered with ants, as you can see in Figure 2-10 on the next page. The acacia trees provide food (nectar and protein

TOPIC: parasitism and mutualism
GO TO: www.scilinks.org
KEYWORD: HE041

ECO-FACT

One South American mite species lives entirely on the blood it sucks from the hind feet of soldier army ants.

41

Wildlife Garden

If you think you might enjoy watching species interact with each other, see pages 396–397 to find out how to create your own wildlife garden.

bodies on the leaves) and nesting sites (hollow thorns) for the ants. In exchange, the ants defend the acacia trees from herbivores such as grasshoppers and beetles. The ants will even attack mammals that interfere with the trees. In one study, ecologist Daniel Janzen removed the ants from some acacias by spraying them with insecticides. He found that the trees grew more slowly and were heavily eaten by herbivores. Janzen had demonstrated that the ants provide an important service for the acacia trees.

Figure 2-10 These ants defend the acacia tree against herbivores. In return, the acacia trees provide food and nesting sites for the ants. This is an example of the relationship called mutualism.

COMMENSALISM

Commensalism is perhaps the rarest and strangest type of species interaction. **Commensalism** is a relationship in which one species benefits and the other is neither harmed nor helped, such as the interaction between remoras and sharks, shown in Figure 2-11. Remoras are fish that attach themselves to sharks and feed on scraps of food left over from the shark's meals. Although the sharks do not seem to benefit by this relationship, they aren't harmed either.

Figure 2-11 This remora attached itself to the shark and benefits by eating food left over from the shark's meals. The shark is neither helped nor harmed by the remora. Commensalism is the name of this kind of relationship.

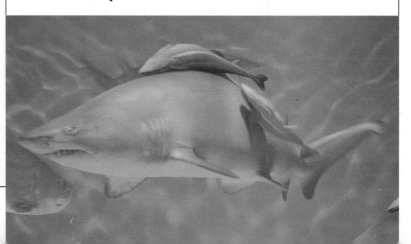

SECTION REVIEW

❶ Give one example of a predator-prey relationship that is not mentioned in this chapter.

❷ What is the difference between mutualism and parasitism?

THINKING CRITICALLY

❸ *Inferring Relationships* Why is it usually advantageous for a parasite to leave its host alive?

❹ *Analyzing Relationships* How could you show that a suspected case of mutualism was not a case of commensalism?

HIGHLIGHTS

SUMMARY

- Ecosystems are ecological units that include all the different organisms living in a certain area, along with their physical environment.

- Living things are organized from the smallest to the largest unit in the following ecological levels: organism, population, community, ecosystem, and biosphere.

- Each organism has a niche, or "lifestyle," and a habitat, or "address."

- Species interact with each other in five major ways—predation, competition, parasitism, mutualism, and commensalism.

- Charles Darwin proposed that, over many generations, populations of organisms become well suited to their environments through evolution by natural selection.

- Coevolution is a type of evolution by natural selection in which two or more species evolve in response to each other.

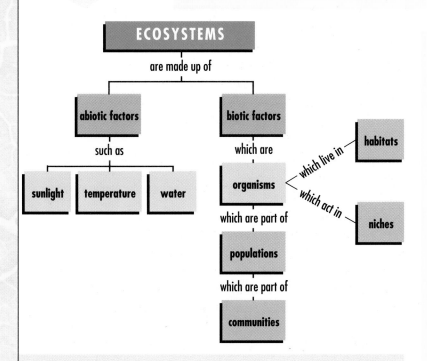

Vocabulary Terms

abiotic factors (p. 35)

adaptation (p. 46)

biotic factors (p. 35)

coevolution (p. 46)

commensalism (p. 42)

community (p. 37)

competition (p. 40)

ecosystem (p. 34)

evolution (p. 44)

extinction (p. 46)

habitat (p. 38)

host (p. 41)

mutualism (p. 41)

natural selection (p. 43)

niche (p. 38)

organism (p. 37)

parasites (p. 41)

parasitism (p. 41)

population (p. 37)

predation (p. 39)

predator (p. 39)

prey (p. 39)

species (p. 37)

EcoLog

Now that you've studied this chapter, revise your answer to the question you answered at the beginning of the chapter, based on what you have learned.

● If all the lions on an African savanna were killed or removed, how might their absence affect the other living things on the savanna?

REVIEW

UNDERSTANDING VOCABULARY

1. For each pair of terms, explain the difference in their meanings.

   a. biotic factors
      abiotic factors

   b. population
      community

   c. niche
      habitat

   d. parasitism
      mutualism

   e. adaptation
      extinction

RELATING CONCEPTS

2. Copy the unfinished concept map below onto a sheet of paper. Then complete the concept map by writing the correct word or phrase in each box containing a question mark.

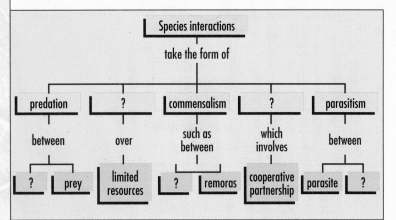

UNDERSTANDING CONCEPTS

Multiple Choice

3. Which is NOT an abiotic factor in an ecosystem?

   a. temperature
   b. air pressure
   c. sunlight
   d. bacteria

4. Which of these sayings most closely describes how an ecosystem operates?

   a. The early bird gets the worm.
   b. A chain is only as strong as its weakest link.
   c. It's always darkest before the dawn.
   d. Curiosity killed the cat.

5. Select the correct order from the choices below.

   a. ecosystem, population, community, organism
   b. population, organism, ecosystem, community
   c. organism, population, community, ecosystem
   d. community, population, organism, ecosystem

6. Which of these organisms could belong to the same population?

   a. a gorilla and an orangutan
   b. two classmates
   c. a zebra and a horse
   d. a rose and a carnation

7. Which is NOT one of the major points in the theory of evolution by natural selection?

   a. Organisms have the ability to produce more offspring than can survive.
   b. Limited resources produce a struggle for existence.
   c. A community includes populations of different species.
   d. Organisms with advantageous traits produce more offspring.

8. Which is an example of coevolution?

   a. flowers that can be pollinated by only one insect species
   b. deer that live in a cold region and have thick fur
   c. dark gray moths that are found near Birmingham, England
   d. desert rats that do not sweat

9. Which is an example of competition?
   a. two species of insects that feed on the same rare plant
   b. a bobcat and a jackrabbit
   c. an African lioness feeding her cubs
   d. a tick living on a dog

10. Ants and acacia trees have a mutualistic relationship because
    a. they benefit each other.
    b. they are part of the same ecosystem.
    c. they are both adapted to a humid climate.
    d. the ants eat parts of the acacia tree.

11. Which of these statements is true of parasitism?
    a. The presence of a parasite does not affect the host.
    b. Parasitism is identical to predation.
    c. The presence of a parasite may make an animal more susceptible to predation.
    d. Parasitism is a cooperative relationship between two species.

Short Answer

12. A tapeworm lives inside the intestines of a cow and feeds by absorbing food that the cow is digesting. Is this an example of predation? Explain your reasoning.

13. As a human, what types of ecological interactions do you participate in with other species? Give at least two examples.

14. Explain how two species can compete for the same resource even if they never come into contact with each other.

15. Snail kites are predatory birds that feed exclusively on snails. They use their hooked, needle-like beaks to pull snails from their shells. Explain how the kites might have evolved their specialized beaks.

16. What would happen to the snail kites mentioned in question 15 if the snails' habitat were destroyed? Explain.

INTERPRETING GRAPHICS

17. Examine the graph below. Each line represents a different species. What type of interaction could be taking place between species A and B? between A and C? Explain the reasoning behind each of your answers.

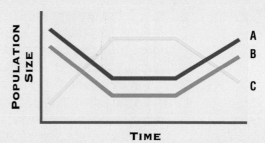

THINKING CRITICALLY

18. *Analyzing Relationships* Imagine that one species becomes extinct as a direct result of the extinction of another species. Which relationship did the two species more likely have, competition or commensalism? Explain your reasoning.

19. *Inferring Relationships* How might humans be affecting the course of evolution?

THEMES IN SCIENCE

20. *Evolution* Why is time an important factor in the process of evolution by natural selection?

21. *Interacting Systems* Why are abiotic factors just as important to an ecosystem as biotic factors?

CROSS-DISCIPLINE CONNECTION

22. *Math* Suppose that scientists introduce a breeding pair of one species into a certain habitat. This species doubles its population size each year. Another species, native to the habitat, keeps its numbers at a stable 500 individuals from one year to the next. In how many years will the introduced species' population have more members than the native species' population?

PORTFOLIO ACTIVITY

Do a special project about the ecosystem in which you live. Try to identify all of the biotic and abiotic factors in your ecosystem. List some interactions that take place among the biotic factors. Then, using your data, develop a series of storyboards to show what might happen if one factor were suddenly removed from this ecosystem.

CHAPTER 2

INVESTIGATION

SHOWDOWN ON THE PRAIRIE

In a quiet rural area of the Midwest, a struggle for survival is going on. In the prairie, exotic or imported grass species are gradually replacing the native grasses. When the plant community changes, it affects the entire ecosystem, possibly threatening the survival of many types of native wildlife.

You are a plant ecologist studying ways to restore native grasses to the prairie. You want to learn why one type of grass might outcompete another and whether different species succeed better under different conditions. In order to answer these questions, you and a team of other biologists will first do a simple plant-competition experiment. You will then devise your own experiment to test the factors that affect competition among grasses.

CHECK OUT THE COMPETITION

1. In your notebook, make a table like the one shown below to record data. Add additional days if desired.

| | Species A Alone | | Species B Alone | | Plants in Mixed Pot | | | |
| | | | | | Species A | | Species B | |
	Max. Height	No. of Leaves	Max. Height	No. of Leaves	Max. Height	No. of Leaves	Max. Height	No. of Leaves
Day 1								
Day 2								
Day 3								
Day 4								
Day 5								
Day 6								
Day 7								

2. Each team of biologists will be given three flowerpots filled with potting soil. One pot has been planted with grass seeds of native species A, another contains grass seeds of exotic species B, and the third contains equal numbers of seeds of species A and B mixed together. The pots with only one species of grass are the controls in this experiment. What is the purpose of having these two pots? Write your answer in your notebook.

3. How do you think the growth of each species in the mixed pot will compare with the growth of each species grown alone? Write your hypothesis in your notebook.

4. Put the pots in a well-lighted area, and check them daily. When the soil seems dry, add the same amount of water to all three pots.

MATERIALS

- flowerpots prepared by teacher
- 3 small flowerpots
- 3 aluminum pie pans
- potting soil
- native grass seeds (buffalo is best)
- imported grass seeds (rye or fescue)
- tape and marker for labeling flowerpots
- metric ruler
- hand lens
- graph paper
- one or more of the following (optional): light source, scissors, fertilizer, other soil additives
- notebook
- pen or pencil

5. As the grasses begin to sprout, count the number of leaves and measure the height of the tallest leaf in millimeters. In order to distinguish the two species in the mixed pot, compare them with the grasses in the two individual pots using a hand lens. Most grass species will differ in the amount and kind of hair, hooks, or spines covering them and in the presence or absence of glands. Color and size are not as reliable for identifying species. Record your observations each day.

6. After a period of 7 to 10 days, use your data table to make two line graphs. One graph should compare the height of the plants in the three pots over time, and the other should compare the number of leaves.

7. How did the growth of each species in the absence of competition differ from its growth in the presence of competition? Was your hypothesis supported?

WEED OUT THE VARIABLES

8. Why is it difficult to simulate competition in a laboratory? In other words, why would the grass that survived best in your competition experiment not necessarily survive best in the wild?

9. Many factors might give one species a competitive edge over another. Select one of the factors listed below to investigate, or come up with your own.

   - amount and frequency of watering   • amount of light
   - grazing (can be simulated by clipping the grasses at timed intervals)
   - level of nitrates in the soil (can be increased by adding fertilizer)

10. Write down a hypothesis regarding the effect of the factor you chose. For example, you might expect grass species A to outcompete grass species B during drought conditions. Explain your reasoning.

11. In your notebook, describe an experiment that will test your hypothesis. Base the design on the preliminary competition experiment you did. Keep in mind that whatever modification you make must be applied to all three pots.

12. Based on your hypothesis, predict what you expect to happen. For example, you might expect grass species A to produce more and longer leaves than species B when an equal number of seeds of the two species are grown together in a pot that is watered infrequently. Write your prediction in your notebook.

PUT THE COMPETITORS TO THE TEST

13. Carry out your experiment. Record your results in a table similar to the one used for the preliminary experiment.

14. Illustrate the results of your experiment using graphs of the data collected.

15. Compare your results with those obtained by other teams. Does one species outcompete the other under most conditions, or does each one do better under its own preferred conditions? Using the information from all experiments done by the class, propose some explanations for why one species might outcompete another under certain conditions.

16. Why is it difficult to draw conclusions concerning plant competition in a natural setting based on simple laboratory experiments? What additional laboratory and field studies could be done to help develop a plan for restoring native grasses to an area that has been taken over by exotics?

Examine the details of the grass leaves to identify the two species in the mixed pot.

Native grasses have been restored to this Kansas prairie that had been invaded by exotic species.

Butterfly Ecologist

Imagine millions of butterflies swirling through the air like autumn leaves, clinging in tightly packed masses to tree trunks and branches, and covering low-lying forest vegetation like a luxurious, moving carpet. According to Alfonso Alonso-Mejía, this is quite a sight to see.

Every winter Alfonso climbs up to the few remote sites in central Mexico where about 200 million monarch butterflies spend the winter. He is researching the monarchs because he wants to help preserve their habitat and the butterflies themselves. His work is also helping him earn a Ph.D. in ecology from the University of Florida.

Alfonso's work is helping Mexican conservationists better understand and protect monarch butterflies.

Monarchs are famous for their long-distance migration. Those that eventually find their way to Mexico come from as far away as the northeastern United States and southern Canada. Some of them travel an amazing 3,200 km (2,000 mi.) before reaching central Mexico.

Unfortunately, the habitat that the monarchs travel such distances to reach is increasingly threatened by logging and other human activities. Only nine of the monarchs' wintering sites remain. Five of those are set aside as sanctuaries for the butterflies, but even these sanctuaries are endangered by people who cut down fir trees for firewood or for commercial purposes.

◄ *Alfonso's research has led to important discoveries about the monarch butterfly.*

Alfonso's work is helping Mexican conservationists better understand and protect monarch butterflies. Especially important is Alfonso's discovery that monarchs depend on bushlike vegetation, called understory vegetation, that grows beneath the fir trees.

Alfonso's research showed that when the temperature dips below freezing (as it often does in the mountains where the monarchs winter), understory vegetation can mean the difference between life and death for some monarchs. This is because low temperatures (–1 to 4°C, or 30 to 40°F) limit the monarchs' movement. In fact, the butterflies are not even able to fly. At extremely cold temperatures (–7 to –1°C, or 20 to 30°F), monarchs resting on the forest floor are in danger of freezing to death. But as long as there is understory vegetation, the monarchs can slowly climb the vegetation until they are at least 10 cm (4 in.) above the ground. This tiny difference in elevation can provide a microclimate that is warm enough to ensure the monarchs' survival.

The importance of understory vegetation was not known before Alfonso did his research. Now, thanks to Alfonso's work, Mexican conservationists will better protect the understory vegetation.

Alfonso is undoubtedly on his way to becoming a world-class monarch butterfly ecologist. When he completes his Ph.D., Alfonso Alonso-Mejía will devote himself to preserving the Mexican habitat of the monarch butterfly.

For More Information . . .

If you are interested in a nationwide monarch-tagging program, write to Monarch Watch, Department of Entomology, 7005 Haworth Hall, University of Kansas, Lawrence, KS 66045.

The monarch butterflies that Alfonso studies migrate up to 3,200 km (2,000 mi.) before reaching the remote mountainous locations in central Mexico.
▼

UNITED STATES

Gulf of California

Gulf of Mexico

MEXICO

BELIZE

PACIFIC OCEAN

GUATEMALA

Mexico City

Monarch Butterfly Sanctuaries

HOW ECOSYSTEMS WORK

"You could cover the whole world with asphalt, but sooner or later green grass would break through."

ILYA EHRENBURG, RUSSIAN WRITER

Ecolog

Before you read this chapter, take a few minutes to answer the following questions in your EcoLog.

❶ What does sunlight have to do with the amount of food available to a hawk, which eats only meat?

❷ How is it possible that an atom of nitrogen in your sandwich was once part of a dinosaur's body?

ENERGY FLOW IN ECOSYSTEMS

AFTER READING THIS SECTION YOU SHOULD BE ABLE TO

❶ describe the roles of producers and consumers.

❷ trace the transfer of energy from the sun to producers and from producers to consumers.

❸ differentiate among different types of consumers.

❹ draw a food chain and a food web.

❺ explain why an energy pyramid is a good representation of trophic levels.

Figure 3-1 These plants are using sunlight to produce food in their leaves.

J ust as a car cannot run without fuel, an organism cannot survive without a supply of energy. How organisms meet this need for energy greatly affects the structure of ecosystems. Where does an organism's energy come from? The answer to that question depends on the organism, but the ultimate source of energy for almost all organisms is the sun.

LIFE DEPENDS ON THE SUN

Plants, algae, and some kinds of bacteria can capture solar energy and store it as food. On a sunny spring day, for instance, a clover plant is producing food in its leaves through the process of photosynthesis. The leaves absorb sunlight, which drives a series of chemical reactions that require water and carbon dioxide. The result is the production of sugar, an energy-rich food.

55

The sun provides light energy.

Grass uses energy from the sun to make organic compounds through photosynthesis.

A mule deer grazes on the grass, getting energy from the organic compounds that the grass produced.

Wolves feed on a deer, and energy is transferred from the deer to the wolves.

Figure 3-2 **Almost all organisms depend on the sun for energy. Most producers, like the grass shown here, get energy directly from the sun.**

Figure 3-3 **The tube worms shown below are part of an ecosystem that is dependent on bacteria.**

When a rabbit eats the clover plant, it gets energy from the food the clover made during photosynthesis. Then, if a coyote eats the rabbit, some of the energy is transferred from the rabbit to the coyote.

In this example, the clover is the **producer.** A producer is an organism that makes its own food. Producers are also called autotrophs (self-feeders). Both the rabbit and the coyote are **consumers,** organisms that get their energy by eating other organisms. Consumers are also called heterotrophs (other-feeders).

The important thing to remember is that almost all organisms get their energy from the sun. Producers get energy *directly* from the sun. Consumers get energy *indirectly* from the sun by eating producers or other organisms that eat producers.

An Exception to the Rule: Deep-Ocean Ecosystems The previous paragraph said that *almost* all organisms get their energy directly or indirectly from the sun. That's because in 1977, scientists discovered areas on the bottom of the ocean off the coast of Ecuador that were teeming with life even though sunlight didn't reach down that far. They found rich communities of fish, worms, clams, crabs, mussels, and barnacles living around cracks in the ocean floor through which hot water escaped. (See Figure 3-3.) These deep-ocean ecosystems exist in total darkness, where photosynthesis cannot occur. So where are the organisms getting their energy? As it turns out, there are bacteria that make food from hydrogen sulfide, which is present in the hot water that escapes from the cracks in the ocean floor. These bacteria are producers that can make food without sunlight. They are eaten by animals and thus support a rich ecosystem.

WHAT EATS WHAT

Figure 3-4 shows what eats what in an ecosystem. Consumers that eat only producers are called **herbivores** (plant-eaters). Rabbits are herbivores, as are cows, sheep, deer, grasshoppers, and many other animals. Consumers that eat only other consumers, such as lions and hawks, are **carnivores** (flesh-eaters). You already know that humans are consumers, but what kind of consumers are we? After all, most humans eat *both* plants and animals. We are considered to be **omnivores** (eaters of all). Bears and pigs are other examples of omnivores. Consumers that get their food by breaking down dead organisms, causing them to rot, are **decomposers.** Bacteria and fungi are examples of decomposers. The decomposers make it possible for the nutrients contained in the rotting material to return to the soil or water.

RESPIRATION: BURNING THE FUEL

So far, you have learned how organisms get energy. But how do they use the energy they get? Take yourself as an example to understand the process. Suppose you have just eaten a large meal. The food you ate contains a lot of energy. Your body gets the energy out of the food by using the oxygen you breathe to break down the food molecules. In this way your body "liberates" the energy stored in the food.

The process of breaking down food to yield energy is called **cellular respiration.** It is similar to combustion in an automobile

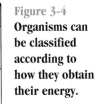

The CALL of the WILD

To some, the howl of a wolf is a thrilling sound. To others, it signals death and destruction. Turn to pages 76–77 to read about the controversy surrounding gray wolves, carnivores of the American Northwest.

Figure 3-4
Organisms can be classified according to how they obtain their energy.

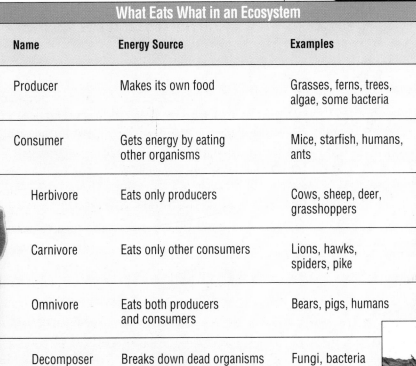

What Eats What in an Ecosystem		
Name	Energy Source	Examples
Producer	Makes its own food	Grasses, ferns, trees, algae, some bacteria
Consumer	Gets energy by eating other organisms	Mice, starfish, humans, ants
Herbivore	Eats only producers	Cows, sheep, deer, grasshoppers
Carnivore	Eats only other consumers	Lions, hawks, spiders, pike
Omnivore	Eats both producers and consumers	Bears, pigs, humans
Decomposer	Breaks down dead organisms in an ecosystem, returning nutrients to the soil or water	Fungi, bacteria

$$6CO_2 + 6H_2O + \text{light energy} \longrightarrow C_6H_{12}O_6 + 6O_2$$

PHOTOSYNTHESIS

$$C_6H_{12}O_6 + 6O_2 \longrightarrow 6CO_2 + 6H_2O + \text{energy}$$

CELLULAR RESPIRATION

Figure 3-5 Notice that cellular respiration is essentially photosynthesis in reverse.

SCI LINKS
NSTA

TOPIC: food chains, food webs
GO TO: www.scilinks.org
KEYWORD: HE058

engine, in which gasoline is burned to obtain the energy to run the car. As you can see in Figure 3-5, cellular respiration is essentially the reverse of photosynthesis. (Don't confuse cellular respiration, which occurs within the cells of the body, with respiration, another name for breathing.) During cellular respiration, sugar and oxygen combine to yield carbon dioxide, water, and, most important, energy.

You use a portion of the energy obtained through cellular respiration to carry out your daily activities, such as walking, breathing, reading this book, thinking, and going to the refrigerator for more food. The energy is also used to make more body tissue, so that you grow, and some of it is stored as fat or sugar.

All living things use cellular respiration to get energy from food molecules. Even organisms that make their own food through photosynthesis use cellular respiration to obtain energy from the food.

ENERGY TRANSFER: FOOD CHAINS, FOOD WEBS, AND TROPHIC LEVELS

Each time one organism eats another organism, a transfer of energy occurs. We can trace the paths that energy follows as it travels through an ecosystem by studying food chains, food webs, and trophic levels.

DDT IN AN AQUATIC FOOD CHAIN

Something strange was happening in the estuaries near Long Island Sound in the 1950s and 1960s. Carnivorous birds of prey that fed on fish in the estuaries, such as ospreys and eagles, had high concentrations of the pesticide DDT in their bodies. But when the water in the estuary was tested, it had low concentrations of DDT.

What accounted for the high levels of DDT in the birds? Poisons that dissolve in fat, such as DDT, can become more concentrated as they move up a food chain in a process called *biological magnification.* When the pesticide enters the water, small aquatic organisms such as algae and bacteria take in the poison. When fish eat the algae and bacteria, the poison dissolves into the fat of the fish rather than diffusing back into the water. Each time a bird feeds on a fish, the bird accumulates more DDT in its fatty tissues. In some estuaries on Long Island Sound, DDT concentrations in fatty tissue were magnified almost 10 million times from the bottom to the top of the food chain.

Long Island Sound lies between Long Island and Connecticut.

58

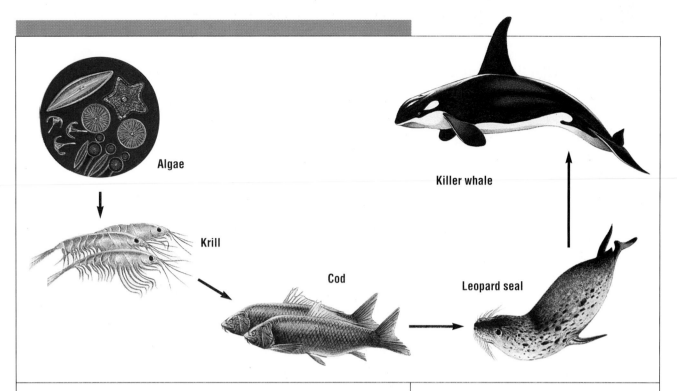

Algae

Krill

Cod

Killer whale

Leopard seal

Food Chains and Food Webs A **food chain** is a sequence in which energy is transferred from one organism to the next as each organism eats another. Figure 3-6 shows a typical food chain in an ocean ecosystem. Algae are eaten by krill, which are eaten by cod, which are eaten by leopard seals, which are eaten by killer whales. (Poisons can also be passed on in a food chain, as discussed in the Case Study about DDT below.)

Figure 3-6 **Energy is transferred from one organism to another in a food chain. Algae are the producers in this ocean food chain.**

This accumulation of toxins damages the carnivore at the top of the food chain. It may kill the carnivore, weaken its immune system, or impair its ability to reproduce successfully. High concentrations of DDT weaken the shells of bird eggs. When the eggs break, the chick embryos die; this causes a tremendous drop in the population of the bird species.

The United States government recognized DDT as an environmental contaminant and in 1972 banned its sale except for emergency use. The aquatic food chains immediately started to recover. Unfortunately, the food chains are still not totally free of DDT.

The pesticide breaks down very slowly in the environment. Also, DDT is still legal in some countries, where it is used in large quantities. As a result, migratory birds may be exposed to DDT while wintering in Latin America or other locations outside the United States.

An osprey catches a perch

THINKING CRITICALLY

❶ *Analyzing Processes* DDT does not dissolve readily in water. If it did, how would the accumulation of the pesticide in organisms be affected?

❷ *Inferring Relationships* Suggest some specific measures that the United States could take to stop the DDT pollution that is still occurring.

Figure 3-7 A food web shows feeding relationships in an ecosystem. What feeding relationships do the krill have?

Killer whale

Elephant seal

Crabeater seal

Leopard seal

Adélie penguin

Squid

Cod

Krill

Algae

Small animals and one-celled organisms

FIELD ACTIVITY

In a park, yard, or lot, measure out a 1-square-meter area. You may use sticks and string to mark off the area. Using glass jars or sealable plastic bags, carefully collect 5 plant species and 3 invertebrate species. Use a field guide to identify the different species, and then return the invertebrates to their original location. Draw a possible food chain or food web that includes the species you have collected.

Ecosystems are much more complicated than a simple food chain. For one thing, ecosystems almost always contain many more species than those present in a single food chain. In addition, most organisms, yourself included, feed on more than one kind of food. So a more accurate illustration of what organisms eat in an ecosystem is a **food web,** such as the one shown in Figure 3-7. A food web shows many of the feeding relationships in an ecosystem. Notice that the food chain in Figure 3-6 is just one strand in the larger food web.

Trophic Levels Each step in the transfer of energy through an ecosystem is known as a **trophic level.** In the ocean example, the algae are in the bottom trophic level, the krill are in the next level, and so on. Each time energy is transferred, less of it is available to organisms at the next trophic level.

What accounts for the decreased amount of energy at each trophic level? Some energy is lost during the process of converting food to energy. Organisms use much of the remaining energy to carry out the functions of living—such as producing new cells, regulating body temperature, and moving around. About 90 percent of the energy at each trophic level is used up in this way. The remaining 10 percent becomes part of the organism's body, stored in its molecules. This 10 percent is all that is available

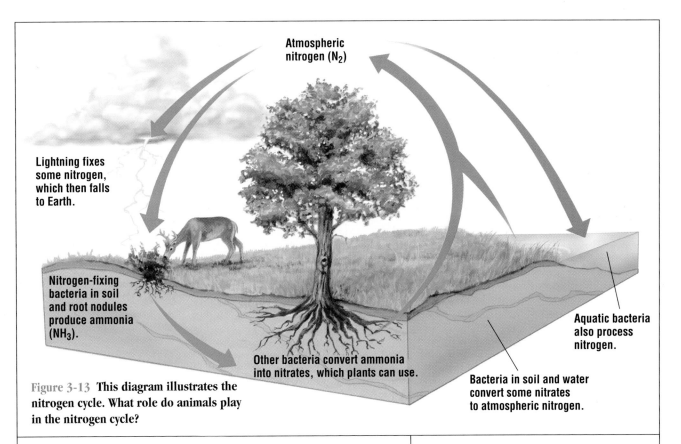

Atmospheric nitrogen (N$_2$)

Lightning fixes some nitrogen, which then falls to Earth.

Nitrogen-fixing bacteria in soil and root nodules produce ammonia (NH$_3$).

Other bacteria convert ammonia into nitrates, which plants can use.

Aquatic bacteria also process nitrogen.

Bacteria in soil and water convert some nitrates to atmospheric nitrogen.

Figure 3-13 **This diagram illustrates the nitrogen cycle. What role do animals play in the nitrogen cycle?**

in Chapter 2—a mutualistic relationship, in which both organisms benefit from the association. The excess nitrogen fixed by the bacteria is released into the soil. In addition, some nitrogen-fixing bacteria live in the soil rather than within roots, and these bacteria also add nitrogen to the soil.

Plants that don't have nitrogen-fixing bacteria in their roots get nitrogen from the soil. Animals get nitrogen by eating plants or other animals, both of which are sources of usable nitrogen.

Closing the Nitrogen Cycle In the nitrogen cycle, nitrogen moves back and forth between the atmosphere and living things. You've learned how nitrogen gets from the atmosphere to living things—through nitrogen-fixing bacteria. But how does the nitrogen return to the atmosphere?

Once again, it is bacteria, along with fungi, that are essential to the nitrogen cycle. These decomposers break down wastes (urine, dung, leaves, and other plant parts) and dead organisms, returning the nitrogen they contain to the soil. If it weren't for decomposers, much of the nitrogen in ecosystems would be locked away in wastes, corpses, and castoff parts such as tree branches. After decomposers return the nitrogen to the soil, bacteria transform a small amount of it into nitrogen gas, which then returns to the atmosphere and completes the nitrogen cycle. Other bacteria incorporate the remaining nitrogen into compounds that plants can use. So once nitrogen enters an ecosystem, most of it stays within the ecosystem, cycling between organisms and the soil in an endless loop.

SECTION REVIEW

❶ Explain how the model water cycle shown in Figure 3-9 is like the real water cycle shown in Figure 3-10.

❷ Describe the role of producers in the carbon cycle.

❸ How are humans altering the carbon cycle?

THINKING CRITICALLY

❹ *Interpreting Graphics* Examine Figure 3-11. What role do animals play in the carbon cycle?

❺ *Relating Concepts* Create a concept map that describes the water cycle. Be sure to include the following terms: water, groundwater, atmosphere, lakes, rivers, precipitation, plants, animals, and humans.

HOW ECOSYSTEMS CHANGE

AFTER READING THIS SECTION YOU SHOULD BE ABLE TO

❶ describe secondary and primary succession.

❷ explain the importance of pioneer species.

❸ explain how soil is formed.

At some time in your life you may have walked through a forest that was hundreds of years old. If your great-grandmother and great-grandfather had walked in the same forest, they probably would have seen the same kinds of plants and animals that you saw. However, the area was not always a forest. A thousand years ago it might have been a meadow or even a shallow lake. Scientists refer to such ecological change as succession.

SUCCESSION

Succession is a regular pattern of changes over time in the types of species in a community. The process of succession may take hundreds or thousands of years.

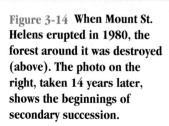

Figure 3-14 When Mount St. Helens erupted in 1980, the forest around it was destroyed (above). The photo on the right, taken 14 years later, shows the beginnings of secondary succession.

What causes succession? Each new community that arises makes it more difficult for the previous one to survive. In a pine forest, for example, the tall pine trees shade the ground and make it impossible for new pine seedlings to grow. But the seedlings of other trees, like oaks and maples, can grow with less light, so they begin to replace the pines.

The community that eventually forms if the land is left undisturbed is called the **climax community.** Even though a climax community continues to change in small ways, the type of community remains similar through time. For example, a maple forest will remain a maple forest as long as no serious disturbances occur.

Secondary Succession In 1980, a volcano called Mount St. Helens erupted in Washington State. Over 18,000 hectares (about 44,460 acres) of forest were burned and flattened. If you visited Mount St. Helens today, you would find that the forest has already begun to regenerate through succession. (See Figure 3-14.) Succession that occurs on a surface where an ecosystem has previously existed, such as in the burned areas around Mount St. Helens, is called **secondary succession.**

Another example of secondary succession is old-field succession, which occurs when farmland is abandoned. Figure 3-16 shows old-field succession on an abandoned farm in Tennessee. When a farmer stops cultivating a field, grasses and weeds quickly move in. These plants are called **pioneers,** the first organisms to colonize any newly available area and start the process of succession. The pioneer grasses and weeds grow rapidly and produce many seeds.

DESTRUCTION
REJUVENATION
DEVASTATION
RENEWAL

What happens when a hurricane ravages an ecosystem? This kind of question could keep a biologist very busy. To find out more, see pages 374–375.

Figure 3-15 **These pine trees shade the ground and make it impossible for young pines to grow there. The young trees you see are the seedlings of maple trees, which thrive in the shade.**

Figure 3-16 **Why do young oak trees begin to appear around year 20 in this example of secondary succession?**

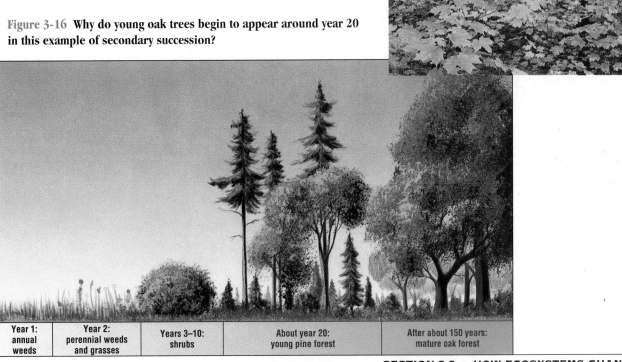

Year 1: annual weeds	Year 2: perennial weeds and grasses	Years 3–10: shrubs	About year 20: young pine forest	After about 150 years: mature oak forest

Then taller plants, such as perennial grasses, move in. These plants shade the ground, which keeps light from the shorter pioneer plants. The long roots of the taller plants also take up much of the water in the soil, depriving the pioneer plants of adequate water. The pioneer plants soon die from lack of sunlight and water.

Later, as succession continues, the taller plants themselves are deprived of light and water. This occurs as small shrubs or trees sprout and mature.

Finally, slower-growing trees, such as oaks, hickories, beeches, and maples, move in and take over, blocking out the sunlight to the smaller trees. After about a century the land returns to the climax community that was there before the farmers cleared it.

FIRE-MAINTAINED COMMUNITIES

Natural fires caused by lightning are a necessary part of secondary succession in some communities. Some species of trees, such as the jack pine, can release their seeds only after they have been exposed to the intense heat of a fire. Minor forest fires remove accumulations of brush and deadwood that would otherwise contribute to major fires that burn out of control. And some animal species depend on occasional fires because they feed on the

ECO-FACT

About 80 percent of all forest fires in the United States are caused by human beings.

FIRES IN YELLOWSTONE

CASE STUDY

What happens when a fire breaks out in a national park? You might expect all available firefighters to rush to the scene. However, since 1972 the policy of the National Park Service has been to manage the national parks as naturally as possible. Since fire is a natural force in forest ecosystems, this policy includes allowing most fires caused by lightning to burn. The only lightning-caused fires that are put out are those that

threaten lives, property, uniquely scenic areas, or endangered species. All human-caused fires are put out.

Between 1972 and 1987, more than 200 naturally caused fires burned in Yellowstone National Park. None of the fires grew excessively large, and all of them went out by themselves. The fire policy of the National Park Service was not really put to the test until the summer of 1988.

Conditions in Yellowstone during the summer of 1988 were unusual because very little rain had fallen during the normally wet summer months. In fact, that summer turned out to be the driest on record, and several of the previous winters had also been drier than normal. All

that was needed to set the dry forest ablaze was a few sparks, which were provided that summer by lightning.

By mid-July, Yellowstone had several fires that had been blazing for nearly a month and 11 others that had come and gone. At this time, the National Park Service began fighting the fires. Several days later in another part of the park, careless humans complicated the control efforts by starting what turned out

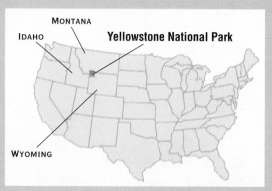

Yellowstone National Park, which spreads across three states, is the oldest national park in the world.

vegetation that sprouts after a fire has cleared the land. Therefore, foresters sometimes allow natural fires to burn unless they threaten human life or property. (See the Case Study below about fires in Yellowstone National Park.)

Primary Succession Succession that occurs on surfaces where no ecosystem existed before is called **primary succession.** Primary succession occurs on new islands created by volcanic eruptions, for example, and in areas exposed when a glacier retreats.

Primary succession is much slower than secondary succession because it begins where there is no soil. It takes several hundred to several thousand years to produce fertile soil naturally.

Imagine that a glacier melts and exposes an area of bare rock. The first pioneer species to colonize the bare rock will probably be bacteria and lichens, which can live without soil. Lichens, shown in Figure 3-17, are important early pioneers in primary succession. They are the colorful, flaky patches that you see on the sides of

Figure 3-17 **Lichens are able to live without soil, which makes them important contributors to primary succession.**

A fire rages in Yellowstone National Park

to be the largest fire of all. Even more fires sprang up around the park in the passing weeks. Some of them persisted through the fall months, and a few were still burning in the winter.

About 25,000 firefighters controlled the fires and managed to protect major tourist sites from significant damage, but the price tag on the firefighting efforts came to $120 million. Final surveys showed that about 35 percent of the park's total land area had been blackened by the fires.

Some politicians and journalists criticized the National Park Service for allowing such widespread destruction. They claimed that the service's policy on fires was irresponsible and dangerous.

Two commissions of experts scrutinized the fire policy. They concluded that the policy was sound, but they recommended stricter limits on when and how long such fires should be allowed to burn. These recommendations were incorporated into Yellowstone's revised fire management plan and approved in April of 1992.

THINKING CRITICALLY

1 *Understanding Processes* Use what you have learned in this chapter about succession and fire-maintained communities to explain why the National Park Service might allow a naturally occurring fire to burn in Yellowstone.

2 *Expressing Viewpoints* Based on what you have read in this Case Study, do you think that the National Park Service's policy for controlling fires adequately protects humans and their property? Explain.

FIELD ACTIVITY

Explore two or three blocks in your neighborhood, and find evidence of succession. Make notes about the location and the evidence of succession that you observe. Pay attention to sidewalks, curbs, streets, vacant lots, and buildings, as well as parks, gardens, fields, and other open areas. Create a map from your data that identifies where succession is taking place in your neighborhood.

SECTION REVIEW

❶ How is primary succession different from secondary succession? How is it similar?

❷ Explain why it may be damaging in the long run to put out some forest fires.

❸ What important role do lichens play in primary succession?

THINKING CRITICALLY

❹ *Analyzing Processes* Over a period of 1,000 years, a lake becomes a maple forest. Is this primary or secondary succession? Explain your answer.

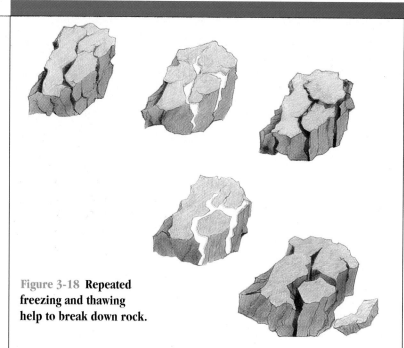

Figure 3-18 **Repeated freezing and thawing help to break down rock.**

trees and rocks. A lichen is actually composed of two species, a fungus and an alga, that have a mutualistic relationship with each other. The alga photosynthesizes, while the fungus absorbs nutrients from rocks. Together, they begin to break down the rock.

Water may freeze and thaw in cracks, breaking up the rock still further. (See Figure 3-18.) Soil slowly accumulates as dust particles in the air are trapped in cracks in the rock and as the dead remains of lichens and bacteria accumulate. Mosses may later gain a hold, breaking up the rock even more. When the mosses die, they decay and are added to the growing pile of soil. Thus, fertile soil is formed from the broken rock, decayed organisms, water, and air.

After some soil is formed, the seeds of small plants are able to germinate and grow. From this point on, the process is similar to secondary succession.

Primary succession can also be seen in any city street. Mosses, lichens, and weeds establish themselves in cracks in a sidewalk. Fungi and mosses invade a roof that needs repair. Even New York City would eventually turn into a cement-filled woodland if it were not constantly cleaned and maintained.

Figure 3-19 **Primary succession on a city sidewalk**

CHAPTER 3 • HOW ECOSYSTEMS WORK

HIGHLIGHTS

SUMMARY

- For the vast majority of the Earth's living things, the ultimate source of energy is the sun. Producer organisms harness the sun's energy directly. Consumer organisms use the energy indirectly, by eating other organisms.

- Only about 10 percent of the energy that an organism consumes is stored and there-fore transferred when that organism is eaten. The rest is lost during digestion and used up in carrying out life functions.

- Materials in ecosystems are endlessly recycled by natural processes.

- Carbon, water, and nitrogen are three materials essential for life, and each follows a recognizable cycle.

- The types of organisms in a community follow a regular pattern of change over time. This process is called succession.

- Eventually, a climax community takes hold and persists until it is disturbed once again.

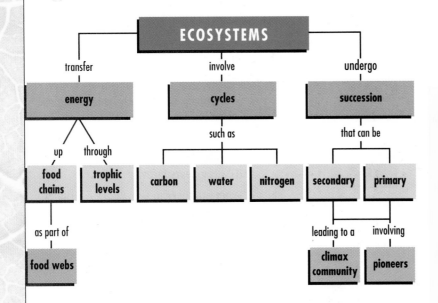

Vocabulary Terms

carnivore (p. 57)

cellular respiration (p. 57)

climax community (p. 67)

consumer (p. 56)

decomposer (p. 57)

food chain (p. 59)

food web (p. 60)

herbivore (p. 57)

nitrogen-fixing bacteria (p. 64)

omnivore (p. 57)

pioneers (p. 67)

precipitation (p. 63)

primary succession (p. 69)

producer (p. 56)

secondary succession (p. 67)

succession (p. 66)

trophic level (p. 60)

water cycle (p. 62)

EcoLog

Now that you've studied this chapter, revise your answers to the questions you answered at the beginning of the chapter, based on what you have learned.

❶ What does sunlight have to do with the amount of food available to a hawk, which eats only meat?

❷ How is it possible that an atom of nitrogen in your sandwich was once part of a dinosaur's body?

REVIEW

UNDERSTANDING VOCABULARY

1. For each pair of terms, explain the difference in their meanings.
   a. producer
      consumer
   b. carnivore
      omnivore
   c. carbon cycle
      nitrogen cycle
   d. food web
      food chain

RELATING CONCEPTS

2. Copy the unfinished concept map below onto a sheet of paper. Then complete the concept map by writing the correct word or phrase in each box containing a question mark.

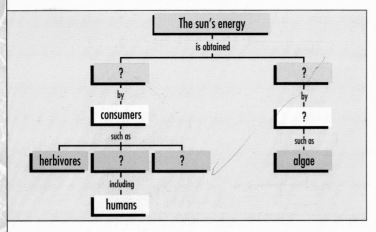

UNDERSTANDING CONCEPTS

Multiple Choice

3. Which is NOT true of consumers?
   a. They get energy indirectly from the sun.
   b. They are also called heterotrophs.
   c. They make their own food.
   d. They sometimes eat other consumers.

4. Which is correctly arranged from the lowest trophic level to the highest?
   a. bacteria, frog, eagle, mushroom
   b. algae, deer, wolf, hawk
   c. grass, mouse, snake, eagle
   d. grass, bass, minnow, snake

5. Communities of bacteria have been found living hundreds of feet underwater. Which is a proper conclusion to draw from this?
   a. Somehow they are conducting photosynthesis.
   b. They are living on borrowed time.
   c. They were somehow introduced by human activities.
   d. They use an energy source other than sunlight.

6. Which of these pairs of organisms probably belong to the same trophic level?
   a. humans, bears
   b. bears, deer
   c. humans, cows
   d. both a and c

7. The energy lost between trophic levels
   a. can be captured only by parasitic organisms.
   b. cools the surrounding environment.
   c. is used in the course of normal living.
   d. disappears forever.

8. From producer to *secondary* consumer, about how much energy is lost?
   a. 10 percent
   b. 90 percent
   c. 99 percent
   d. 100 percent

9. Which is NOT true of the nitrogen cycle?
   a. Animals get nitrogen by eating plants or other animals.
   b. Plants generate nitrogen in their roots.
   c. Nitrogen moves back and forth between the atmosphere and living things.
   d. Decomposers break down waste to yield ammonia.

10. The water cycle
    a. was instituted to save scarce water.
    b. is the process by which water is used and reused in nature.
    c. is the cycle by which water is broken down chemically and turned into other compounds.
    d. is the cycle in which water evaporates and is lost forever.

11. Vegetation slowly returns after a woodland is destroyed by fire. This is an example of
    a. primary succession.
    b. secondary succession.
    c. a climax community.
    d. the carbon cycle.

12. Simple organisms colonize the barren lava produced by a volcanic eruption. This is an example of
    a. primary succession.
    b. secondary succession.
    c. the rock cycle.
    d. a climax community.

13. Which of these are MOST likely to be the pioneer organisms on an area of bare rock?
    a. saplings
    b. shrubs
    c. lichens
    d. perennial grasses

Short Answer

14. Explain the relationship of cellular respiration to photosynthesis.

15. Why can't there be an unlimited number of trophic levels?

16. Why are decomposers an essential part of an ecosystem?

17. Is there a starting point to the water cycle? Is there an ending point? Explain.

18. Describe the role of carbon dioxide in the carbon cycle.

INTERPRETING GRAPHICS

19. **Examine the graph below.** It shows the sea level over a period of thousands of years, sometime in the past. Since water is not usually destroyed but is instead recycled through the water cycle, what does this graph tell you about the location of the Earth's water during the time indicated? Where might the water have been?

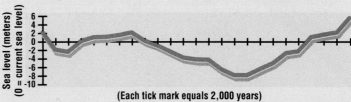

(Each tick mark equals 2,000 years)

THINKING CRITICALLY

20. *Comparing Processes* How are producers and decomposers in some ways opposites of each other?

21. *Inferring Relationships* Abandoned fields in the southwestern part of the United States are often taken over by mesquite trees, which can grow in nutrient-poor soil. If the land is later cleared of mesquite, the soil is often found to be enriched with nitrogen and is therefore more suitable for crops. What might be the reason for this phenomenon?

THEMES IN SCIENCE

22. *Evolution* Compare the process of succession with the process of evolution. How are the two processes similar? How are they different?

23. *Interacting Systems* Suppose that a plague eliminates all the primary consumers in an ecosystem. What will most likely happen to organisms in other trophic levels?

CROSS-DISCIPLINE CONNECTION

24. *Math* If a lake contains 600,000 kg of plankton and the top consumers are a population of 40 pike, each weighing an average of 15 kg, how many trophic levels does the lake contain?

PORTFOLIO ACTIVITY

Do a special project on succession. Find areas in your community that have been cleared of vegetation and left unattended at different times in the past. Ideally, you should find several areas that were cleared at different times, from recently to decades ago. Photograph each area, and arrange the pictures to show how succession takes place in your geographic region.

 internetconnect

SCLINKS NSTA National Science Teachers Association On-Line Resources www.scilinks.org

When you see a SciLinks logo, visit the NSTA Web site and type in the keyword. There you will find current information relevant to that section or topic.

INVESTIGATION

WHAT'S IN AN ECOSYSTEM?

How well do you know the environment around your home or school? You may walk through it every day without noticing most of the living things it contains or thinking about how they survive. Ecologists, on the other hand, notice and seek to understand how ecosystems work. Ecology is the study of the relationships between living things and their environments. In this Investigation, you will play the role of an ecologist by observing an environmental site in detail. You will collect data about both its physical features, or *abiotic* factors, and the organisms that live there, or *biotic* factors. You will then examine the interrelationships among these factors.

MAP A SITE

1. CAUTION: Before beginning your field study, review the safety guidelines on pages 409–412. Remember to approach all plants and animals with caution.

2. With a tape measure or meter stick, measure a 10 m × 10 m square site to be studied. Place one stake at each corner of the site. Loop the string around each stake, running the string from one to the next, to form boundaries for the site.

3. Mark off as large a square as possible on the poster board to serve as a map of your site. Draw the physical features of the site on the map. For example, show the location of streams, sidewalks, trails, or large rocks, and indicate the direction of any noticeable slope.

4. Think of a set of symbols to represent the organisms at your site. For example, you might use green triangles to represent trees, blue circles to represent insects, brown squares to represent animal burrows or nests, and so on. At the bottom or side of the poster board, make a key to your symbols.

MATERIALS

- tape measure or meter stick
- 4 stakes
- string (about 50 m)
- poster board
- markers or felt-tip pens of several different colors
- notebook
- pen or pencil

Use stakes and string to mark off a site that you will observe in detail.

5. Draw your symbols on the map to show the location and relative abundance of organisms. If there is not enough space on your map to indicate the specific kinds of plants and animals you observed, record them in your notebook.

6. Which symbols represent producers? Which represent consumers? Which represent decomposers? Write your answers in your notebook.

7. In your notebook, record any observations of organisms interacting with each other or with their environment. (For example, note if you see insects feeding on plants or seeking shelter under rocks.)

8. After completing the maps and observations, rewind the string and remove the stakes. Do not destroy or remove anything from the site.

ANALYZE RELATIONSHIPS

9. Return to the classroom, and display your site map. Use your site map and those of your classmates, together with your notes, to answer the following questions. Write your answers in your notebook.

10. List two food chains found on the maps, each containing a producer and two consumers.

11. Remember that as energy is transferred through food chains in an ecosystem, the amount of energy available decreases at successively higher trophic levels. Given this fact, would you expect there to be more producers or more consumers in the sites you mapped? Do your observations confirm this expectation? Consider both the number of organisms and their biomass (volume and weight). If your observation does not match your expectation, suggest an explanation for the situation you observed.

12. What decomposers did you observe? What additional decomposers might be present, though not visible?

13. What role do decomposers play in the environment? What would happen to the producers and consumers if there were no decomposers?

14. How are the biotic factors (organisms) affected by the abiotic factors (nonliving things)? How are the abiotic factors affected by the biotic factors?

EXPLORE FURTHER

15. Based on what you have learned, think of a question that explores how the components of the ecosystem you observed interact with each other. For example, you might want to consider the influence of humans on the site; study a particular food chain in more detail; or explore the effect of physical features, such as water or sunlight, on the growth or behavior of organisms. Describe how you would investigate this question.

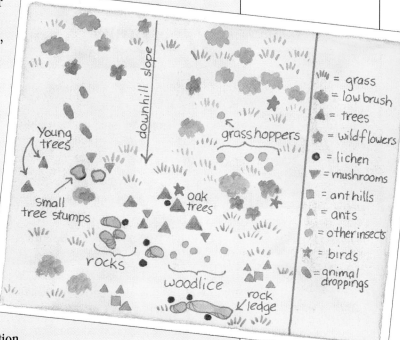

In this site map, which symbols represent producers, and which represent consumers?

Where Should the Wolves Roam?

n the 1920s the gray wolf was exterminated from much of the northwestern United States. Ranchers and federal agents killed the animal to protect livestock. Today the gray wolf is an endangered species. In January 1995, the U.S. Fish and Wildlife Service reintroduced 41 wolves to Yellowstone National Park and 35 wolves to central Idaho. As of 1997, there were 80–90 wolves in each location. The goal is to establish a population of at least 100 wolves at each location by 2002. However, some ranchers and hunters are uneasy about the plan, and some environmentalists and wolf enthusiasts think that the plan doesn't go far enough to protect wolves. Read the following points of view, and then analyze the issue for yourself.

WOLVES SHOULD BE REINTRODUCED

The gray wolf has lost most of its breeding range in the contiguous United States (left). Under the current plan, wolves will be reintroduced to parts of Montana, Wyoming, and Idaho (right).

Many environmentalists and scientists believe that the reintroduction plan could bring Yellowstone National Park and two other areas into ecological balance for the first time in 60 years. They believe that the wolves will eliminate old and weak animals in elk, moose, and deer populations and help keep the populations of these animals from growing beyond the resources of their environment. If the project continues as planned, wolves may be removed from the endangered species list by the year 2002.

In response to ranchers' concerns that wolves will kill livestock, some biologists offer evidence that most wolves living near areas with adequate populations of deer, elk, moose, and other prey do not attack livestock. In fact, from 1995–1997 fewer than five wolf attacks on livestock were reported.

In response to fears that the wolves pose a threat to humans, proponents of the plan say that there have been no substantiated or documented attacks on humans by healthy wolves in North America. Wolves are shy animals that prefer to keep their distance from people, supporters of the plan say.

Most wolf enthusiasts readily admit that there are places where wolves belong and places where wolves do not belong. They believe that the selected reintroduction zones offer environments where wolves can carry out a vital role without becoming a serious liability to humans.

A naturalist at the International Wolf Center, in Minnesota, describes wolf behavior to visitors.

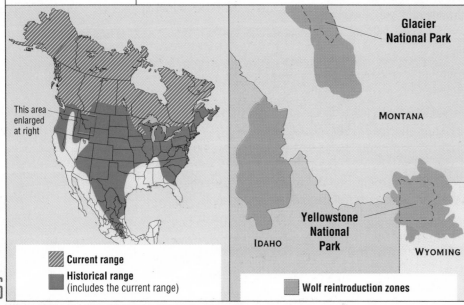

This area enlarged at right

Current range

Historical range
(includes the current range)

Glacier National Park

MONTANA

Yellowstone National Park

IDAHO

WYOMING

Wolf reintroduction zones

Some opponents of the reintroduction plan argue that wolves should not be classified as endangered at all. According to data from biologists, there are 1,500 to 2,000 wolves in Minnesota, 6,000 to 10,000 in Alaska, and 40,000 to 50,000 in Canada. With such numbers, many people feel that the animal should not receive the special treatment given to endangered species.

Hunters oppose the plan because they worry that wolves will kill a large share of the total number of animals that can be hunted. They cite studies that say large game animal populations cannot withstand hunting by both humans and wolves. This is a problem, they say, not only because it limits their hunting success, but also because hunting has a significant positive impact on the economies of the Western states. Furthermore, hunting is a valuable tool that park rangers use to control wildlife populations and to obtain funds for programs that are designed to help wildlife, such as habitat improvement and wildlife studies.

Ranchers are concerned that wolves will kill livestock. These losses could result in a tremendous financial burden to ranchers. A compensation program established by an environmental group to help reimburse ranchers will be in effect only as long as the wolf is classified as an endangered species. Ranchers point out that when wolves are plentiful enough to warrant removal from the endangered species list, the problem of wolf predation will be critical and yet compensation will no longer be available.

Gray wolf in Montana

ANALYZE THE ISSUE

1. ***Expressing Viewpoints*** Supporters of the reintroduction plan suggest that much of the controversy surrounding the reintroduction of the gray wolf stems from a fear of wolves created by myths and legends about "the big, bad wolf." Do you think it is possible that society has given the gray wolf a negative reputation that it simply does not deserve? Support your opinion with examples.

2. ***Analyzing Viewpoints*** Opponents of the reintroduction plan often say that defenders of the gray wolf have had little, if any, direct experience with the animal and its ferocious instinct to kill. Do you think a person needs to have direct experience with a wolf to have an informed opinion about this issue? Explain.

4

KINDS OF ECOSYSTEMS

"In all things of nature there is something of the marvelous."

ARISTOTLE, GREEK PHILOSOPHER

EcoLog

Before you read this chapter, take a few minutes to answer the following questions in your EcoLog.

❶ What are the general characteristics of the ecosystem in which you live? Are there ecosystems similar to yours in other parts of the world?

❷ Describe a plant or animal that lives in your area, and describe its survival strategy.

FORESTS

AFTER READING THIS SECTION YOU SHOULD BE ABLE TO

❶ define *biome.*

❷ compare and contrast the world's forest biomes.

❸ describe plant and animal adaptations in each kind of forest.

Earth is covered by hundreds of types of ecosystems. For convenience, ecologists group these into a few biomes. **Biomes** are areas that have distinctive climates and organisms. Each biome contains many individual ecosystems. The locations of the major biomes are shown in Figure 4-1. Biomes are usually named for their plant life because the plants that can grow in an area determine what other organisms can live there. But what determines which plants can grow in a certain area? The main determinant is climate. *Climate* refers to weather conditions in an area—temperature, precipitation, humidity, and winds—over a long period of time. Temperature and precipitation (rain, sleet, and snow) are the two most important factors in a region's climate. These and other aspects of climate are discussed in greater detail in Chapter 7.

In this chapter, you'll take a tour through the major biomes of the world—from lush rain forests to scorching deserts, and from the depths of the ocean to the icy polar regions. When reading about each biome, notice the adaptations of the organisms to their very different environments.

Figure 4-1 **The world's ecosystems can be grouped into regions known as biomes based on the dominant plants, animals, and climates present.**

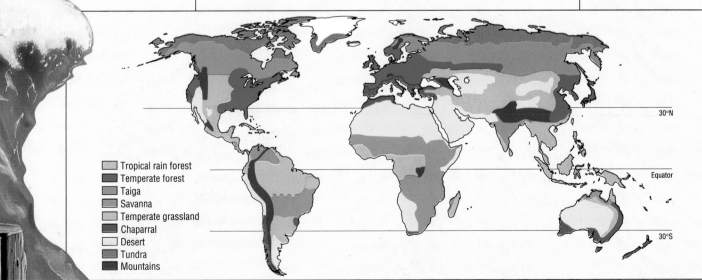

- Tropical rain forest
- Temperate forest
- Taiga
- Savanna
- Temperate grassland
- Chaparral
- Desert
- Tundra
- Mountains

30°N

Equator

30°S

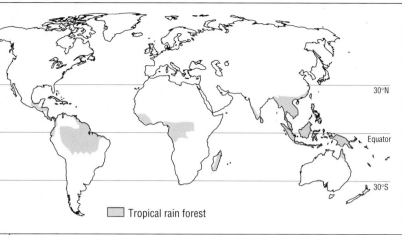

30°N

Equator

30°S

Tropical rain forest

Figure 4-2 The world's tropical rain forests are characterized by heavy rainfall and fairly constant warm temperatures year-round.

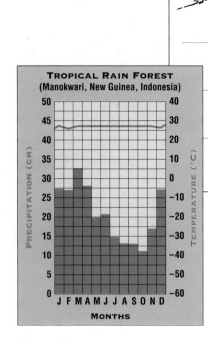

TROPICAL RAIN FOREST
(Manokwari, New Guinea, Indonesia)

PRECIPITATION (CM)

TEMPERATURE (°C)

J F M A M J J A S O N D
MONTHS

Figure 4-3 Tropical rain forests, which contain perhaps half of all species on Earth, have the greatest biological diversity of any biome.

TROPICAL RAIN FORESTS

The air is hot and heavy with humidity. You walk through the shade of the rain forest, stepping carefully over tangles of roots and vines and brushing past enormous leaves. Life is all around you, but you see little on the surprisingly bare forest floor. Birds call, and monkeys chatter high above.

Tropical rain forests occur in a belt around the Earth near the equator, as shown in Figure 4-2. They are always humid and

Tropical rain forest, Trinidad

Arum lily, Costa Rica

Malayan lacewing butterfly, Malaysia

Bromeliad and orchid on tree trunks, Costa Rica

The world's largest flower, ► *Rafflesia keithii,* Borneo

warm and get about 250 cm (100 in.) of rain a year. Because they are near the equator, tropical rain forests get strong sunlight year-round, maintaining a climate with little seasonal variation in temperature.

The climate is ideal for growing plants, which flourish in tropical forests year-round. The warm, wet conditions also nourish more plant species than any other biome. While 1 hectare of temperate forest contains about 10 species of trees, the same area of a tropical rain forest may contain over 100 species.

You might think that this profusion of plants grows on rich soil, but it does not. Rapid decay of plants and animals returns nutrients to the soil, but these nutrients are just as quickly picked up by the plants. The remaining nutrients are washed away by rainfall, so the soil is usually thin and poor. Many of the trees form aboveground roots that grow sideways from the trees, providing extra support in the thin soil.

Monkey ladder vine, Trinidad

Golden lion marmoset, Brazil

Young scarlet macaws, Peru

Figure 4-4 The vegetation of the rain forest forms distinct layers. The plants of each layer are adapted to a particular level of light.

Emergent trees

Bright light

Upper canopy

Lower canopy

Filtered light

Understory

Dense shade

Plant Adaptations In tropical rain forests, plants grow in layers, as shown in Figure 4-4. Trees more than 30 m (100 ft.) tall form a dense **canopy** that absorbs at least 95 percent of the sunlight. Above the canopy, the tallest trees emerge into direct sunlight. Below the canopy, little light reaches the understory, and only trees and shrubs adapted to shade can grow there. Herbs with large flat leaves capture the small amount of sunlight that penetrates to the forest floor.

When fallen trees create an opening in the canopy, tree seedlings that are adapted to grow quickly outcompete other seedlings for sunlight. Many plants, such as orchids and monkey ladder vines, use the tall tree trunks for support high in the canopy, where there is light for photosynthesis.

Animal Adaptations The incredible diversity of rain-forest vegetation may have led to the evolution of the greatest diversity of animals anywhere on Earth. Most rain-forest animals are *specialists,* organisms adapted to exploit a specific resource in a particular way to avoid competition. For example, there are several species of birds called antwrens that eat insects, but each species catches insects in a different layer of forest vegetation. Another example is flowering plants that can be pollinated by only one species of insect, bat, or bird that can reach the flower's nectar.

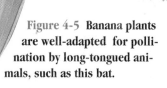

Figure 4-5 Banana plants are well-adapted for pollination by long-tongued animals, such as this bat.

Figure 4-6 This Brazilian butterfly mimics a dead leaf to hide from predators.

Some rain-forest animals have evolved elaborate methods for escaping predators, and others have evolved equally sophisticated methods for snaring prey. Camouflage is common. Insects, such as the butterfly shown in Figure 4-6, may be shaped like leaves or twigs. Some frogs blend in perfectly with plants; others have poisons in their skin that are advertised with bright colors to warn predators.

Threats to Rain Forests

Tropical rain forests used to cover about 20 percent of the Earth's surface. Today they cover about 7 percent. Every year an area of tropical rain forest the size of North and South Carolina combined is stripped by logging operations or cleared for farming or cattle grazing. (See Figure 4-7.) With the disappearance of these and other habitats, plants and animals become extinct. And native peoples, such as the Malaysian nomads shown in Figure 4-8, are often displaced, their culture and traditions lost.

You can help save rain forests by buying products that promote the sustainable use of rain forests. Look for "rain-forest friendly" labels on products such as brazil nuts, tropical fruits, and coffee. You can also support organizations that help preserve tropical forests. To learn more about a country that is saving some of its rain forests, read the Case Study about Costa Rica on pages 84–85.

Figure 4-7 **Forest on this Costa Rican hillside was cleared for cattle ranching.**

TOPIC: threats to rain forests
GO TO: www.scilinks.org
KEYWORD: HE083

Figure 4-8 **The nomadic people shown at left are attempting to block the logging of the Malaysian rain forests where they have lived for generations.**

SC*LINKS*

NSTA

TOPIC: temperate forests
GO TO: www.scilinks.org
KEYWORD: HEØ84

TEMPERATE FORESTS

Temperate rain forests occur in North and South America, Australia, and New Zealand. The Pacific Northwest is home to North America's only temperate rain forest, where tree branches are draped with mosses and tree trunks are clothed in lichens. The forest floor is blanketed with lush ferns. Towering, 300-ft.-tall evergreen trees such as Sitka spruce and Douglas fir dominate the

SAVING COSTA RICAN BIOMES

CASE STUDY

Today human actions are altering virtually every biome on Earth. Many countries are attempting to preserve particularly interesting areas as national parks and wildlife preserves. This concern is clearly evident in Costa Rica, a small country in Central America. Once almost entirely covered by magnificent forests, Costa Rica has suffered an extremely high rate of deforestation in the past 20 years. But Costa Rica still has many unique and beautiful ecosystems,

and Costa Rican leaders hope to protect them.

About 25 percent of Costa Rica is now set aside in national parks and preserves. The protected areas include every major biome type in tropical Central America. Sections of rain forests, deciduous forests, coral reefs, volcanic mountain regions, and páramo (high open plains) are all protected in the nation's program.

One goal is to link many of the parks and preserves with forest corridors. The corridors will allow species a larger area from which to choose their breeding partners. This is an important step in helping species remain healthy and fertile because it allows for a constant exchange

of genetic material.

Another goal of the program is to encourage practices that do not cause permanent damage to the country's land and wildlife, such as sustainable agriculture. An increasing number of Costa Rican wildlife specialists are helping to further this effort.

Other Costa Rican residents are taking a scientific interest in the diversity of plants and animals

Costa Rica is in Central America.

forest. Moisture pervades everything in this cool, humid forest.

Although the forest is located at about 48° north latitude, it rarely freezes because nearby Pacific Ocean waters moderate the temperature. In this area, winds travel from west to east. Ocean winds pick up moisture that is dropped on the coastal forests because the Olympic Mountains block the winds' passage eastward. The high rainfall and moderate temperatures have created an ideal ecosystem for the abundant growth of forest plants.

This area of the United States has become the subject of controversy in recent years because of conflicts over logging. You can read about the logging controversy in Chapters 8 and 10.

TEMPERATE DECIDUOUS FORESTS

To walk through a North American deciduous forest in the fall is to immerse yourself in color. Leaves in every shade of orange, red, and yellow crackle beneath your feet. The forest is quieter than it was in the summer. Most birds have flown south. You see mostly chipmunks and squirrels gathering and storing the food they'll need during the long, cold winter.

These tourists are enjoying the beauty of Manuel Antonio National Park, in Costa Rica.

that live in the country's rain forests. For example, a group of residents is helping an American pharmaceutical company study rain-forest plants and animals in the hopes of finding ingredients for medicines. A portion of the American company's licensing fees and possible future profits will be used to help preserve the forest's resources.

Organizations around the world also recognize the value of Costa Rica's resources. Environmental groups help Costa Rica obtain funds for protecting its natural treasures. Students help by establishing international children's rain forests. "Adopt-an-Acre" programs, which enable a person to adopt one or more acres of rain forest, successfully draw hundreds of thousands of dollars each year.

Costa Rica is also encouraging tourism. Tourist dollars provide a strong incentive for Costa Ricans to conserve the natural resources of their country. Tourist interest and appreciation also lead residents to take pride in those treasures.

These are just a few of the many aspects of Costa Rica's conservation program. The fact that the program is ambitious and yet successful has captured the world's attention. Many other countries are now taking similar steps to ensure the conservation of their own unique natural resources.

THINKING CRITICALLY

❶ *Making Inferences* Why might a country's policy makers hesitate before enacting serious conservation measures?

❷ *Understanding Relationships* Why would encouraging national pride in a country's resources be part of a conservation program? What else have Costa Rican officials done to change the attitudes of Costa Rican residents?

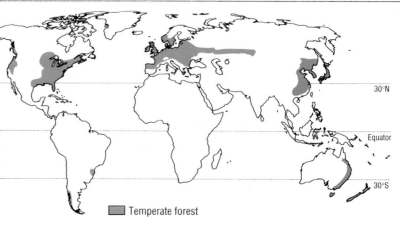

Figure 4-10 **Temperate deciduous forests experience extreme changes in temperature from summer to winter.**

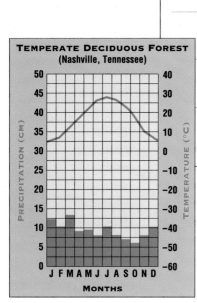

TEMPERATE DECIDUOUS FOREST
(Nashville, Tennessee)

PRECIPITATION (CM) / TEMPERATURE (°C)

J F M A M J J A S O N D
MONTHS

In **temperate deciduous forests,** trees drop their broad, flat leaves each fall. These forests once dominated vast regions of the Earth, including parts of North America, Europe, and Asia. (See Figure 4-13.) Deciduous forests generally occur between 30° and 50° north latitude, so seasonal variations can be extreme, and the growing season lasts only four to six months. Summer temperatures can soar to 35°C (95°F). Winter temperatures often plummet well below freezing.

Deciduous forests are moist, receiving 75–250 cm (30–100 in.) of precipitation annually. The rain and snow help decompose dead organic matter, such as fallen leaves, which in turn contributes to the rich, deep soils of deciduous forests.

Plant Adaptations As in rain forests, the plants in deciduous forests grow in layers. The forest canopy is dominated by tall trees

Figure 4-11 **A temperate deciduous forest in Woodstock, New York, in summer, fall, and winter.**

such as maple, oak, and birch. Small trees, shrubs, and bushes abound in the understory. The forest floor gets more light than that of a rain forest, and more plants—ferns, herbs, and mosses— grow there as a consequence.

Temperate-forest plants are adapted to survive seasonal changes. In winter, when ice locks up moisture in the soil, deciduous trees shed their leaves. Herb seeds, bulbs, and rhizomes (underground stems) become dormant in the ground, somewhat insulated by the cover of leaf litter and snow. In spring, as sunlight increases and temperatures rise, trees put out new leaves, seeds germinate, and rhizomes and roots put forth new shoots.

Animal Adaptations The animals of deciduous forests are adapted to exploit the forest plants for food and shelter. Squirrels eat the nuts, seeds, and fruits in the treetops. Bears feast on the leaves and sweet berries of forest plants. Deer and other browsers nibble leaves from trees and shrubs.

Many birds nest in the relative safety of the canopy. Most of these birds are migratory. Because they cannot survive the harsh winters, each fall they fly south to warmer weather and available food. Each spring they return north to nest in temperate forests and feed on the abundance of food. Animals that do not migrate use various strategies for surviving the winter. Mammals such as bears and squirrels become inactive. Insects also enter a state of very low metabolic activity.

Figure 4-12 **Deer, squirrels, and bears are among the numerous animals of the temperate deciduous forest.**

Figure 4-13 **The original forests of the United States have dwindled since Europeans settled in North America.**

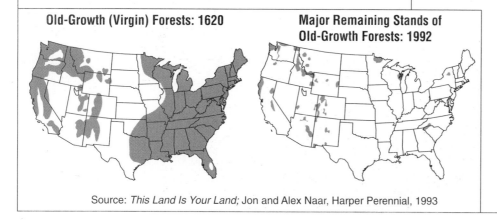

Old-Growth (Virgin) Forests: 1620

Major Remaining Stands of Old-Growth Forests: 1992

Source: *This Land Is Your Land;* Jon and Alex Naar, Harper Perennial, 1993

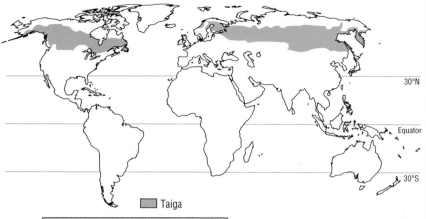

Taiga

TAIGA

In the taiga, or "boreal forest," the terrain is rough and the forest floor is sparsely vegetated. From the ground, many trees seem like straight, dead shafts of bark and wood—until you look up and see their green tops.

The **taiga** is the northern coniferous forest, which stretches in a broad band across the northern hemisphere just below the Arctic Circle. As shown in Figure 4-14, winters are long (6 to 10 months) and extremely cold, with average subfreezing temperatures that often plummet to −20°C (−4°F). The frost-free growing season may be as short as 50 days depending on latitude. Plant growth, however, is enhanced by constant daylight during the summer. Most of the precipitation falls as snow.

Plant Adaptations A conifer is a tree whose seeds develop in cones. Most conifers do not shed their needle-shaped leaves, which help them survive harsh winters. The leaves' narrow shape and waxy coating retain water for the tree when the moisture in the ground is frozen. A conifer's typical pointed shape helps it shed snow whose weight would otherwise crush it. These and other adaptations are shown in Figure 4-16. Dominant tree species include pine, hemlock, fir, and spruce.

Conifer needles contain acidic substances that acidify the soil when the needles fall. Most plants can't grow in acidic soil,

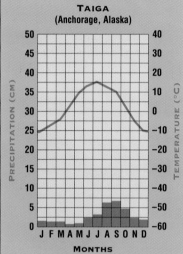

Figure 4-14 **The taiga has long, cold winters and low precipitation.**

Figure 4-15 **The taiga is characterized by conifers, trees whose seeds grow in cones.**

which is one reason the forest floor is bare of most plants except blueberries, a few ferns, and mosses. Soil forms slowly because the climate and acidity of the leaf litter hinder decomposition.

Animal Adaptations The taiga is dotted with lakes and swamps that in summer attract birds that feed on insects, fish, or other wetland organisms. Many birds migrate south to avoid winter in the taiga. Some year-round residents, such as shrews and voles, may burrow underground during the winter, insulated by the deep snow cover. Moose and arctic hares eat what vegetation they can find. As shown in Figure 4-18, hares have adapted to avoid predation by lynx, wolves, and foxes by shedding their brown summer fur and growing white fur that camouflages them against the winter snow.

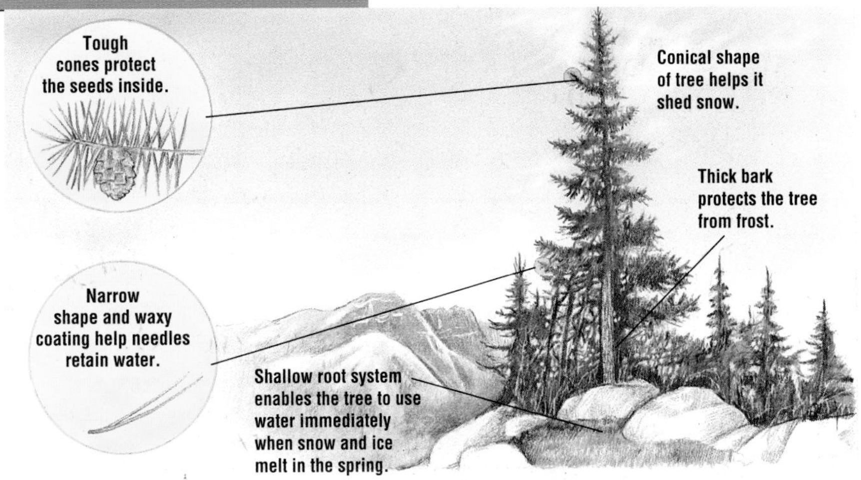

Tough cones protect the seeds inside.

Conical shape of tree helps it shed snow.

Thick bark protects the tree from frost.

Narrow shape and waxy coating help needles retain water.

Shallow root system enables the tree to use water immediately when snow and ice melt in the spring.

Figure 4-16 **Coniferous trees have adaptations that help them survive the snow and extreme cold of winter.**

Figure 4-17 **These year-round residents of the taiga have thick fur that helps them survive the long winter.**

Gray wolves, Canada

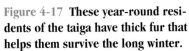
Lynx, Canada

Moose, Alaska

Figure 4-18 **The hare's fur changes color according to the season to help camouflage it from predators.**

❶ Which aspects of climate are most important to forest ecosystems?

❷ How does a temperate rain forest differ from the taiga?

❸ Which would be better suited for agriculture, the soil of a tropical rain forest, or that of a temperate deciduous forest? Explain.

THINKING CRITICALLY

❹ *Relating Concepts* Draw a concept map about the four types of forest ecosystems. Include at least one plant or animal from each forest type.

GRASSLANDS, CHAPARRAL, DESERTS, AND TUNDRA

AFTER READING THIS SECTION YOU SHOULD BE ABLE TO

❶ describe the factors that shape and characterize grassland, chaparral, desert, and tundra ecosystems.

❷ explain how the adaptations of plants and animals in each ecosystem help them to survive.

In climates where there is less rainfall, forests give way to savannas, grasslands, and chaparral, which in turn give way to deserts. As precipitation decreases, so too does the diversity of species present. But while the number of different species is often smaller, the number of individuals of each species present may be staggering. Far to the north, another type of "desert" occurs—the tundra. Like the desert, little precipitation occurs in the tundra, but unlike the desert, temperatures stay very cold year-round.

Figure 4-19 Savannas have periods of heavy rainfall followed by periods of drought.

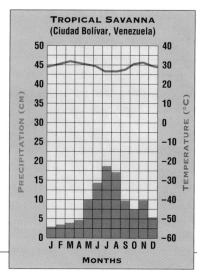

SAVANNAS

The West African plains, called **savannas,** contain the greatest collection of grazing animals on Earth—along with the magnificent predators that hunt them. Savannas are found in the tropics, near the equator. Yet they get too little rain for many trees to grow. As Figure 4-19 shows, rain falls mainly at certain times of the year. Grass fires may sweep across the savanna during the dry season.

Plant Adaptations

Savanna trees and grasses have large underground root systems that survive fire, so plants regrow quickly after a fire. The root systems also help the plants survive during the parched dry season. The coarse savanna grasses have vertical leaves that further help them conserve water. Trees and shrubs often have thorns or razor-sharp leaves that deter hungry herbivores.

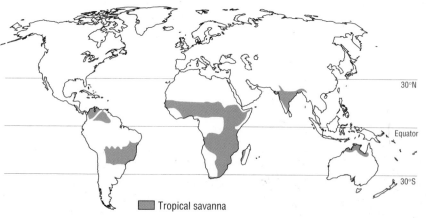

Tropical savanna

Figure 4-20 **Savanna, Tarangire National Park, Tanzania**

Animal Adaptations Large, grazing herbivores have adopted a migratory way of life; they follow the rains to areas of newly sprouted grass. Some predators follow this mobile food source. Many savanna animals give birth only during the rainy season, when food is most abundant and the young are more likely to survive. Herbivores avoid competition for food by eating vegetation at different heights; small gazelles graze on grasses, black rhinos browse on shrubs, and giraffes feed on tree leaves.

Figure 4-21 **Savanna herbivores reduce competition for food by feeding on vegetation at different heights. Giraffes feed on tree leaves, while impala graze on grasses.**

Figure 4-22 **To find freshly sprouted grasses, wildebeests migrate in huge herds over long distances. The wildebeests shown below are crossing the Mara River in Kenya.**

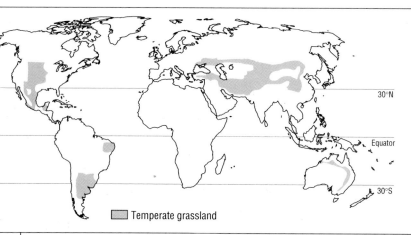

Figure 4-23 **Temperate grasslands are characterized by low rainfall, periodic droughts, and high temperatures.**

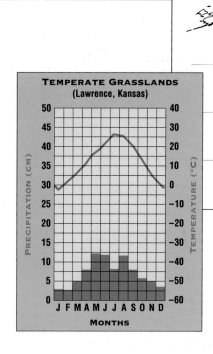

TEMPERATE GRASSLANDS
(Lawrence, Kansas)

Figure 4-24 **Grasslands occur on many continents and are known by several different names.**

TEMPERATE GRASSLANDS: PRAIRIES, STEPPES, AND PAMPAS

In eighteenth-century North America, Conestoga wagons were swallowed up by the 12-ft.-high grasses of the tallgrass prairies. Oxen sometimes died of thirst as wagon trains pushed west over the vast, dry shortgrass prairies. Although they seemed formidable, grasslands have the most fertile soil of any biome. It is no surprise, then, that most grasslands have been replaced with crops of corn, soybean, and wheat. The world's grasslands once covered about 42 percent of the total land surface of the Earth. Today, temperate grasslands occupy only about 12 percent of the Earth's surface. (See Figure 4-23.)

Temperate grasslands are found in the interiors of continents where there is too little rainfall for trees to grow. In addition to the prairies, there are the steppes of Russia and Ukraine and the pampas of South America. Mountains often play a crucial role in maintaining grasslands. For example, in North America, rain clouds from the west

Shortgrass prairie, Colorado

Steppe, Mongolia

Pampa, Argentina

are blocked by the Rocky Mountains, so the shortgrass prairie east of the mountains gets only about 25 cm (10 in.) of rain a year. Rainfall increases as you move eastward, so taller grasses and some shrubs can grow. Heavy precipitation is rare; sizzling temperatures in summer make the grasslands a tinderbox. Thus, fire is common in the grassland biome.

Plant Adaptations Prairie grasses are perennials, surviving from year to year. Their root systems form dense mats that survive drought and fire and hold the soil in place. The amount of rainfall determines what types of grasses will grow in an area. Figure 4-25 shows how root depth and grass height vary with rainfall. Few trees survive on the grassland because of drought, fire, and the constant battering of winds that roar over the land.

Animal Adaptations Grazing animals, such as pronghorn antelope and American buffalo (also called bison), have large, flat back teeth for chewing the coarse prairie grasses. Along with other large mammals, such as wolves, these grazers cope with severe winters by growing thick coats of fur that they shed in spring. Other plains animals, such as badgers, prairie dogs, and even owls, live protected in underground burrows. The burrows shield them from fire and the elements and protect them from predators on the open grasslands.

Threats to Temperate Grasslands Cultivation and overgrazing have changed the grasslands. The grain crops that have replaced native grasses cannot hold the soil in place as well because their roots are shallow, and soil erosion results. Overgrazed grasses are constantly chewed down and cannot regenerate or hold the soil, causing further erosion.

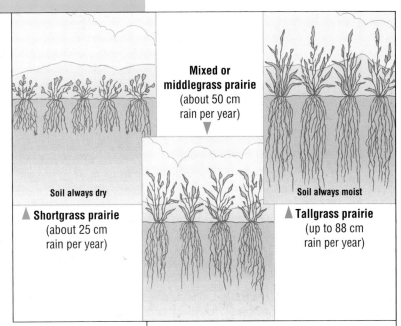

Mixed or middlegrass prairie (about 50 cm rain per year)

Soil always dry

▲ Shortgrass prairie (about 25 cm rain per year)

Soil always moist

▲ Tallgrass prairie (up to 88 cm rain per year)

Figure 4-25 **The height of grassland plants as well as the depth of roots depends on the amount of rainfall.**

Figure 4-26 **The prairie dogs shown below live in the Black Hills of South Dakota.**

Figure 4-27 **Because the soil is so fertile, most of the world's tallgrass prairies have been plowed under for crops. At left is a tallgrass prairie in central Iowa.**

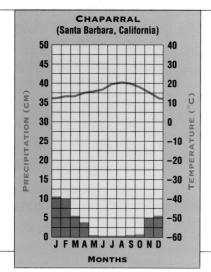

CHAPARRAL
(Santa Barbara, California)

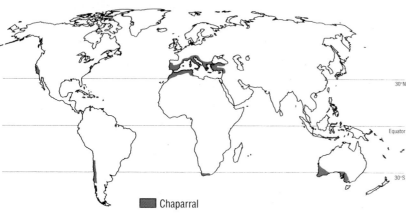

Figure 4-28 **Chaparral occurs in areas with Mediterranean climates.**

Figure 4-29 **The chaparral surrounding the famous Hollywood sign is home to plants such as the manzanita, shown in the inset at right.**

CHAPARRAL

Picture the famous white letters that spell *Hollywood* across green and brown California hills. Now imagine the scrub-covered settings common in old westerns—they are similar to deserts but have more vegetation. This landscape is part of a biome known as chaparral.

Chaparral is a biome that occurs in the mid-latitudes, about 30 degrees north and south of the equator. It lies primarily in coastal areas that have Mediterranean climates. As shown in Figure 4-28, these areas are known for their hot, dry summers; mild, wet winters; and slight variations in seasonal temperature.

Plant Adaptations Chaparral plants are mostly low-lying evergreen shrubs and small trees. Common chaparral plants include chamise, manzanita, scrub oak, olive trees, and cooking herbs such as sage and bay. These plants have small, leathery leaves that resist water loss. The leaves also contain oils that promote burning, which is an advantage because natural fires destroy trees that might compete with chaparral plants for light and space. Chaparral plants are so well adapted to fire that they can resprout from small bits of surviving tissue. The flammable oils give plants such as sage their characteristic taste and smell.

Animal Adaptations A common adaptation of chaparral animals is camouflage—shape or coloring that allows an animal to blend into its environment. Animals such as quail, lizards, chipmunks, and mule deer have brownish gray coats that let them move unseen through the drab brush. (See Figure 4-30.) Chaparral animals are also adapted to seasonal differences in food. The scrub jay, for example, has a beak adapted for a varied diet of insects, seeds, other birds' eggs, and occasionally even baby birds!

Threats to Chaparral Worldwide, the biggest threat to chaparral is human development. Because the biome has lots of sun, access to the ocean, and a mild year-round climate, people have developed much of the chaparral landscape.

DESERTS

When some people think of deserts, they think of Lawrence of Arabia riding a camel over towering sand dunes. Others picture the Sonoran Desert with its mighty saguaro cacti, the California desert graced with Joshua trees, or the magnificent rock formations of Monument Valley, in Arizona and Utah. There are many different kinds of deserts, but one characteristic they all share is that they are the driest places on Earth.

Deserts are defined as areas that receive less than 25 cm (10 in.) of precipitation a year. Hot deserts, such as Arizona's Sonoran Desert, occur closer to the equator than cold deserts, such as the Great Basin area. Deserts often occur in the rain shadow of mountains that block the passage of moisture-filled clouds. (See Figure 4-32.)

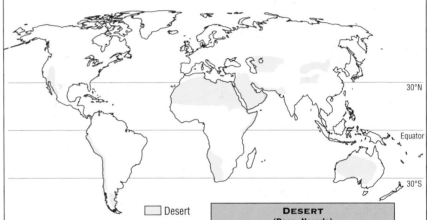

Figure 4-30 **This California quail uses camouflage to hide from predators such as hawks and coyotes.**

Figure 4-31 **Deserts are the driest places on Earth.**

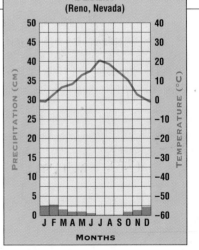

DESERT
(Reno, Nevada)

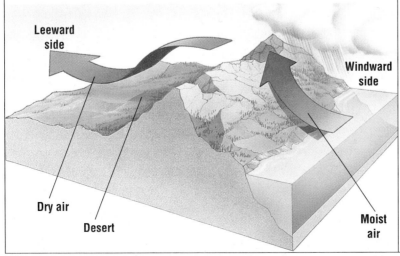

Figure 4-32 **Mountains sometimes block the passage of rain, creating a "rain shadow" where deserts form.**

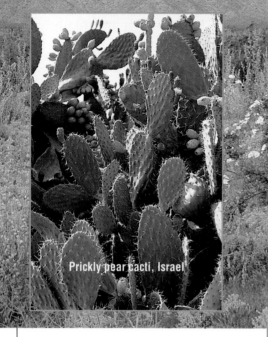
Prickly pear cacti, Israel

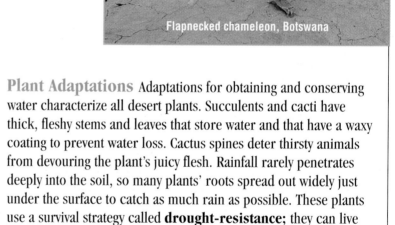
Flapnecked chameleon, Botswana

Figure 4-33 Desert organisms are adapted to survive in a place with little water.

FIELD ACTIVITY

Create a miniature desert by growing a small cactus garden. Purchase two or three small cactus plants, or take several cuttings from a large cactus. To take cuttings, carefully break off the shoots growing at the base of the parent cactus. Place the plants in rocky or sandy soil similar to the soil in a desert. Keep the cacti in bright sunlight, and water them infrequently.

Plant Adaptations Adaptations for obtaining and conserving water characterize all desert plants. Succulents and cacti have thick, fleshy stems and leaves that store water and that have a waxy coating to prevent water loss. Cactus spines deter thirsty animals from devouring the plant's juicy flesh. Rainfall rarely penetrates deeply into the soil, so many plants' roots spread out widely just under the surface to catch as much rain as possible. These plants use a survival strategy called **drought-resistance;** they can live through the worst desert conditions.

Instead of resisting dry conditions, some desert plants are adapted to escape drought. When it gets too dry, the plants die, dropping seeds that lie dormant in the soil until the next rainfall. Then new plants quickly germinate, grow, and bloom before the soil becomes dry again.

Animal Adaptations Reptiles, such as Gila monsters and rattlesnakes, have thick, scaly skin that prevents water loss. Amphibians, such as the spadefoot toad, survive scorching desert summers by **estivating**—burying themselves in the ground and sleeping through the dry season. Desert insects and spiders are covered with body armor that helps them retain water. In addition, most desert animals are active mainly at night or at dusk, when the air is cooler.

Figure 4-34 The sidewinder has a unique way of moving so that only small portions of its body are in contact with the hot sands at any one time. This photograph was taken in the Namib Desert of Namibia.

Threats to Deserts Residential development continues to encroach upon desert areas in the American West. Off-road and all-terrain vehicles kill desert vegetation, destroying the habitat of endangered animals such as the desert tortoise. Some desert plants are prized by collectors, who selectively remove them, often endangering plant populations.

TUNDRA

Tundra is a biome without tall trees that lies north of the Arctic Circle. The frozen tundra soil supports mostly tough grasses and shrubs. As shown in Figure 4-35, summers are short in the tundra so that only the top few inches of soil thaw. Underneath lies the **permafrost,** permanently frozen soil. Because permafrost is impermeable, the tundra becomes dotted with bogs and swamps

Figure 4-35 **Next to deserts, the tundra is the driest place on Earth.**

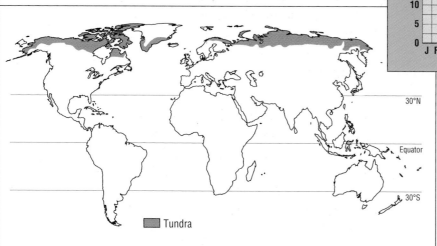

Tundra

Figure 4-36 **During its brief summer, the Alaskan tundra comes alive with many plants and lichens.**

Figure 4-37 **By growing close to the ground, dwarf shrubs and trees, such as these dwarf willows in Banks Islands, Canada, are protected from the battering wind.**

when the top layer of soil thaws. In summer, these are ideal breeding grounds for huge numbers of swarming insects such as mosquitoes and blackflies and for the many birds that feed on them.

Plant Adaptations Mosses and lichens, which can grow without soil, cover acres of rocks in the tundra. Where soil exists, it is thin, and plants have wide, shallow roots that also anchor them against the arctic winds. Most flowering plants of the tundra, such as moss campion and gentian, are tiny. Hugging the ground keeps them out of the wind and helps them absorb heat from the sunlit soil. Woody plants and perennials such as willow and juniper have evolved dwarf forms, growing flat or trailing along the ground. Tundra plants make optimal use of the brief spell of summer sunshine, growing and flowering very quickly. (See Figure 4-36.)

Figure 4-38 Many animals, such as caribou (right) and geese (below), return to the tundra each year.

Animal Adaptations Millions of migratory birds breed in the tundra in summer. Food is abundant in the form of plants, mollusks, worms, and especially insects. Other tundra migrants are the caribou in North America and the reindeer in northern Europe. Being excellent hunters, wolves prey on caribou, deer, and moose as well as smaller animals such as lemmings, mice, and rabbits. Rodents burrow underground during the winter, though they are still active. Many year-round residents, such as arctic foxes, don white fur or feathers as winter camouflage. Animals that stay the winter are extremely well insulated. The musk ox's dense, shaggy coat makes the lumbering herbivore impervious to the cold.

Threats to the Tundra The tundra is one of the most fragile biomes on the planet. The food chains are relatively simple and thus easily disrupted. Because conditions are so extreme, the land is easily damaged and slow to recover. Until recently, these areas were undisturbed by humans. But oil has been found in some tundra regions, such as Prudhoe Bay in northern Alaska. Many fear the impact that oil extraction and transport will have on the land.

EXPLORATION

Do oil and ice mix? Will oil exploration do irreparable damage to the tundra? See pages 118–119.

SECTION REVIEW

❶ How are tundras and deserts similar?

❷ Some people have questioned the wisdom of building large cities in desert regions. Do you agree? Explain your reasoning.

THINKING CRITICALLY

❸ *Identifying Relationships* Former grasslands are among the most productive farming regions. What do you think are some reasons for this?

❹ *Analyzing Relationships* How can fire, a destructive event, actually be beneficial to the grassland ecosystem?

FRESHWATER ECOSYSTEMS

AFTER READING THIS SECTION YOU SHOULD BE ABLE TO

❶ describe the characteristics of the different freshwater ecosystems.

❷ compare survival adaptations of organisms in moving and standing freshwater ecosystems.

Freshwater ecosystems include the sluggish waters of lakes and ponds, the moving waters of rivers and streams, and the areas where land and water come together, known as wetlands. Fresh water is water that contains relatively little dissolved salt. The plant and animal life found in a freshwater ecosystem depends on the depth of the water, how fast the water moves, and the amount of mineral nutrients, sunlight, and oxygen.

LAKES AND PONDS

In the shallow areas close to the shores of lakes and ponds, aquatic life is diverse and abundant. This nutrient-rich area is known as the **littoral zone.** Farther out from the shore, the open water that gets enough sunlight for photosynthesis is dominated by tiny plants and animals known as phytoplankton and zooplankton. As shown in Figure 4-39, the types of organisms present depend on the amount of sunlight available.

Some bodies of fresh water have areas so deep that there is too little light for photosynthesis to occur. Dead plants and animals that drift down from above are decomposed by bacteria, and a few fish adapted for cooler, darker water also live here. Eventually, dead and decaying organisms reach the **benthic zone,** the bottom of a body of water, which is inhabited by decomposers, insect larvae, and clams.

A lake with a large amount of plant nutrients is known as a

SC*LINKS*

NSTA

TOPIC: lakes and ponds
GO TO: www.scilinks.org
KEYWORD: HE1ØØ

Figure 4-39 A pond or lake ecosystem is structured according to how much light is available.

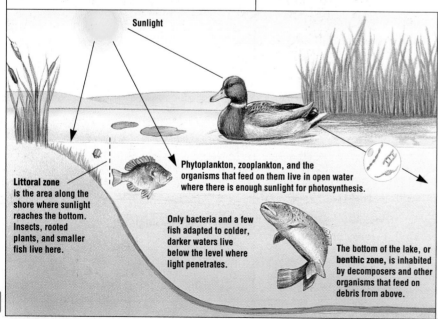

Sunlight

Littoral zone is the area along the shore where sunlight reaches the bottom. Insects, rooted plants, and smaller fish live here.

Phytoplankton, zooplankton, and the organisms that feed on them live in open water where there is enough sunlight for photosynthesis.

Only bacteria and a few fish adapted to colder, darker waters live below the level where light penetrates.

The bottom of the lake, or benthic zone, is inhabited by decomposers and other organisms that feed on debris from above.

Figure 4-40 Water moves very slowly through lakes, such as this one in Maine. Water flows much more quickly through rivers and streams.

eutrophic lake. As the amount of plants and algae grows, the number of bacteria feeding on the decaying organisms also grows. These bacteria use up the oxygen dissolved in the lake's waters. Eventually, the diversity of species declines. Lakes naturally become eutrophic over a long period of time. However, the process of eutrophication can be accelerated by runoff containing sewage, fertilizers, and animal wastes.

Plant and Animal Adaptations

Along the shore, plants such as cattails and reeds are rooted in the bottom mud, their upper leaves and stems emerging above the water. Deeper water contains floating plants, such as pond lilies. Some species of water beetles use hairs under their bodies to trap surface air to breathe during their dives for food. Whiskers help catfish sense food as they swim over dark lake bottoms. Fish are adapted to certain temperature

Bullfrog, North Carolina ▶

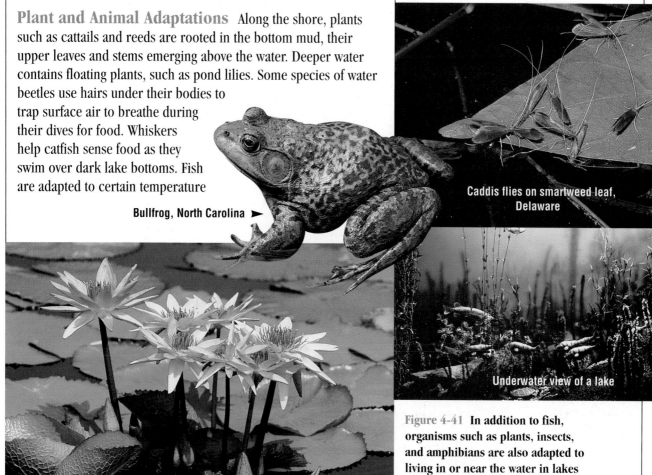

Caddis flies on smartweed leaf, Delaware

Underwater view of a lake

Water lily

Figure 4-41 In addition to fish, organisms such as plants, insects, and amphibians are also adapted to living in or near the water in lakes and ponds.

Figure 4-42 This map shows the locations of wetlands in the United States.

Wetlands

Figure 4-43 A marsh is a type of wetland that contains nonwoody plants. This is a marsh in New Jersey.

ranges; lake trout need cold water, while bass prefer warmer waters. In regions where lakes partially freeze in winter, amphibians burrow into the littoral mud.

WETLANDS

Wetlands are areas of land that are covered with water for at least part of the year. The two main types of freshwater wetlands are marshes, which contain nonwoody plants, and swamps, which contain woody plants or shrubs. (Estuaries, which are a type of saltwater wetland, are discussed in the next section.) Wetlands perform several important environmental functions. Many of the freshwater game fish caught in the United States each year use the wetlands for feeding and spawning. In addition, these areas provide a home for native and migratory wildlife, including endangered and threatened species. Wetland vegetation traps carbon that would otherwise be released as carbon dioxide, which may be linked to rising atmospheric temperatures. Finally, wetlands remove pollutants from the water, control flooding by absorbing extra water when rivers overflow, and produce many commercially important products such as cranberries, blueberries, and peat moss.

Marshes In the shallow water of marshes, plants such as reeds, rushes, and cattails are rooted in the rich bottom sediments, but their leaves are above water. The benthic zone is rich, containing plants and numerous decomposers and scavengers. Waterfowl such as grebes and ducks have beaks adapted for eating marsh vegetation. Water birds such as herons have spearlike beaks that they use to grasp small fish and frogs. Marshes attract many nesting birds, such as blackbirds.

There are several kinds of marshes, each characterized by its salinity (salt content). Brackish marshes have slightly saline water; tidal marshes contain saltier water. In each marsh type, organisms are adapted to live within the ecosystem's range of salinity. The Florida Everglades is the largest freshwater marsh in the United States.

Swamps Swamps occur on flat, poorly drained land, often near streams. Swamps are dominated by shrubs or water-tolerant trees such as red maple, cedar, oak, or cypress, depending on the latitude and climate in which the swamps occur. Mangrove swamps occur in warm climates near the ocean, so their water is saline. Swamps are the ideal habitat for many amphibians, such as green frogs and salamanders, and they attract birds such as wood ducks that nest in hollow swamp trees near or over water.

Threats to Wetlands Wetlands were previously considered to be wasteland—noxious breeding grounds for pesky insects. Thus they've been relentlessly "improved"—drained and cleared for farms or residential or commercial development. The importance of wetlands as purifiers of wastewater and absorbers of otherwise hazardous flood waters is now recognized. Wetlands are also vitally important as habitats for wildlife. Herons, storks, and other birds depend on wetlands for nesting. Wetlands are also home to many amphibians and reptiles, such as alligators and crocodiles. The federal government and most states now prohibit destruction of certain wetlands.

RIVERS

Many rivers originate from snowmelt in mountains. At its headwaters, a river is usually very cold and highly oxygenated, running swiftly through a shallow riverbed. As it tumbles down the mountain, a river may broaden, become warmer, lose oxygen, and flow more slowly. A river's characteristics may vary with changes in the land and climate through which it flows. Runoff, for example, may wash nutrients and sediment from the surrounding land into a river. These materials can affect the growth and health of the organisms in the river.

Figure 4-44 Plants such as these bladderworts in a Louisiana swamp have underwater, "bladder-shaped" leaves that they use to trap insects.

SC*L*INKS
NSTA

TOPIC: threats to wetlands
GO TO: www.scilinks.org
KEYWORD: HE1Ø3

Figure 4-45 **The water flow of a river slows and the habitat changes as narrow headwaters give way to wide channels downstream.**

SECTION REVIEW

❶ Which of the life zones of a lake, the area with sunlight or the area without, is likely to be more biologically diverse? Why?

❷ Imagine that a city wishes to clear and drain the wetlands along a river bottom to control flooding and improve the river's water quality. Is this a good idea? Why or why not?

THINKING CRITICALLY

❸ *Identifying Relationships* Most of the naturally occurring lakes in North America are found either high in the mountains or at latitudes above about 45°N. How might you explain this?

❹ *Analyzing Processes* Explain how fertilizing your yard and applying pesticides can affect the health of a river ecosystem.

Plant and Animal Adaptations Near the churning headwaters, mosses anchor themselves to rocks using rootlike structures called rhizoids. Mayfly nymphs use hooks on their legs to cling to any stable surface. Trout and minnows are adapted to thrive in the cold, oxygen-rich headwaters. Trout have streamlined bodies that present less resistance to the strong current, and they're powerful swimmers. Further downstream, catfish and carp prefer the warmer, calmer waters. Carp are adapted to gliding over the river bottom but not to swimming against the current. Here, freshwater aquatic plants such as water crowfoot set roots down into the rich sediment. Figure 4-46 shows how the arrowhead plant's leaf shape varies according to the strength of a river's current.

Threats to Rivers Industries use river water in manufacturing processes and as a receptacle for waste. For ages, people have used rivers to "take away" their sewage and garbage. These practices have polluted rivers with toxins, killing river organisms and making river fish inedible. Today, runoff from the land puts pesticides and other poisons into rivers and coats riverbeds with toxic sediments. Dams alter river flow and may destroy fish habitat.

Figure 4-46 **The arrowhead plant's leaves differ according to the speed of the water the plant grows in.**

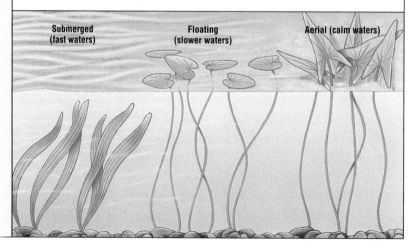

Submerged (fast waters)   Floating (slower waters)   Aerial (calm waters)

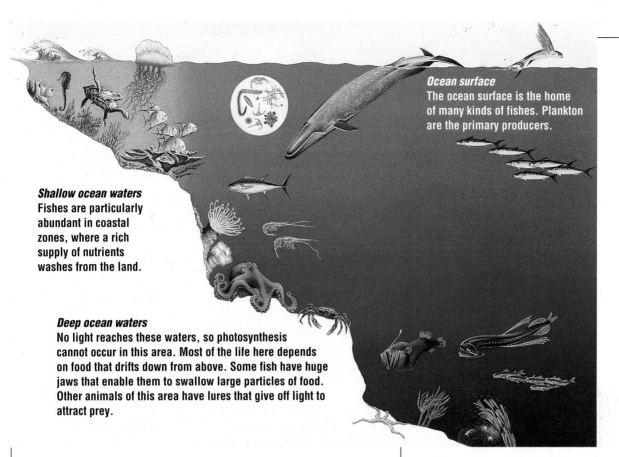

Ocean surface
The ocean surface is the home of many kinds of fishes. Plankton are the primary producers.

Shallow ocean waters
Fishes are particularly abundant in coastal zones, where a rich supply of nutrients washes from the land.

Deep ocean waters
No light reaches these waters, so photosynthesis cannot occur in this area. Most of the life here depends on food that drifts down from above. Some fish have huge jaws that enable them to swallow large particles of food. Other animals of this area have lures that give off light to attract prey.

result, the open ocean is one of the least productive of all ecosystems. (See Figure 4-55.) The depths of the ocean are perpetually dark, and most of the food consists of dead organisms that fall from the surface.

Plant Adaptations Flowering plants are absent from oceans, except around the edges. Food for herbivores in the open ocean is provided by the abundant phytoplankton. (See Figure 4-56.) These tiny cells all have buoyancy devices that prevent them from sinking

Figure 4-54 The amount of sunlight determines which organisms can live in each layer of the ocean.

Figure 4-55 The open ocean is among the least productive of all ecosystems.

Figure 4-56 Diatoms form one of the major groups of marine phytoplankton.

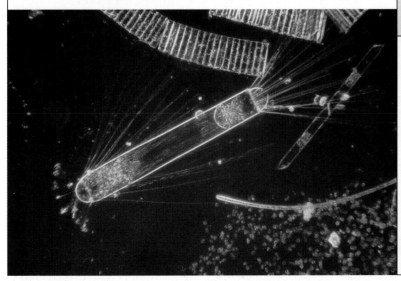

Ecosystem Productivity	
Ecosystem Type	**Average Net Primary Productivity** (grams of plant organic matter produced/sq. m/year)
Coral reef	2,500
Tropical rain forest	2,200
Estuary	1,800
Temperate forest	1,250
Tropical savanna	900
Taiga	800
Lake	500
Continental shelf	360
Open ocean	125
Tundra	90
Extreme desert	3

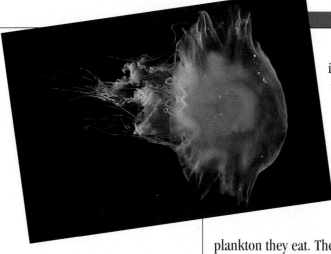

Figure 4-57 **The density of salt water permits many jellylike animals, such as this red medusa jellyfish, to remain buoyant and move through the seas.**

into deep water that is too dark for photosynthesis. Some float by means of long spines or whiplike flagella. Others contain oil droplets that act as floats. When they die, the phytoplankton sink toward the bottom, sometimes in vast numbers.

Animal Adaptations The sea's smallest herbivores are the zooplankton, which live near the surface with the phytoplankton they eat. The zooplankton include jellyfish, tiny shrimp, and the larvae of fish and bottom-dwelling animals such as oysters and lobsters. Dozens of fish feed on the plankton as do marine mammals such as seals and whales.

Many creatures of the open ocean have evolved sleek, tapered shapes for moving through dense water. Most fish that swim near the surface are tinged a silvery color, a protective camouflage for life in the open water with no place to hide. Many of them also have buoyancy devices that permit them to stay at one level in the water. Sharks have huge oily livers that act as floats. Many bony fish contain gas-filled swim bladders. Reptiles and mammals have lungs in place of swim bladders, and their lungs are used as floats as well as for breathing.

Water absorbs light, so sunlight penetrates only about 100 m (330 ft.) into the sea before it is all absorbed. Below this level there is no light for photosynthesis. In the depths of the ocean live decomposers, filter feeders, and the organisms that eat them.

Figure 4-58 **The viper fish (right) is unmistakably a predator. This deep-sea fish lives at depths of 600 m or more.**

Figure 4-59 **This flashlight fish in the Coral Sea uses light to communicate.**

Also in the ocean depths, flashlight fish and other species use light for communication. Their bursts or blinks of light are produced by luminous bacteria incorporated into their bodies. Visibility is poor underwater, but sound carries extremely well over long distances. Whales communicate with beautiful, haunting "songs." Other marine mammals, such as dolphins, communicate by emitting clicks and calls.

Threats to the Oceans Although oceans are huge, they are becoming steadily more polluted. Most ocean pollution arises from activities on land. The pollutants are the same ones that cause problems on land. For instance, plant nutrients washing off the land as runoff from fertilized fields may cause blooms of algae, some of which are poisonous. Industrial waste and sewage discharged into rivers is the biggest source of coastal pollution in the United States. A modern addition to the list of substances that pollute the oceans is radioactive waste, particularly from nuclear power plants. Until 1970, much of this waste was dumped into deep water in drums and glass containers that have subsequently leaked.

Overfishing and certain fishing methods are destroying fishing grounds. Immense trawl nets entangle every living thing larger than the net holes. Most of the catch is not used, and the dead fish are thrown back into the ocean. Marine mammals such as dolphins, which must breathe air, drown in the nets. Although it is against the law, some ships discard fishing lines into the ocean, where they can strangle fish and seals. The toll is so vast that reduced reproduction is endangering many species.

POLAR ECOSYSTEMS

The ice-covered polar caps at the North and South Poles can be considered marine ecosystems because nearly all food is provided by phytoplankton in the ocean. In other ways, the two poles are very different from each other. The South Pole lies on the continent

SC*i*LINKS
NSTA
TOPIC: threats to oceans
GO TO: www.scilinks.org
KEYWORD: HE111

Figure 4-60 **Humpback whales feed in the Arctic Ocean.**

of Antarctica, where it is covered with a permanent icecap that melts only around the edges of the continent in summer. The North Pole is not on land at all. It lies in the Arctic Ocean, much of which is frozen into a huge iceberg throughout the year, with smaller icebergs drifting around the edges.

The Arctic The Arctic Ocean is relatively shallow, so its waters are rich in nutrients from the surrounding landmasses, and it supports large populations of plankton. These in turn provide the food for a rich diversity of fish, which live in the open water and under the ice. In open waters, whales and ocean birds prey on the fish. The birds and many species of seals bear young on the ice. The seals keep holes open in the ice so that they can dive to catch fish. The seals and birds in turn provide food for the few humans who live in the Arctic and for the top predators, polar bears.

The Antarctic The Antarctic is the only continent never colonized by humans. It is governed by an international commission and is used mainly for research on the unusual animals that live there. Even during the summer, only a few plants grow at the rocky edges of the continent. As in the Arctic, plankton forms the basis of the Antarctic food web. The plankton nourish large numbers of fish, whales, and birds such as penguins, which cannot fly because their wings have become adapted for swimming.

Threats to Polar Ecosystems Both the Arctic and the Antarctic contain reserves of minerals, such as oil, whose extraction would disrupt these largely untouched ecosystems. Conservationists want the Antarctic to be made into a world wildlife refuge so that this unique ecosystem can be preserved. Meanwhile, the main threat to wildlife is an increase in tourism in recent years. The garbage left by tourists is difficult to dispose of in a climate so cold that nothing decays. Research stations and tour operators are working to solve this problem.

SECTION REVIEW

❶ Coral reefs are especially sensitive to environmental disturbances. What are some of the factors that can damage coral reefs?

❷ Why are estuaries particularly vulnerable to the effects of pollution? Why is this important to humans?

THINKING CRITICALLY

❸ *Predicting Outcomes* Suppose the sea level were suddenly to rise by 100 m. What would happen to the world's coral reefs? Explain.

❹ *Analyzing Processes* The parts of the ocean most remote from land are biological deserts. They contain far less life (in terms of mass per unit of surface) than most deserts on land. What do you think are some reasons for this?

CHAPTER 4

HIGHLIGHTS

SUMMARY

- Scientists classify the ecosystems of the world into classes called biomes. Biomes are usually named according to their plant life because the plants that grow in an area determine what other organisms live there.

- The major land biomes of the world include tropical rain forests, temperate forests, taiga, savannas, temperate grasslands, chaparral, desert, and tundra.

- In each biome, plants and animals have adapted to specific environmental conditions. These conditions, however, are threatened by human activities.

- Water ecosystems can be freshwater or marine. As in biomes, the plants and animals in water ecosystems are adapted to specific environmental conditions. These conditions are also threatened by human activities.

- Freshwater ecosystems include lakes and ponds, rivers and streams, and wetlands. The types of freshwater ecosystems are distinguished by the depth of the water, how fast the water moves, and the availability of mineral nutrients, sunlight, and oxygen.

- Marine ecosystems, which are identified by the presence of salt water, include estuaries, coral reefs, and oceans. The icecaps at the North and South Poles are also considered marine ecosystems because organisms living there obtain almost all their food from the ocean.

WATER ECOSYSTEMS

may be

- **freshwater**
  - such as
    - lakes
    - rivers
    - wetlands
      - which include
        - swamps
        - marshes
- **marine**
  - such as
    - estuaries
    - coral reefs

Vocabulary Terms

benthic zone (p. 100)

biome (p. 79)

canopy (p. 82)

chaparral (p. 94)

coral reef (p. 107)

desert (p. 95)

drought-resistance (p. 96)

estivating (p. 96)

estuary (p. 105)

littoral zone (p. 100)

permafrost (p. 97)

taiga (p. 88)

temperate forest (p. 84)

temperate grasslands (p. 92)

tropical rain forest (p. 80)

savanna (p. 90)

tundra (p. 97)

wetlands (p. 102)

Ecolog

Now that you've studied this chapter, revise your answers to the questions you answered at the beginning of the chapter, based on what you have learned.

❶ What are the general characteristics of the ecosystem in which you live? Are there ecosystems similar to yours in other parts of the world?

❷ Describe a plant or animal that lives in your area, and describe its survival strategy.

REVIEW

UNDERSTANDING VOCABULARY

1. For each pair of terms, explain the difference in their meanings.
   a. savanna
      steppe
   b. biome
      ecosystem
   c. littoral zone
      benthic zone
   d. taiga
      tundra

RELATING CONCEPTS

2. Copy the unfinished concept map below onto a sheet of paper. Then complete the concept map by writing the correct word or phrase in each box containing a question mark.

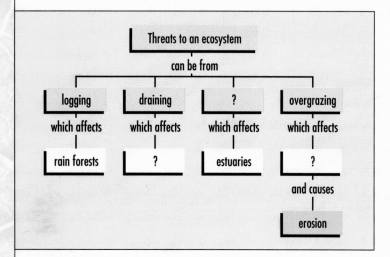

UNDERSTANDING CONCEPTS

Multiple Choice

3. Tropical rain forests contain approximately what percent of the Earth's species?
   a. 7
   b. 20
   c. 50
   d. 80

4. Animal species of the tropical rain forest
   a. compete more fiercely for available resources than do species native to other environments.
   b. specialize to avoid competition.
   c. have adaptations to cope with extreme climatic variations.
   d. never use camouflage.

5. Migration of animals in the savanna is largely a response to
   a. predation.
   b. altitude.
   c. rainfall.
   d. temperature.

6. Compared with temperate deciduous forests, temperate grasslands receive
   a. more rainfall.
   b. less rainfall.
   c. about the same amount of rainfall.
   d. sometimes more, sometimes less rainfall.

7. Spadefoot toads survive the dry conditions of the desert by
   a. migrating to seasonal watering holes.
   b. locating underground springs.
   c. burying themselves in the ground.
   d. drinking cactus juice.

8. The tundra would most likely be suitable to an animal that
   a. required nesting sites in tall trees.
   b. was coldblooded.
   c. had a green outer skin for camouflage.
   d. could migrate hundreds of kilometers each summer.

9. Wetlands are important to fishermen in the United States because
   a. wetlands are the easiest place to catch fish.
   b. wetlands breed insects eaten by fish.
   c. wetlands provide the most desirable species of fish.
   d. many of the fish caught each year use the wetlands for feeding and spawning.

10. Estuarine animals
  a. tend to produce few offspring.
  b. are usually found in unpolluted environments.
  c. must be adapted to varying levels of salinity.
  d. are adapted to cold-water conditions.

11. Bacteria cause eutrophication in lakes containing large amounts of plant nutrients by
  a. feeding on decaying plants and algae.
  b. reducing oxygen dissolved in the water.
  c. both a and b
  d. neither a nor b

12. Seals would MOST likely be found in which of the following?
  a. estuaries
  b. open ocean
  c. marshes
  d. benthic zone

13. Polar regions are considered marine ecosystems because
  a. they contain an enormous amount of frozen sea water.
  b. they are inhabited by few organisms.
  c. sunlight is limited.
  d. phytoplankton form the basis of polar food webs.

Short Answer

14. Unlike depictions of jungles seen in movies, the floor of an undisturbed tropical rain forest is largely devoid of vegetation. Why is this so?

15. When considering a grassland ecosystem, what is the relationship between root systems and erosion?

16. How do mountains affect the distribution of biomes?

17. Well-preserved mammoths have been found buried in the tundra. Explain why the tundra would be a good preserver of animal remains.

18. How does the phrase "best of both worlds" relate to an estuary?

INTERPRETING GRAPHICS

19. **Examine the diagram below.** It shows how the relationship between temperature and rainfall affects the location of the biomes. According to the diagram, what type of climate would be found in the grasslands? in the tropical rain forest? in the tundra? Notice that there are two desert locations shown. Explain.

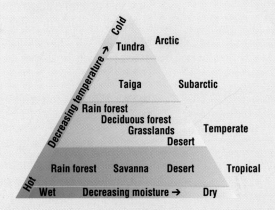

THINKING CRITICALLY

20. *Analyzing Relationships* Explain the relationship between the speed of a river and its oxygen content.

THEMES IN SCIENCE

21. *Evolution* There is evidence that in the past humans purposefully set prairies on fire to maintain them for grazing wildlife. How might this practice have affected the evolution of fire-resistance in prairie grasses?

CROSS-DISCIPLINE CONNECTION

22. *Geography* Using a world map, identify locations of the various biomes you learned about in this chapter. Then mount photos or illustrations of plants and animals native to each of the biomes.

PORTFOLIO ACTIVITY

Do a special project on the ecosystems found in your community. Using field guides of your area and other resources, find out what plants and animals make their home in the ecosystems you identify in your community. With the information you find, draw a food web that shows how the organisms in each ecosystem could be related.

 internetconnect

SCiLINKS National Science Teachers Association
NSTA On-Line Resources www.scilinks.org

When you see a SciLinks logo, visit the NSTA Web site and type in the keyword. There you will find current information relevant to that section or topic.

INVESTIGATION

IDENTIFY YOUR LOCAL BIOME

What sort of biome do you call home? Do you live in a temperate deciduous forest, a desert, or a prairie or other temperate grassland? In this Investigation, you will explore certain characteristics of the biome where you live. With the information you gather, you will be able to identify which biome you inhabit.

COLLECT INFORMATION FROM LOCAL RESOURCES

1. Using a globe or map, determine the latitude at which you live. Record this information in your notebook.

2. Consider the topography of the place where you live. To do this, study the contour lines on a map or surface variations on a globe. What clues do you find that might help identify your biome? For example, is your local area located in a rain shadow? Record your findings in your notebook.

3. Prepare a climatogram. A climatogram is a graph that shows average monthly values for two climatic factors—temperature and precipitation. Temperature is expressed in degrees Celsius and is plotted as a smooth curve. Precipitation values are given in centimeters and are plotted as a histogram. The climatogram for a city in Texas is shown below.

MATERIALS

- globe or map
- field guide to local flora and fauna
- binoculars (optional)
- notebook
- pencil or pen
- ruler
- graph paper (optional)

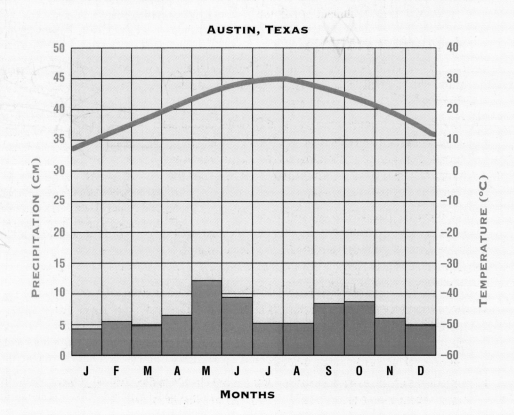

OUR WATER RESOURCES

AFTER READING THIS SECTION YOU SHOULD BE ABLE TO

① explain why fresh water is a precious resource.

② describe our main sources of fresh water.

③ explain why fresh water is often in short supply.

The next time you quench your thirst with some cold, clear water, think about this: that water may have been part of a rainstorm that pounded the Earth before life existed. It may have been part of a plant or fish that lived millions of years ago. Much of the water we drink today has been around since water first formed on Earth billions of years ago. When you drink water, you are actually sharing an ancient drink with the entire biosphere, both past and present.

Clean, fresh water is essential to life. People can survive for more than a month without food but can live for only a few days without water. Clean water is critical to human health. One of the main reasons people live longer today than they did 200 years ago is clean water: water to drink, water to bathe in, water to wash dishes and clothes, water to flush away sewage, and water to irrigate crops. Figure 5-1 shows how fresh water is used in the United States.

Figure 5-1
Agriculture and power plants account for most of the water usage in the United States.

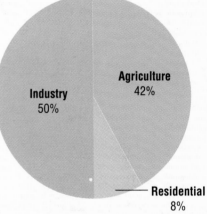

**WATER USAGE
IN THE UNITED STATES**

Source: U.S. Geological Survey, 1995

Figure 5-2 **Life as we know it would be impossible without water. Living organisms contain more water than any other substance.**

Water is a renewable resource. As you learned in Chapter 3, water is endlessly circulated by means of the water cycle. Water evaporates from the surface of the Earth, where it is held in oceans, lakes, rivers, soil, and living organisms. The water rises into the air, leaving behind salts, impurities, and other materials. Then the water vapor in the air condenses into clouds and falls as rain or snow. When rain or snow falls on land, it replenishes the land's fresh water.

WATER, WATER EVERYWHERE, BUT . . .

The Earth is often called the water planet. Look at a globe or at photographs of the Earth taken from space, and you'll see why. Most of what you see is blue. About 70 percent of the Earth's surface is water. The Earth and its atmosphere contain an estimated 336 million cu. mi. of water, enough for every person on Earth to get about 1 trillion gal. each if the water were divided evenly. It would seem that a lack of water couldn't possibly be a concern on this planet.

However, if you look at the globe again, you can see one reason why water shortages are often a problem. As shown in Figure 5-3, 97 percent of the water on Earth is salt water and only 3 percent is fresh water. Most human uses, such as agriculture and drinking, require fresh water. But there's a catch there too. Most of the fresh water—about 77 percent, in fact—is frozen solid in the polar icecaps. Thus, only a tiny fraction of the Earth's water supply is available for our use. The water we require for all of our everyday needs comes from two sources: surface water and groundwater.

Figure 5-3 **The diagram below shows how the Earth's water is distributed. How much of the fresh water is in lakes and rivers?**

97% Oceans

3% Fresh water

77% Icecaps and glaciers

22% Groundwater

1% Other water:
- Lakes, rivers
- Soil moisture
- Atmosphere

Source: U.S. Geological Survey

Figure 5-4 **More than half of the world's fresh water is frozen solid in the polar icecaps. This photograph shows frozen fresh water on Ellesmere Island, Canada.**

SURFACE WATER

Most large cities depend on surface water for their water supplies. **Surface water** is fresh water that is aboveground in lakes, ponds, rivers, and streams. Throughout history, human societies have flourished where surface water was abundant. The water not only provided the supplies needed for life but also allowed travel by boat.

You know that all water is part of the water cycle. But when you look at a huge river like the Mississippi, it may be difficult to believe that all of the water in the river fell to the Earth in the form of rain, sleet, or snow. Yet all rivers are the result of precipitation. The mighty Mississippi, the Columbia, the Colorado, the Missouri, and even the Amazon and Nile exist because of precipitation. In the case of the Mississippi, the river drains water that has fallen on thousands of square kilometers of land. As rain falls and snow melts, water drains into the Mississippi from mountaintops, hills, plateaus, and plains. The entire area of land that is drained by a river is known as its **watershed.** The watershed of the Mississippi River is shown in the map in Figure 5-5.

The amount of water that falls on a watershed varies from year to year and can have a significant effect on the amount of water that a river carries. As a result, it can be very dangerous for communities in some parts of the country to rely only on river water for their water supply. Lakes can provide more-stable sources of water than rivers can, but lakes also depend on precipitation and the flow of water from rivers and streams for their water supply.

Figure 5-5 The Mississippi River is the longest river in the United States. The map at the right shows its watershed.

TROOPER

Diane Stout says you wouldn't believe the things she encounters along Oregon rivers. Find out more on pages 378–379.

SCLINKS
NSTA

TOPIC: watersheds
GO TO: www.scilinks.org
KEYWORD: HE123

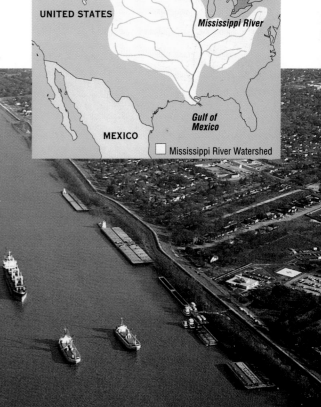

CANADA

UNITED STATES

Mississippi River

Gulf of Mexico

MEXICO

☐ Mississippi River Watershed

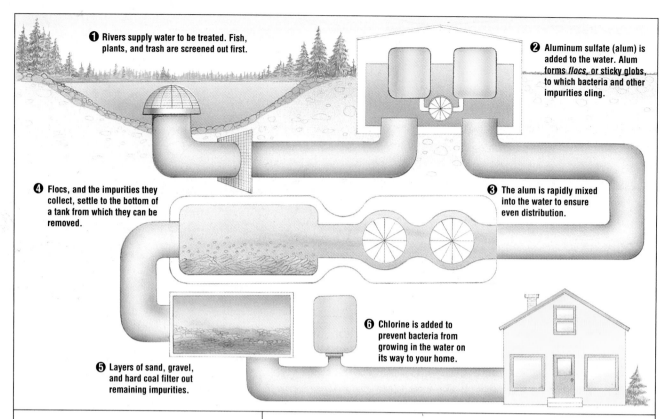

❶ Rivers supply water to be treated. Fish, plants, and trash are screened out first.

❷ Aluminum sulfate (alum) is added to the water. Alum forms *flocs*, or sticky globs, to which bacteria and other impurities cling.

❹ Flocs, and the impurities they collect, settle to the bottom of a tank from which they can be removed.

❸ The alum is rapidly mixed into the water to ensure even distribution.

❻ Chlorine is added to prevent bacteria from growing in the water on its way to your home.

❺ Layers of sand, gravel, and hard coal filter out remaining impurities.

Figure 5-6 The diagram above shows what happens to water from a river before it reaches homes. Water from lakes and reservoirs undergoes the same process.

Rivers of Controversy River water is in such high demand that disputes arise over it. In the United States, for example, Arizona and California have fought over water rights to the Colorado River for a long time. The Colorado River is one of the largest bodies of water in the western United States. It flows for 2,335 km (1,450 mi.), passing through the Grand Canyon on its way to the Gulf of California. (See the map in Figure 5-7.) However, by the time the Colorado gets close to the gulf, very little water is left because so much water has been removed along the way.

Figure 5-7 As you can see in the map above, the Colorado River winds through the western United States. Because of heavy usage, the river trickles away in the deserts of Mexico, as shown in the photograph at right.

Disputes over rivers are not limited to the United States. Forty percent of the world's people rely on water that originates in another country, so conflicts over water rights are common. How much of a river's water does the country upstream have the right to use? How much water will the country downstream receive? Who will decide these issues and regulate international water rights? These are extremely difficult questions to answer.

Conflicts between countries are particularly common when dams are built on rivers. For example, Turkey is building a series of dams that will dramatically reduce the amount of water that flows into Syria and Iraq. One of the dams is shown in Figure 5-8. The problem is being negotiated, but with little success so far.

The problem of water rights is likely to get worse in the future. As the human population increases, the demand for fresh water also increases. Many of the "shared" rivers flow through developing nations that want to build industries and irrigate their farmlands, which will require enormous amounts of water.

Dams A dam is a structure built across a river or stream that restricts the flow of water traveling downstream. The water that is prevented from flowing downstream collects behind the dam and forms a reservoir, an artificial lake. (See the dam and reservoir in Figure 5-9.) Water from reservoirs is used for drinking and irrigation, and in manufacturing. When there is a drought, the reserves of water in the reservoir can be used to supply the water needs of the population. Dams can also provide flood control and electricity. Millions of people depend on dams for these services.

However, dams are a mixed blessing. When a dam is built, the dry land behind the dam is completely covered with water, which destroys the existing ecosystem. In addition, ecosystems downstream are disrupted because they receive less water.

Figure 5-8 This Turkish soldier is guarding one of the dams that will reduce the amount of water flowing into Syria and Iraq. Construction of the dams has caused conflict between Turkey and its neighbors.

Figure 5-9 This is the Lake Owyhee Dam in Oregon. Notice the reservoir of water that forms behind the dam.

Because of environmental problems and the fact that dams have already been built at the most favorable sites, the era of building big dams in the United States is probably over. Still, all countries will probably continue to build some dams.

GROUNDWATER

Not all of the water that falls to Earth as precipitation drains into rivers and streams. Some of the water soaks into the ground. Plants collect and use some of this water, but much of it seeps down through the soil. Water that seeps underground in this way is called **groundwater.**

Large amounts of groundwater are found in underground rock formations called **aquifers.** (See Figure 5-10, on page 128.) Aquifers usually consist of rocks, sand, and gravel with a lot of air spaces in which water can accumulate. Occasionally, aquifers contain large areas of water without any rocks in them. Limestone, for instance, may dissolve to leave large caves full of water.

Aquifers continuously receive water that percolates down from the surface, but this process is very slow. It may take millions of

THE OGALLALA AQUIFER:

AN UNDERGROUND TREASURE

Agriculture seemed a ridiculous prospect for settlers in the hot and dry Great Plains region of the United States. But when these settlers discovered that the enormous Ogallala Aquifer lay beneath the ground, the idea no longer seemed so absurd. Wells were dug, pipes were laid, and soon the Great Plains was bathed in an excess of water.

Decades passed, and landowners enjoyed a seemingly limitless water supply. But the Ogallala has begun to show its limits. Although the aquifer is still considered the largest underground water source in the United States, water is being withdrawn 10 to 40 times faster than it is being replenished. Most of the water is withdrawn to irrigate crops. In some places the water level has dropped more than 30 m (100 ft.) since pumping began. Many people have abandoned their wells and moved because digging any deeper was just too expensive.

In some areas, the Ogallala Aquifer flows onto the land's surface. These areas provide vital habitat for many animals, especially birds. Unfortunately, these wetlands are often the first to disappear when crop irrigation lowers the water level in the aquifer.

Some farmers have begun to limit their crop irrigation to permit surface water levels to rise during bird migrations. Others have adopted water-saving practices such as drip irrigation systems or modified

The Ogallala Aquifer holds about 4 quadrillion liters of water, enough to fill Lake Huron (one of the five Great Lakes).

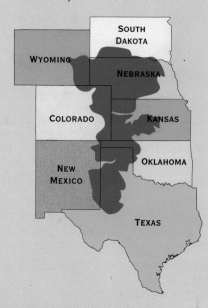

CHAPTER 5 • WATER

years for a large aquifer to form. The area of land from which the groundwater originates is called its **recharge zone.**

Some large cities, as well as many rural communities and individual farms and ranches, depend on aquifers for their water needs. The United States has several huge aquifers that together supply millions of gallons of water for homes and agriculture. This resource is tapped by drilling a well into the ground until the hole reaches the groundwater. In some areas, the well must be drilled 1,000 m deep to reach the groundwater. In other locations, the water is so close to the surface that it bubbles out of the ground as a spring. In either case, a pump is installed to force the water from the ground and through pipes to homes and other buildings.

Aquifers Are Running Low The problem with aquifers is that people are pumping out the water faster than it can be replaced naturally. Consequently, the water levels of many aquifers are dropping rapidly. One aquifer that is being rapidly depleted is the largest aquifer in the United States, the Ogallala Aquifer, discussed in the Case Study below. Some communities that once depended on aquifers are now using other sources of fresh water.

centerpivot sprinklers that deliver water directly to plant roots and reduce evaporation losses by as much as 98 percent. Still other farmers are turning to dry-land agriculture, which involves planting crops such as wheat or grain sorghum, which need less water than crops such as corn or cotton.

For a farmer, reducing the amount of water used is not as simple as it may seem. Governmental policies often actually discourage such practices. For example, government money granted to grow corn may not be granted to grow crops that require less water. In addition, if a farmer uses less water than he or she has been allocated, the government may withdraw the farmer's future legal rights to that water. Thus, farmers are compelled to "use it or lose it."

Nevertheless, many farmers and other plains residents are recognizing the value of the Ogallala and are fighting to preserve it. They are pressuring politicians to replace policies that encourage wasting water with policies that promote water conservation. These improved management practices may help save the Ogallala Aquifer.

These sandhill cranes are among the many birds that rely on the surface water generated by the Ogallala Aquifer.

THINKING CRITICALLY

1. *Applying Ideas* Why couldn't the Ogallala be replenished by watering its recharge zone?

2. *Expressing Viewpoints* Do you think residents of the Great Plains are the only citizens who should be responsible for conserving the Ogallala? Why or why not?

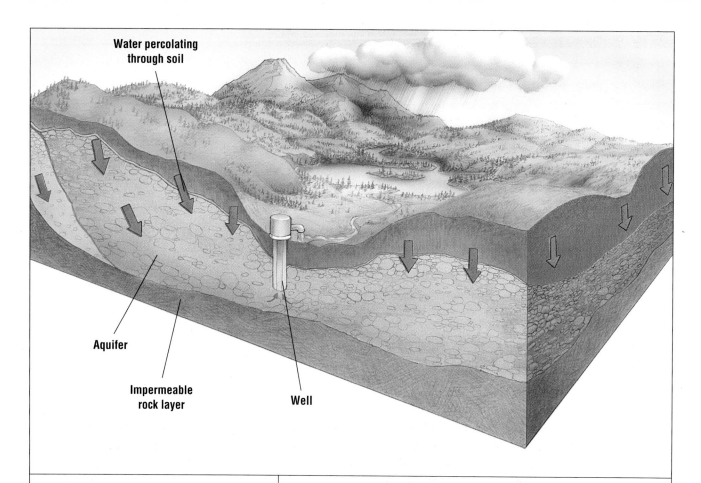

Water percolating
through soil

Aquifer

Impermeable
rock layer

Well

Figure 5-10 Aquifers are
underground rock formations
that hold water.

SOLUTIONS TO WATER SHORTAGES

While there are numerous potential solutions to water shortages, it is unlikely that any one is sufficient by itself. We need to develop new sources of fresh water, to use less by practicing conservation, and to minimize pollution. Here are some small-scale techniques that may one day prevent areas from running out of fresh water.

Desalting the Sea Some coastal countries and communities are attempting to solve their water shortages by removing the salt from salt water, a process called **desalinization** (also called desalination). Salt water cannot be used for drinking, and it ruins the soil if used for irrigation. Nearly all the drinkable water in desert countries, such as Saudi Arabia, is produced by desalinization. Some California cities built desalinization plants after they experienced droughts.

The two main methods of desalinization are distillation and reverse osmosis. (See Figure 5-11.) In distillation, heat is used to evaporate fresh water from salt water, leaving the salts behind. In reverse osmosis, pressure is used to push the water through a semipermeable membrane that will not permit the salts to pass.

Unfortunately, obtaining fresh water through desalinization is expensive. New technologies may someday reduce the cost, but today desalinization is still too expensive for many nations in dire need of fresh water.

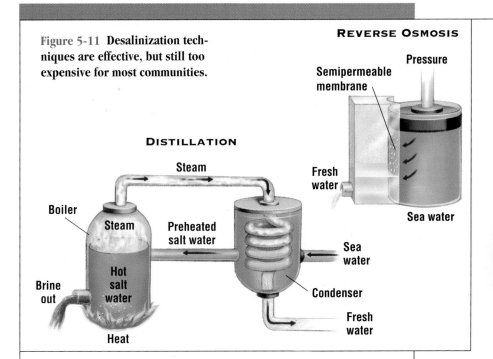

Figure 5-11 Desalinization techniques are effective, but still too expensive for most communities.

DISTILLATION

Steam

Boiler
Steam
Preheated salt water
Hot salt water
Brine out
Heat

Sea water
Condenser
Fresh water

REVERSE OSMOSIS

Pressure
Semipermeable membrane
Fresh water
Sea water

FLUSHING LESS WATER

Did you know that every time you flush, you are probably sending far too much water down the drain? Don't worry; it's easy to fix. See page 404.

Towing Water For years people have considered the possibility of towing water from one place to another to solve water shortage problems. One possibility is transporting icebergs. Saudi Arabia, where water costs more than oil, recently commissioned a series of experiments on towing icebergs. The potential problems are obvious: icebergs are hard to tow, they melt rapidly as they get near the equator, and they would be difficult to transport on land. Furthermore, the removal of large quantities of ice could disrupt polar ecosystems.

Alaska, which has more than 40 percent of the United States' fresh water, is experimenting with sending some of its water south in huge plastic bags and selling it. The idea is to float the bags down the Pacific coast to California, which is often short of water.

Figure 5-12 The average person uses about 295 L of water each day.

Water Conservation Water goes around and comes around, but its passage through the water cycle still takes time. The amount of fresh water that is available for use at any given time is limited, so people must do everything they can to use it wisely.

As more people realize that fresh water is a precious and limited resource, they are doing more to conserve it. More people are installing low-flow faucets and shower heads and turning off the tap while they brush their teeth or shave.

Indoor Water Use		
Typical Daily Water Use Per Person		
Use	Approximate Percentage of Daily Use	Liters of Water
Toilets	39	115
Showers	33	100
Laundry	10	30
Washing dishes	5	15
Cooking and drinking	5	15
Brushing teeth	4	10
Cleaning	4	10
Source: Clean Water Action, Inc.		

129

Figure 5-13 Planting native plants in yards instead of grass helps conserve water because the native plants do not need extra watering.

More people are watering their lawns at night to reduce water loss by evaporation. People in desert regions are replacing high-maintenance grass lawns with native plants like the ones shown in Figure 5-13. Some people are even putting filled water bottles inside their toilet tanks to reduce the water used for each flush. See Figure 5-14 for more water-conservation ideas.

Can one person make a difference? When you multiply one by the millions of people who are trying to conserve water, it makes a big difference.

Figure 5-14 **How could you save water?**

What You Can Do to Conserve Water
1. Take shorter showers, and avoid taking baths unless you keep the water level low.
2. Install a low-flow shower head in your shower.
3. Install inexpensive low-flow faucet aerators in your water faucets at home.
4. Install a water-saving device in your toilet, or purchase a modern low-flow toilet. See page 404.
5. Don't let the water run while you are brushing your teeth.
6. Fill up the sink basin rather than letting the water run when you are shaving, washing your hands or face, or washing dishes.
7. Water your lawn in the evening to avoid losing much of the water to evaporation.

SECTION REVIEW

❶ Why is fresh water considered a limited resource?

❷ What is groundwater, and why should we take care not to use it too quickly?

❸ What are some things you can do to help conserve the world's water supply? Give at least two examples.

THINKING CRITICALLY

❹ *Making Decisions* How should disputes over water rights, such as the one over the dams in Turkey, be settled? Explain your reasoning.

❺ *Inferring Relationships* What if the world's supply of fresh water ran almost completely dry tomorrow? How would this affect your life? How would this affect the world?

Water pollution can be harmful to human health. And in fish, toxic chemicals can cause cancers, scale rot, and fin rot. Toxic chemicals can also accumulate in fish tissues, making many fish too dangerous for humans to eat. In addition, some of the heavy metals and toxic chemicals that end up in waterways cause cancer or birth defects in humans, and others affect reproduction or damage the nervous system, liver, or kidneys.

ARTIFICIAL EUTROPHICATION

Lakes and slow-moving streams can become eutrophic, which means that they contain an abundance of nutrients. This occurs naturally over a long period of time as organisms die and decompose, adding nutrients to the water. The process of decomposition uses up large amounts of oxygen dissolved in the water, which can affect the types of fish and other animals that can survive in the water. Plants take root in the nutrient-rich sediment at the bottom and start to fill the shallow waters. Eventually, the body of water becomes a swamp or marsh. This process is an example of secondary succession, which you learned about in Chapter 3.

The natural process of eutrophication can be accelerated when inorganic plant nutrients, such as phosphorus and nitrogen, get into the water from sewage and fertilizer runoff. Eutrophication caused by humans in this way is called **artificial eutrophication.** Phosphorus—a plant nutrient contained in detergents, animal wastes, and fertilizers—causes the excessive growth of algae. The algae can form large mats, called *algal blooms,* that float on the water, as shown in Figure 5-23. As the algae die and decompose, large amounts of dissolved oxygen are used. Fish suffocate in the oxygen-depleted water.

In an effort to alleviate the problem, some states have banned phosphate detergents, which contain phosphorus. Others have limited the amount of phosphates in detergents.

THERMAL POLLUTION

When excessive amounts of heat are added to a body of water, **thermal pollution** can result, as shown in Figure 5-24. Thermal pollution occurs when power plants and other industries located along lakes or rivers use the water in their cooling systems. Cool water from the river or lake is circulated around engines to absorb waste heat. The warm water is then returned to the lake or river, creating an unnatural warm area.

Thermal pollution can cause massive fish kills when the discharged water is too warm for the fish to tolerate. Furthermore, because warm water cannot hold as much oxygen as cool water can, aquatic organisms are deprived of oxygen and may suffocate. A constant influx of warm water may totally disrupt an aquatic ecosystem if the organisms are unable to adjust to the higher

Are there heavy metals in our drinking water? Not if Elizabeth Philip has anything to say about it!
Find out more on pages 148–149.

Figure 5-23 **Algal blooms are caused by high levels of phosphates in the water.**

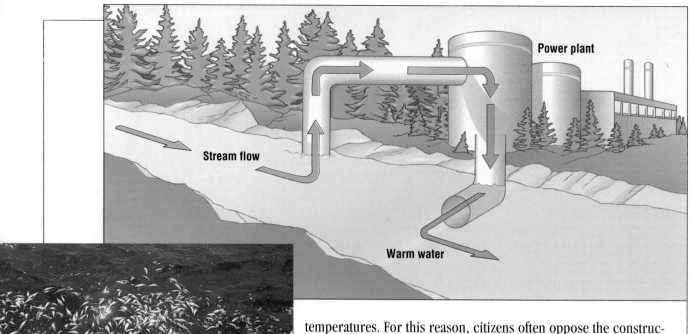

Stream flow

Power plant

Warm water

Figure 5-24 **The diagram above shows thermal pollution, and the photograph shows a massive fish kill that resulted from this type of pollution.**

Figure 5-25 **Some progress has been made in cleaning up our water, but much work remains to be done.**

temperatures. For this reason, citizens often oppose the construction of power plants on lakes and rivers or insist on cooling systems that reduce the temperature of the water before it is returned to the waterway.

CLEANING UP WATER POLLUTION

In 1972, Congress passed the Clean Water Act (CWA). The stated purpose of the act was to "restore and maintain the chemical, physical, and biological integrity of the nation's waters." The goal was to make all surface waters clean enough for fishing and swimming. Other water-quality legislation is described in Figure 5-25. Since 1972, many states have passed their own, even stricter water-quality standards. Together, federal and state regulations have had some positive effects on surface water. For instance, many toxic metals are now removed from wastewater, and many industrial wastes are treated prior to disposal.

Despite these successes in curbing point pollution, non-point pollution continues to be a problem that requires the cooperation of individuals and businesses throughout the nation. Progress has been made. Some agricultural wastes are channeled into lagoons, where pollutants are decomposed before the water is released into waterways. Similar waste-treatment processes have been adopted by some industries, including a few paper and

Water Quality Legislation in the United States

Here is a list of the main federal laws designed to improve water quality in the United States.

- **1972 Clean Water Act** (CWA). This is technically the **Water Pollution Control Act.** The act set a national goal of making all natural surface waters fit for fishing and swimming by 1983 and of banning pollutant discharge into these waters by 1985. The Act required that metals be removed from wastewater beginning in the early 1980s.

- **1972 Marine Protection, Research, and Sanctuaries Act,** amended 1988. This act empowered the Environmental Protection Agency to control the dumping of sewage wastes and toxic chemicals in the ocean.

- **1975 Safe Drinking Water Act.** This act introduced programs to protect both groundwater and surface water from pollution.

- **1980 Comprehensive Environmental Response Compensation and Liability Act** (CERCLA). This is the Superfund Act, which makes owners, operators, and customers of hazardous waste sites responsible for their cleanup. It has reduced the pollution of groundwater by toxic substances leached from hazardous waste dumps.

- **1987 Water Quality Act.** This act was formed to support state and local efforts to clean polluted runoff. It also established loan funds to pay for new wastewater treatment plants and created programs to protect major estuaries.

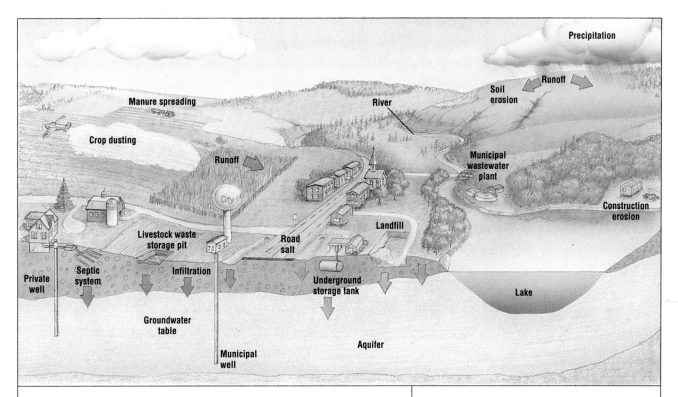

Precipitation

Runoff

Soil erosion

Manure spreading

River

Crop dusting

Runoff

Municipal wastewater plant

Construction erosion

Livestock waste storage pit

Road salt

Landfill

Private well

Septic system

Infiltration

Underground storage tank

Lake

Groundwater table

Aquifer

Municipal well

Figure 5-26 **How pollutants get into groundwater**

pulp mills. Some companies have even implemented innovative water-recycling processes that greatly reduce pollution.

THE SPECIAL PROBLEM OF GROUNDWATER POLLUTION

Groundwater pollution is likely to plague us for centuries to come. Pesticides, chemical fertilizers, and other agricultural chemicals are common pollutants that seep into groundwater. Leaky chemical storage tanks and industrial wastewater lagoons also contribute to the problem. Figure 5-26 illustrates how pollutants get into groundwater. The Environmental Protection Agency has detected at least 200 hazardous chemicals that can seep through the soil and into groundwater.

Unfortunately, even if groundwater pollution stopped tomorrow, the water would still be polluted generations from now. As you have learned, groundwater recharges very slowly. In addition, it is hard to decontaminate aquifers because the water is dispersed among sand and rocks and because it clings to sand grains.

BOTTLED WATER

Sales of bottled water have soared as more and more people have decided that their tap water is not fit to drink. Where does bottled water come from? Most people assume that it comes straight from a pure mountain stream. Much more often, however, bottled water is simply tap water that has been filtered and treated with various chemicals. Bottled-water plants are regulated by the government, but bottled water is not tested for pollutants as often as the public water supply is.

OCEAN POLLUTION

AFTER READING THIS SECTION YOU SHOULD BE ABLE TO

❶ explain how and why the oceans are polluted and describe the effects of pollution on marine life.

❷ discuss the effects of polluted oceans on humans.

❸ explain how individuals can prevent ocean pollution.

"There isn't a clean spot in the Atlantic from Bermuda to the African coast," reported a sailor who made the journey. "A river of polystyrene cups and bits of plastic stretches across the ocean." If you walk along a beach, you can see some of these plastic cups, bottles, and bags that have washed up out of the ocean.

How much waste can the oceans absorb? How long will the waste take to decompose? Little research is being done on vital questions like these. And when we find the answers, often it is too late. However, we do know the answer to one question: Where does the ocean pollution come from?

HOW POLLUTANTS GET INTO OCEANS

At least 85 percent of ocean pollution, including most of the oil polluting the oceans, comes from activities on land. When pollutants enter rivers as runoff, the rivers may carry the polluted water to the ocean. Most activities that pollute oceans occur near the coasts, where much of the world's human population lives. As you might imagine, sensitive coastal ecosystems, such as coral reefs and estuaries, are hardest hit.

TOPIC: ocean pollution
GO TO: www.scilinks.org
KEYWORD: HE14Ø

Figure 5-27 Pollution off the coast of Oahu, Hawaii

Pollutants are also dumped directly into the oceans. For example, scientists think that burns seen on the shells of lobsters and other shellfish are caused by sludge, an end product of wastewater treatment that has been dumped into the ocean. Oceangoing ships have also dumped wastewater and garbage overboard.

Accidental oil spills also contaminate ocean water. Disasters such as the 1989 *Exxon Valdez* oil spill, in Prince William Sound, Alaska, make front-page news around the world. (See Figure 5-28.) However, such disasters are responsible for only about 5 percent of the oil polluting the oceans. Much of the oil pollution in the seas comes from less spectacular events. Small oil tankers also have accidents and leaks, for example, and there is often some spillage when tankers are loaded and unloaded. Offshore oil rigs sometimes leak petroleum as well.

Plastic is also a significant ocean pollutant because it does not break down easily. When plastic fishing lines are discarded into the sea, marine mammals that become entangled in them can be strangled or disabled. Turtles may eat clear plastic bags that look like jellyfish and die from suffocation or blockage of the digestive system. Plastic six-pack rings end up around the necks of sea birds, strangling them, or around the bodies of fish, which die as the plastic cuts into their flesh.

PREVENTING OCEAN POLLUTION

There are laws that regulate or prohibit pollution of the seas. MARPOL (the International Convention for the Prevention of Pollution From Ships) prohibits the discharge

Figure 5-28 **The sea otter (left) was one of the numerous marine animals covered in oil from the *Exxon Valdez* oil spill. The map above shows the location of the spill, Prince William Sound.**

Figure 5-29 **Left unaided, this elephant seal would strangle from the plastic ring around its neck.**

of oil and the disposal or abandonment of plastics in ocean or coastal waters.

The 1974 Helsinki Convention, supported by 120 nations, seeks to control land-based sources of ocean pollution such as toxic dumping, runoff, and discharging raw wastewater. So far, prohibitions against the dumping of toxins such as DDT, cadmium, and mercury have been enacted. Nations have also worked together to create 15 marine refuges to protect endangered marine species such as sea turtles and monk seals.

The United States has strengthened its laws against ocean dumping by enacting the Marine Protection, Research, and Sanctuaries Act. In addition, the Oil Pollution Act of 1990 requires all oil tankers arriving in United States waters to have double hulls as an added protection against oil spills. The Marine Mammal Protection Act prohibits any actions that could harm the many endangered marine mammals in our oceans.

However, as you might imagine, it is very difficult to monitor every ship on the ocean to ensure that none are discharging oil, throwing garbage overboard, or abandoning plastic fishing lines. To stop ocean pollution, individuals, businesses, and nations must first be convinced of the wisdom of obeying the laws and honoring the agreements.

Who Owns the Oceans? Part of the problem of ocean pollution is uncertainty about who has jurisdiction over the oceans. In the past, international law has permitted nations to exercise complete control over their territorial waters, extending 3 mi. from the coast. The rest of the world's oceans were high seas, open to everyone. In the twentieth century, some countries claimed to extend their territorial waters to 12 mi., and sometimes to 200 mi., from their coasts.

In an attempt to clarify the situation, the Third United Nations Conference on the Law of the Sea met between the years 1973 and 1982. The conference resulted in the Law of the Sea Treaty.

The Law of the Sea Treaty states that the laws of a coastal nation extend to 22 km (12 nautical mi.) from its coastline. This area is called a nation's *territorial sea.* The area that extends 370 km (200 nautical mi.) from land is called a nation's *exclusive economic zone.* A nation has control over economic activity, environmental preservation, and research in this area. The rest of the world's oceans are designated as communal property to be controlled by the International Seabed Authority.

The final agreement was signed by 134 countries. However, some of the most powerful developed nations, including the United States, did not sign the treaty. Several of these nations objected to the treaty's restrictions on seabed mineral mining.

SECTION REVIEW

❶ Where does most ocean pollution come from? What kind of pollution is it?

❷ What are three major sources of oil pollution in the ocean?

❸ Why is plastic considered an ocean pollutant? What are its sources, and how can it be eliminated?

THINKING CRITICALLY

❹ *Inferring Relationships* What long-term effects on ocean life can be expected if ocean pollution is not reduced?

❺ *Applying Ideas* What can individuals do in their own homes and communities to decrease ocean pollution? Give at least three examples.

HIGHLIGHTS

SUMMARY

- Only a tiny fraction of Earth's large water supply is suitable for drinking and other human activities. The tiny percentage of water used for everyday human needs comes from two sources: surface water and groundwater.

- Rivers, which collect water precipitated into watersheds, are an important source of surface water. Groundwater is precipitation that collects underground and is stored in rocky formations called aquifers. Water is pumped from aquifers to supply fresh water to agriculture, industry, and residences. Overpumping is depleting many aquifers.

- Water may become polluted by chemical, physical, or biological material or by excess heat. Water pollution may be easily identified point pollution, or it may be nonpoint pollution, the source of which is often difficult to determine.

- Government actions, such as the Clean Water Act of 1972, have partially succeeded in curbing surface-water pollution. But even so, groundwater pollution will be with us for years to come. Ocean pollution is primarily due to runoff from the land, though pollutants are also sometimes dumped directly into the ocean.

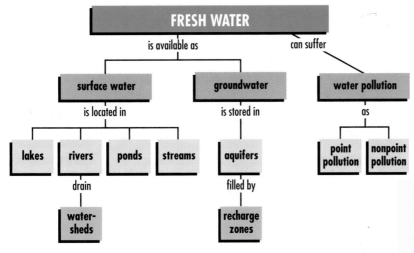

FRESH WATER

is available as / can suffer

- **surface water** — is located in — **lakes**, **rivers**, **ponds**, **streams**
- **rivers** — drain — **water-sheds**
- **groundwater** — is stored in — **aquifers** — filled by — **recharge zones**
- **water pollution** — as — **point pollution**, **nonpoint pollution**

Vocabulary Terms

aquifer (p. 126)
artificial eutrophication (p. 137)
biological magnification (p. 136)
desalinization (p. 128)
groundwater (p. 126)
nonpoint pollution (p. 133)
point pollution (p. 132)
recharge zone (p. 127)
surface water (p. 123)
thermal pollution (p. 137)
water pollution (p. 131)
watershed (p. 123)

EcoLog

Now that you've studied this chapter, revise your answers to the questions you answered at the beginning of the chapter, based on what you have learned.

❶ Describe as best you can where the water in your home comes from.

❷ Do you think the water you drink at home is pure or polluted? Explain your answer.

REVIEW

UNDERSTANDING VOCABULARY

1. For each pair of terms, explain the difference in their meanings.
   a. surface water
      groundwater
   b. watershed
      recharge zone
   c. point pollution
      nonpoint pollution
   d. water pollution
      thermal pollution

RELATING CONCEPTS

2. Copy the unfinished concept map below onto a sheet of paper. Then complete the concept map by writing the correct word or phrase in each box containing a question mark.

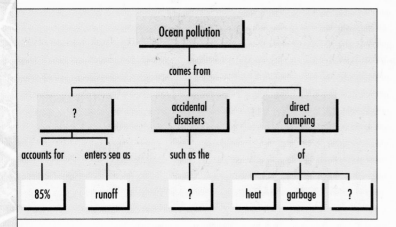

UNDERSTANDING CONCEPTS

Multiple Choice

3. The water in your drinking glass may have once been part of
   a. a primordial ocean.
   b. a dinosaur's bloodstream.
   c. water your neighbor used to water his lawn.
   d. all of the above

4. Lakes can provide more stable sources of water than rivers can because
   a. they tend to flow quickly.
   b. riverbeds keep changing direction.
   c. lakes do not depend directly on watersheds.
   d. rivers contain more salt than lakes do.

5. A major reason the era of building huge dams in the United States has come to a close is that
   a. smaller dams are more economical.
   b. we have all of the water and electricity we need.
   c. they are now too expensive to build.
   d. the environmental consequences are too great.

6. A possible result of pumping large amounts of water from an aquifer is that
   a. farms produce fewer crops.
   b. the recharge zone shrinks.
   c. the aquifer cannot be recharged fast enough.
   d. groundwater stops being collected.

7. Sludge is difficult to dispose of because
   a. it sinks to the bottom of wastewater-treatment plants.
   b. it often contains toxic or hazardous materials.
   c. there is so much of it.
   d. it is noncombustible.

8. Thermal pollution affects aquatic environments because it
   a. can make water too warm for fish to tolerate.
   b. reduces oxygen in the water.
   c. has been circulated around power-plant engines.
   d. both a and b

9. Severe oil-tanker spills account for what percentage of oil polluting the ocean?
   a. 5
   b. 10
   c. 25
   d. 65

ACID PRECIPITATION

AFTER READING THIS SECTION YOU SHOULD BE ABLE TO

① explain what causes acid precipitation.

② explain how acid precipitation affects ecosystems.

③ describe ways that countries are working together to solve the problem of acid precipitation.

Imagine that you are hiking through the vast forests of New York's Adirondack Mountains. You come to a scenic lake and sit down to rest. You marvel at how clear the water is, so clear that you can see the bottom of the lake. But after a few minutes you become uneasy. Something is wrong. What is it? You realize that there are no fish in the lake.

This lake, like thousands of others throughout the world, is a victim of acid precipitation, also known as acid rain. **Acid precipitation** is highly acidic precipitation (rain, sleet, or snow) that results from the burning of fossil fuels. When fossil fuels are burned, they release oxides of sulfur and nitrogen as by-products. When the oxides combine with water in the atmosphere, they form sulfuric acid and nitric acid, which fall as precipitation. Figure 6-16 shows how these acids form. Acid precipitation can kill living things, as it

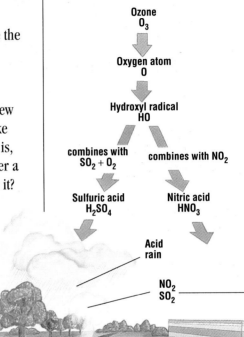

Figure 6-16 **How acid precipitation forms**

Figure 6-17 **Nearly all of the fish in this lake in the Adirondack Mountains have been killed by acid precipitation.**

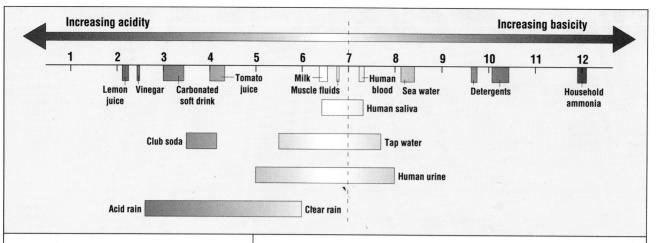

Figure 6-18 **The pH of some common substances**

FIELD ACTIVITY

When it rains, place sterilized glass jars on windowsills or in open areas where the jars can collect the rain. Then test the pH of the rain with pH paper. Repeat this activity as often as possible, and graph the results. In the winter, you could test the pH of snow to see if the snow could cause acid shock when it melts in the spring.

Figure 6-19 **Acid precipitation has damaged this frieze on the Parthenon in Athens, Greece.**

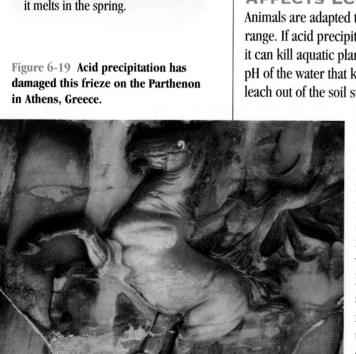

did in the Adirondack Mountains, and can even destroy entire ecosystems.

Precipitation is considered to be acid precipitation if it has a pH of less than 5.6. A pH number is a measure of how acidic or basic a substance is. A pH scale is shown in Figure 6-18. Each whole number on the pH scale indicates a tenfold change in acidity. In highly industrialized regions, acid precipitation can be extreme. The northeastern United States sometimes gets "soda-pop" rain with a pH of 3.5 to 4.0, similar to the pH of soft drinks.

Acid precipitation dissolves the calcium carbonate in common building materials such as concrete and limestone. Some of the world's most prized and historic monuments are being eaten away by acid precipitation. (See Figure 6-19.)

HOW ACID PRECIPITATION AFFECTS ECOSYSTEMS

Animals are adapted to live in an environment with a particular pH range. If acid precipitation falls on a lake and changes the water's pH, it can kill aquatic plants, fish, and other animals. It is not only the pH of the water that kills fish. Acid precipitation causes aluminum to leach out of the soil surrounding a lake. The aluminum accumulates on the gills of fish, stimulating mucus production. Many fish slowly suffocate from the buildup of mucus on their gills.

The effects of acid precipitation are worst in the spring, when acidic snow that accumulated all winter melts and rushes into lakes and other bodies of water. This sudden influx of acidic water causes **acid shock,** which can be so intense that entire populations of fish are wiped out. Acid shock also affects the reproduction of fish and amphibians. They produce fewer eggs, and these usually do not hatch. The young that do hatch are often defective and cannot reproduce.

To counteract the effects of acid precipitation on aquatic ecosystems, some states and countries spray tons of powdered lime on acidified lakes in the spring to help restore their natural pH. Because lime has a pH that is basic, it counteracts the acidic pH of the water. Unfortunately, we cannot spread enough lime to offset all acid damage to lakes.

Forest ecosystems are also affected by acid precipitation. Trees, like other organisms, can tolerate only specific pH ranges. If the water they take up through their roots is too acidic, they will die. Millions of hectares of forests in the northeastern United States and Canada are dying, partly due to acid precipitation. As the trees and other plants die, the animals they support die too. The ecologist shown in Figure 6-20 is attempting to determine the amount of acidity that plants can tolerate.

Figure 6-20 **An ecologist monitors the effects of acid precipitation on plants.**

INTERNATIONAL CONFLICT AND COOPERATION

One problem in controlling acid precipitation is that pollutants may be released in one geographical area and fall to the ground hundreds of miles away. In North America, for example, most of the acid precipitation in New England and southeastern Canada results from pollution produced in the midwestern and eastern United States.

Similarly, emissions from the highly industrialized Ruhr Valley in Germany have spread over many of the other nations in Europe. Weather patterns usually carry pollutants northward toward the Scandinavian countries, which have the most serious acid precipitation problems

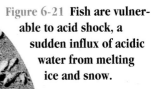

Figure 6-21 **Fish are vulnerable to acid shock, a sudden influx of acidic water from melting ice and snow.**

Figure 6-22 **An acidic lake can often be saved, as shown here, by neutralizing the acid with a basic substance, such as lime.**

Figure 6-23 **This forest in Karkonoski National Park, Poland, suffers from the effects of acid precipitation.**

SCI LINKS.
NSTA
TOPIC: acid rain agreements
GO TO: www.scilinks.org
KEYWORD: HE164

in Europe. Figure 6-24 shows which regions produce pollutants and which are affected by acid precipitation.

In 1985, the United Nations Helsinki Declaration was enacted, which requires countries to cut sulfur-oxide emissions by 30 percent over 10 years. The declaration was signed by 18 nations. The United States did not sign this agreement. In 1988, 27 nations signed the United Nations Sofia Protocol, which required a reduction in nitrogen-oxide emissions. The United States agreed to this protocol in 1989. In 1990 and 1997, the United States strengthened its own clean-air standards.

Later, the European Union, a coalition of European countries, mandated that refineries reduce the sulfur content in diesel fuel by more than 30 percent by 1994 and by another 80 percent by 1996. It is clear that even more international agreements such as these will be necessary to control the acid-precipitation problem.

SECTION REVIEW

1. What human activities contribute to acid precipitation?

2. Why is international cooperation necessary to reduce acid precipitation?

THINKING CRITICALLY

3. *Inferring Relationships* Why might normal rainwater be more acidic than pure water?

4. *Interpreting Graphics* Lime is sprayed on lakes to counteract the effect of acid precipitation. Look at Figure 6-18, and predict whether lime has a pH above or below 7. Explain your reasoning.

Figure 6-24 **A global look at acid precipitation**

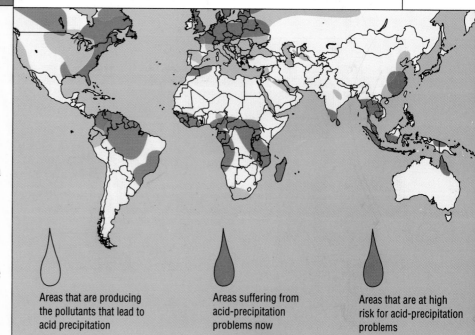

Areas that are producing the pollutants that lead to acid precipitation

Areas suffering from acid-precipitation problems now

Areas that are at high risk for acid-precipitation problems

8. Clean up your work area and wash your hands before leaving the lab.

9. After 24 hours, count the seeds that have germinated (begun to sprout) in each dish. Record your results in your data table. Express the results as a percentage of the total number of seeds in each dish.

10. What was the effect of "acid precipitation" on the seeds? If a farmer planted 10,000 seeds in soil that had been exposed to acid precipitation, how many plants would he lose? Record your conclusions in your notebook.

After soaking the seeds overnight and observing any changes, pour them into petri dishes to germinate.

FORM A HYPOTHESIS

11. What factors do you think might influence how severely acid precipitation affects plants? For example:

   • Would the effects differ depending on the rain's level of acidity?
   • Are different types of seeds affected differently?
   • Will the type of rocks present make a difference? (In nature, some rocks and soils can help to neutralize acid precipitation.)

   Develop a hypothesis about one way that the effects of acid precipitation on plants might vary. Write your hypothesis in your notebook.

DESIGN AN EXPERIMENT

12. Think of an experiment to test your hypothesis. In addition to the materials you used in the first part of this Investigation, you may want to use some of the following materials:

   • a stronger or weaker "acid precipitation" solution
   • beans, corn, or other seeds
   • limestone chips and other rock fragments

   In your notebook, write down your experimental procedure. Remember to include a control. (You will need at least three or four beakers in your new experiment—what will be in them?)

13. Based on your hypothesis, what results do you expect to see from your experiment? Write your prediction in your notebook.

TEST YOUR PREDICTION

14. Carry out your experiment, recording your results in a table in your notebook.

15. Did your results agree with your prediction? Was your hypothesis supported?

16. In what ways did your experiment mimic the real-world effects of acid precipitation? In what ways was it different from a real-world situation? How might your experiment be modified to make it more realistic?

Are Electric Cars the Cure for Air Pollution?

Automobile emissions are responsible for at least half of all urban air pollution and a quarter of all carbon dioxide released into the atmosphere. Therefore, the production of a car that emits no polluting gases in its exhaust is a significant accomplishment. The only such vehicle currently available is the electric car. Electric cars are powered by batteries, so they do not produce exhaust gases. Supporters believe that a switch to electric cars will reduce air pollution in this country. But critics believe that the reduction in pollution won't be as great as promised and that not enough people will buy electric cars to make a difference. Two points of view:

ELECTRIC CARS WILL HELP REDUCE AIR POLLUTION

According to supporters, a switch to electric cars such as this one will reduce air pollution.

More cars are on the road every year, especially in big cities, and even the cleanest and most modern of these cars emit pollutants into the air. Supporters of a switch to electric cars believe the switch is needed to reduce pollution in congested cities.

Some critics suggest that a switch to electric cars will simply move the source of pollution from a car's tailpipe to the power plant's smokestack, because electricity is often generated by burning coal. But supporters contend that moving the source of air pollution away from streets has an important benefit. Electric cars move pollution away from urban areas, where most people live and work. And in California, where electric cars would have the greatest impact, most electricity is produced by burning natural gas, which releases less air pollution than does burning coal. In addition, solar cells, hydroelectric dams, and wind turbines release no pollutants into the air when they generate electricity. Supporters argue that a switch to electric cars will reduce urban air pollution immediately and that a further reduction will result when power plants convert to these cleaner sources of energy.

Electric cars are expensive now, but prices are expected to drop as more are produced and sold. Within 10 years of widespread introduction, electric cars should be competitively priced.

Two new technologies may reduce the price of electric cars even sooner. One, called a hybrid electric vehicle, adds a small gasoline engine to provide extra power and recharge the batteries. Another uses hydrogen fuel cells instead of batteries. These cells use the hydrogen present in more conventional fuels, such as gasoline or ethanol, to produce an electric current that powers the car.

Advocates say that electric cars will reduce air pollution even more significantly when power plants begin using cleaner sources of energy, such as natural gas.

ELECTRIC CARS WON'T LIVE UP TO THEIR PROMISE

In 1990, California passed a law requiring that 10 percent of all new cars sold in the state by the year 2003 be zero-emission vehicles, meaning that they emit no exhaust gases. Other states adopted similar regulations. However, in 1997 California revised the law, allowing for other options in low-emission vehicles. Opponents of electric vehicles suggest that California's experience demonstrates that there are cheaper, easier ways to improve air quality.

Although the purchase price of electric cars is expected to drop, they still cost more than gasoline-powered cars. Even though car dealers have offered large rebates, consumers have not been willing to pay the higher prices.

In addition to being more expensive, electric cars are inconvenient. They must be recharged every 80 to 160 km (50 to 100 mi.). Some types of batteries have to be replaced every two or three years at a cost of about $2,000. More-advanced

batteries last much longer, but they cost even more. Furthermore, electric-car batteries do not work well in cold weather, making them impractical for many areas.

Also, electric cars will likely replace the cleanest cars on the road, not the dirtiest. And older, poorly maintained cars may emit a hundred times more pollution than a newer car. Instead of paying millions of dollars to develop electric cars, that money should be used to get older, polluting cars off the road.

Finally, there are an increasing number of alternatives to electric cars. Cars using natural gas and hydrogen fuel cells are more practical than purely electric cars, and they still produce far less pollution than conventional cars.

Critics say that electric cars will probably not replace older, poorly maintained cars, which may emit 100 times more pollutants than newer models.

This electric car is plugged into a recharging outlet. Some critics think that electric cars are too inconvenient because their batteries have to be recharged so often.

ANALYZE THE ISSUE

1. *Expressing Viewpoints* In your opinion, are electric cars the best solution to the air pollution problem? Why or why not? What are some alternative solutions for reducing air pollution?

2. *Making Decisions* Would you be willing to drive an electric car? Do you think the benefits would outweigh the sacrifices? Explain your reasoning.

ATMOSPHERE AND CLIMATE

"The atmosphere is the key symbol of global interdependence."

MARGARET MEAD, AMERICAN ANTHROPOLOGIST

EcoLog

Before you read this chapter, take a few minutes to answer the following questions in your EcoLog.

❶ Why do you think the warming of the Earth by gases such as carbon dioxide is called "the greenhouse effect"?

❷ You learned in Chapter 6 that ozone is an air pollutant. Why, then, might scientists be concerned about the loss of ozone from the ozone layer?

172

THE ATMOSPHERE

AFTER READING THIS SECTION YOU SHOULD BE ABLE TO

① explain how the atmosphere makes life possible on Earth.

② explain how photosynthesis and respiration keep the amount of carbon dioxide in the air nearly constant.

③ describe how the atmosphere is structured in layers.

The nearby planets Mars and Venus are barren and life-less. Why does our planet teem with life? One thing that makes life possible on Earth is its atmosphere. The **atmosphere** is a thin layer of gases, shown in the photograph in Figure 7-1, that surrounds the Earth. It extends from the surface of the Earth to hundreds of kilometers above the surface.

The atmosphere is 78 percent nitrogen and 21 percent oxygen. The remaining 1 percent is made up of water vapor, argon, carbon dioxide,

"When you look out across our atmosphere, it looks like the skin of an onion."

COL. CHARLES BOLDEN, SPACE SHUTTLE COMMANDER

Figure 7-1 **The Earth's atmosphere as seen from space**

The Earth's diameter is 12,756 km (7,911 mi.), and the troposphere and stratosphere extend about 50 km (about 30 mi.) from the surface. You can get a visual image of how thin these layers are in relation to the Earth by following these instructions. On a paved area like a parking lot, use colored chalk to draw a circle with a diameter of 4 m (about 13 ft.) to represent the Earth. This is easy if you tie the chalk to a string 2 m (about 6.5 ft.) long and have one person hold the end of the string on the ground while another person moves around drawing the circle. Calculate how thick the combined troposphere and stratosphere need to be on your drawing to be in proportion to your "Earth." Then use white chalk to draw another circle around the first one to represent these two layers. Are they thinner than you guessed they would be?

neon, helium, and other gases. We call this entire mixture *air*. The most important of the air's gases for organisms are oxygen and carbon dioxide. As you have learned in previous chapters, oxygen is necessary for cellular respiration, and carbon dioxide is necessary for photosynthesis.

The Earth's atmosphere also protects living things from most of the sun's harmful ultraviolet radiation. At the same time, the atmosphere allows visible light to reach the Earth's surface, supplying energy and making photosynthesis possible. The atmosphere also radiates some heat back to the Earth, thereby warming the planet. Without the atmosphere, life on Earth would cease to exist.

HOW PHOTOSYNTHESIS CHANGED THE ATMOSPHERE

Living things played a very important role in forming the atmosphere we know today. The Earth's early atmosphere probably contained very little oxygen, unlike today's atmosphere. Then about 4 billion years ago, the first living things appeared. These early organisms began to change the Earth's atmosphere slowly but drastically.

Certain bacteria evolved the ability to perform photosynthesis—the process of making food from water and carbon dioxide using sunlight for energy. During photosynthesis, some of the oxygen from the water and some from the carbon dioxide form oxygen gas, which enters the air. As these ancestors of plants multiplied, the amount of oxygen in the air began to increase. Oxygen now makes up about 21 percent of the gases in our atmosphere.

When organisms break down food molecules during cellular respiration, carbon dioxide is released into the atmosphere. Figure 7-2 shows how the balance between photosynthesis and

Figure 7-2 **Photosynthesis and respiration affect the composition of the atmosphere.**

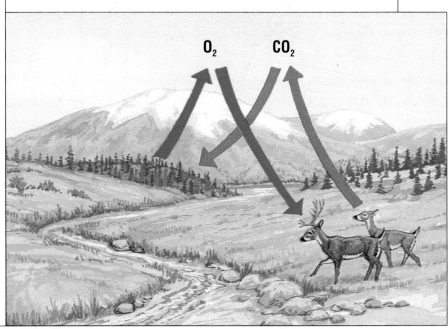

respiration keeps the amount of carbon dioxide in the atmosphere nearly constant. Even though carbon dioxide makes up only .03 percent of the gases in the atmosphere, this small amount helps to keep the Earth within a temperature range that can support life.

THE FIVE LAYERS

Scientists have found it useful to think of the atmosphere as five individual layers, which are shown in Figure 7-4. The layers become less dense the farther they are from the Earth's surface.

The **troposphere** extends from the Earth's surface to about 10 km (about 6 mi.) above the surface. It contains nearly 90 percent of the atmosphere's gases. The air we breathe is part of the troposphere. The troposphere is also the layer in which most weather occurs, as air currents flow and swirl. The air currents may bring dry, icy air from the Arctic, for example, or hot, humid air from the Gulf of Mexico.

Above the troposphere is the **stratosphere,** which extends from 10 km to about 50 km (about 30 mi.) above the Earth. The air in the stratosphere is less dense. Winds blow, but without the swirling turbulence of the troposphere. Commercial airliners often travel in the lower part of the stratosphere. The stratosphere contains the ozone layer, which protects us from harmful ultraviolet light from the sun. You will read about the ozone layer in Section 7.4. Beyond the stratosphere are the mesosphere, the thermosphere, and the exosphere. The gases in the exosphere become thinner and thinner until the exosphere merges with outer space.

Figure 7-4 **The Earth's atmosphere has five layers. The closest layer is the troposphere, which is where the weather we experience occurs. The next layer, the stratosphere, contains the ozone layer.**

Gases in the Atmosphere	
Gas	Percentage of Total
Nitrogen	78
Oxygen	21
Water vapor, argon, carbon dioxide, neon, helium, and other gases	1

Figure 7-3 **Nitrogen and oxygen make up 99 percent of the gases in the atmosphere.**

Earth is the only place in the solar system where oxygen gas exists in significant amounts.

SECTION REVIEW

❶ Name two characteristics of the atmosphere that make life possible on Earth.

❷ What caused the amount of oxygen in the Earth's atmosphere to increase?

❸ In which atmospheric layer do we live?

THINKING CRITICALLY

❹ *Interpreting Graphics* Study the illustration in Figure 7-2. What process is represented by the arrow from the animal to carbon dioxide?

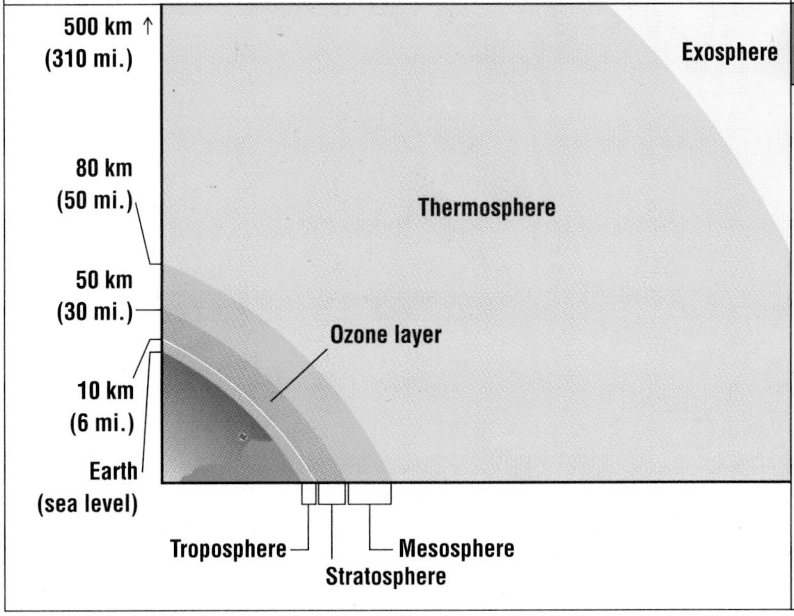

500 km ↑
(310 mi.)

Exosphere

80 km
(50 mi.)

Thermosphere

50 km
(30 mi.)

Ozone layer

10 km
(6 mi.)

Earth
(sea level)

Troposphere — ⊔ ⊔ ⊔ — Mesosphere
Stratosphere

175

CLIMATE

AFTER READING THIS SECTION YOU SHOULD BE ABLE TO

❶ explain why different parts of the world have different climates.

❷ explain what causes the seasons.

You learned in Section 7.1 that weather occurs mostly in the troposphere, the atmospheric layer that touches the Earth's surface. But what *is* weather? **Weather** is simply what is happening in the atmosphere at a particular place at a particular moment. **Climate,** on the other hand, is the average weather in an area over a long period of time. To understand the difference between weather and climate, consider Seattle and Phoenix. These two cities have the same weather on a certain day if it is raining in both places. But their climates are quite different—Seattle is cool and moist, while Phoenix is hot and dry.

Important aspects of climate are temperature, humidity, wind, and precipitation (rain, snow, hail, and sleet). Climate, particularly temperature and precipitation, determines what types of organisms are able to live in a region.

WHAT DETERMINES CLIMATE?

Climate is determined by a variety of factors, including latitude, air circulation, ocean currents, and the local geography of an area. The most important of these factors is latitude.

What does the world look like 45 km (about 28 mi.) up? No one knows better than Richard Somerville. See pages 384–385 for an interview with this climate researcher.

NSTA

TOPIC: weather vs. climate
GO TO: www.scilinks.org
KEYWORD: HE176

Figure 7-5 Seattle, Washington (left), and Phoenix, Arizona (right), could have the same weather on a certain day, but the two cities have quite different climates.

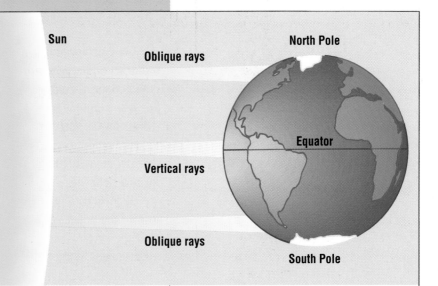

Latitude Latitude is the distance from the equator, measured in degrees north or south of the equator. The equator is defined as 0° (zero degrees). The most northerly latitude is the North Pole, at 90° north, while the most southerly latitude is the South Pole, at 90° south.

Latitude strongly influences climate because the amount of solar energy an area receives depends on its latitude. More solar energy falls on areas near the equator than on areas closer to the poles. Figure 7-6 shows why. At the equator, the sun is directly overhead, and its rays hit the Earth directly. The incoming solar energy is concentrated on a small area of the surface.

At higher latitudes (closer to the poles), the sun is lower in the sky. This reduces the amount of energy arriving at the surface. Sunlight hits the Earth at an oblique angle and spreads over a larger area of the surface than it does at the equator.

Atmospheric Circulation Patterns Three important properties of air will help you understand how air circulation affects climate. First, cold air sinks and warms as it sinks. Second, warm air rises and cools as it rises. Third, warm air can hold more water vapor than cold air can. This means that if warm air is cooled, the water vapor it contains may condense into liquid water, forming rain, snow, or fog.

Solar energy heats the ground, which warms the air above it. This warm air rises, and cooler air moves in to replace it. Heating of the atmosphere therefore causes wind, or the movement of air within the atmosphere. Because different latitudes receive different amounts of solar energy, the patterns of global circulation shown in Figure 7-7 result. This circulation pattern determines the global patterns of precipitation. For instance, the intense solar energy striking the Earth's surface at the equator causes the surface as well as the air above it to become very warm. This warm air can hold large amounts of water that evaporates from the oceans and land. As the air rises, however, it cools and loses some of its ability to hold water. Thus, it rains heavily at the equator; some areas receive over 450 cm (177 in.) of rain per year.

Figure 7-6 This diagram shows why latitude influences climate. At the equator, sunlight hits the Earth vertically. The sunlight is concentrated on a small surface area. Away from the equator, sunlight hits the Earth at an oblique angle and spreads over a larger surface area.

Figure 7-7 This diagram shows the major patterns of atmospheric circulation. How does solar energy affect these patterns?

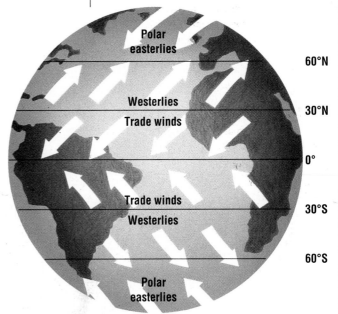

Cool air normally sinks, but the cool air over the equator cannot descend because hot air is moving up below it. So this cool air is forced away from the equator, toward the poles. It sinks back to Earth at a latitude of about 30°, warming as it falls. As this warm, dry air moves across the surface, it causes water to evaporate from the land below, creating dry conditions. Most of the world's deserts, including those in southwestern North America, are located near 30°.

Air descending at 30° moves either toward the equator or toward the poles. Air moving toward the poles warms while it is near the surface, and then it rises again at about 60°. Cold, dry air descends at the poles, which are essentially very cold deserts. Their covering of ice and snow is precipitation that has accumulated over many years because it cannot melt or evaporate in the cold climate.

Ocean Circulation Patterns   Ocean currents have a great effect on climate because water holds large amounts of heat. The movement of surface ocean currents is caused largely by winds and the rotation of the Earth. You can see the major ocean currents in Figure 7-8. These currents redistribute warm and cool masses of water. For instance, the warm Gulf Stream moves along the east coast of the United States and then flows across the Atlantic Ocean, where it warms Western Europe.

Oceans tend to make climates more moderate, so coastal areas usually have warmer winters and cooler summers than inland areas. And since the ocean is the source of most of the water that falls as precipitation, coastal areas typically get more moisture than inland areas.

Local Geography   Kilimanjaro, a mountain in Tanzania, is only about 3° south of the equator, but snow covers its peak year-round. Kilimanjaro illustrates the important effect that height above sea

Figure 7-8 **Surface ocean currents are caused mainly by winds and the rotation of the Earth. The currents redistribute warm and cold masses of water around the world.**

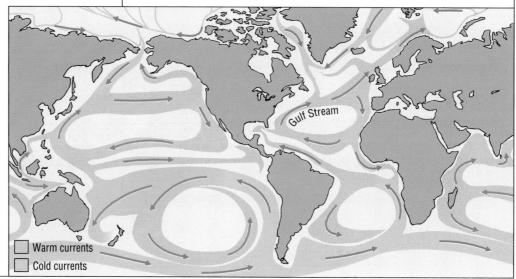

Gulf Stream

☐ Warm currents
☐ Cold currents

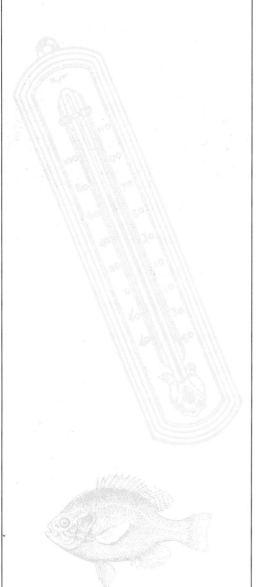

level has on climate. Temperatures fall by about 6°C (about 11°F) for every 1,000 m (3,300 ft.) increase in elevation. Because of this temperature decrease, plants and animals living on high mountains often resemble those living in cold, northern climates.

Mountains and mountain ranges also influence the distribution of precipitation. For instance, consider the Sierra Nevada mountains of California. Air full of moisture blows from the Pacific Ocean in an eastward direction. When it reaches the Sierras, it is deflected upward. This cools the air and causes it to release its moisture on the coastal side of the mountains. When the air crosses the mountains, it is dry. As it descends, it warms and draws up moisture from the surface. The Great Basin Desert of the western United States is the result. (See Figure 7-9.)

SEASONAL CHANGES IN CLIMATE

You know that temperature and precipitation change with the seasons. But do you know what causes the seasons? The seasons are the result of the Earth's orbit around the sun, as illustrated in Figure 7-10. The Earth is tilted at about 23° relative to the path of its orbit. This tilt means that the angle at which the sun's rays strike the Earth changes as the Earth moves around the sun.

During spring and summer in the Northern Hemisphere, the Northern Hemisphere tilts toward the sun and receives concentrated, direct sunlight. The Southern Hemisphere tilts away from the sun and receives less concentrated sunlight. During fall and winter in the Northern Hemisphere, the situation is reversed: the Southern Hemisphere is inclined toward the sun, while the Northern Hemisphere is tilted away.

The four seasons familiar to many people in the world do not occur in the tropics, which are the regions close to the equator. In the tropics, temperatures are high and constant throughout the year because most areas receive nearly direct sunlight year-round.

Figure 7-9 **The coastal side of the Sierra Nevada mountains (above) receives a great deal of rain. Just 20 mi. east of the mountains, however, the land is a desert (below). What accounts for this difference?**

Figure 7-10 **The Earth's orbit around the sun causes seasonal changes.**

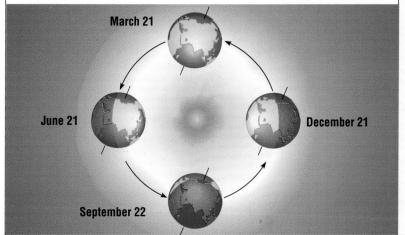

March 21

June 21

December 21

September 22

SECTION REVIEW

❶ Explain why the equator receives more direct sunlight than do the poles.

❷ Dublin, Ireland, and Moscow, Russia, are at nearly the same latitude. Yet Dublin is coastal and Moscow lies inland. How does this difference affect the climates of these two cities?

THINKING CRITICALLY

❸ *Analyzing Processes* If the Earth were not tilted in its orbit, how would the climates and seasons be affected at the equator and in the temperate zones?

❹ *Relating Concepts* Make a concept map showing what determines climate.

179

GREENHOUSE EARTH

AFTER READING THIS SECTION YOU SHOULD BE ABLE TO

❶ explain why the Earth and its atmosphere are like a greenhouse.

❷ explain why carbon dioxide levels in the atmosphere are rising.

❸ explain why many scientists think that the Earth's climate will get warmer.

❹ describe what a warmer Earth might be like.

Have you ever gotten into a car that has been sitting in the sun for a while with all its windows closed? Even if the day is cool, the air inside the car is much warmer than the air outside. On a hot summer day, opening the door to the car can seem like opening the door of a blast furnace.

The reason heat builds up inside the car is that the sun's energy streams into the car through the clear glass windows in the form of sunlight. The carpets and upholstery in the car absorb the light and change it into heat energy. Heat energy does not pass through glass as easily as light energy does. Sunlight keeps pouring into the car through the glass, but heat cannot get out. It just continues to build up, trapped inside the car. A greenhouse, like the one shown in Figure 7-11, works the same way. By building a house of glass, gardeners can trap the sun's energy and grow delicate plants in the warm air inside the greenhouse even when there is snow on the ground outside.

Figure 7-11 How is the Earth like a greenhouse?

THE GREENHOUSE EFFECT

The Earth is similar to a greenhouse. We live inside "greenhouse Earth" like delicate plants, surrounded by the icy coldness of outer space. The Earth's atmosphere acts like the glass in a greenhouse. As shown in Figure 7-12, sunlight streams through the atmosphere and heats the Earth. As heat radiates up from the Earth, some of it escapes into space. The rest of the heat is trapped by gases in the troposphere and warms the air. This process is called the **greenhouse effect.**

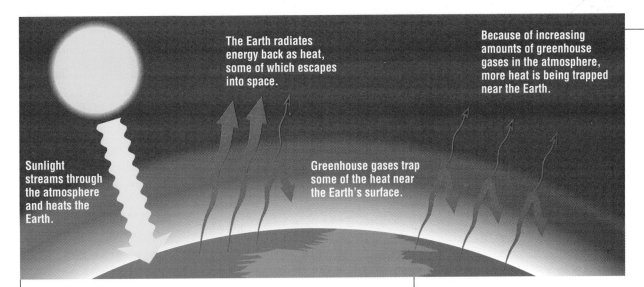

The Earth radiates energy back as heat, some of which escapes into space.

Because of increasing amounts of greenhouse gases in the atmosphere, more heat is being trapped near the Earth.

Sunlight streams through the atmosphere and heats the Earth.

Greenhouse gases trap some of the heat near the Earth's surface.

Figure 7-12 **How the greenhouse effect works**

Not every gas in our atmosphere traps heat in this way. The gases that do trap and radiate heat are called **greenhouse gases.** The major greenhouse gases are water vapor, carbon dioxide, chlorofluorocarbons (CFCs), methane, and nitrous oxide. After water vapor, carbon dioxide is the most important of the greenhouse gases.

MORE CARBON DIOXIDE IN OUR ATMOSPHERE

In 1958, a geochemist named Charles Keeling installed an instrument at the top of a tall tower on the volcano Mauna Loa in Hawaii. An absolute perfectionist, Keeling wanted to measure the amount of carbon dioxide in the air very precisely, far away from forests and cities. In a forest, carbon dioxide levels rise and fall with the daily rhythms of photosynthesis. Near cities, carbon dioxide from traffic and industrial pollution raises the local concentration of the gas. The winds that blow steadily over Mauna Loa have come thousands of miles across the Pacific Ocean, far from forests and human activities, swirling and mixing as they traveled. Keeling reasoned that at Mauna Loa, the average carbon dioxide levels in the air could be measured for the entire Earth.

Keeling's first measurement, in March of 1958, was 314 parts per million of carbon dioxide in the air, or .0314 percent. The next month the levels rose slightly. By summer the levels were falling, but in the winter they rose again. During the summer, growing plants use more carbon dioxide for photosynthesis than they release in respiration. This causes carbon dioxide levels in the air to decrease in the summer. In the winter, dying grasses and fallen leaves decay, releasing the carbon that was stored in them during the summer, and carbon dioxide levels rise.

After only a few years of measuring carbon dioxide levels, it became obvious that they were changing in ways other than just the seasonal fluctuations. Each year, the high carbon dioxide levels of winter were higher, and the summer levels did not fall as low. Figure 7-13, on the next page, shows the carbon dioxide levels measured from 1958 to 1994. As you can see, the average

SC*LINKS*
NSTA

TOPIC: greenhouse effect
GO TO: www.scilinks.org
KEYWORD: HE181

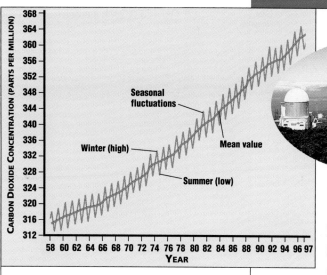

Figure 7-13 **The graph shows the increase in carbon dioxide in the air since 1958. The photograph shows the Mauna Loa research station, in Hawaii.**

amount of carbon dioxide in the air has increased since 1958. By 1994, the average level of carbon dioxide was about 358 parts per million.

WHERE IS THE EXTRA CARBON DIOXIDE COMING FROM?

During photosynthesis, a plant takes in carbon dioxide from the air. Some of the carbon in the carbon dioxide becomes part of the plant's body. This carbon is not returned to the air until the leaves fall or the plant dies and decays.

Some plants, however, never completely decay. Instead, they are covered by sand and silt. After millions of years underground,

COMPUTER MODELS AND EARTH'S FUTURE CLIMATE

CASE STUDY

Most climate researchers think that the increase in greenhouse gases will result in a warmer Earth. But exactly how much warmer? Will sea levels rise? How much? How will the climate of Kansas or China or Peru be different in 50 years?

Scientists would like to be able to give definite answers, such as "The average world temperature will be 2.3°C warmer by the year 2050." But they are unable to make such precise predictions because climatic patterns are far too complicated, and too many variables must be taken into account.

Predictions about climatic change are based on computer models. These models are mathematical representations of how different variables affect the Earth's climate. Scientists write equations representing the atmosphere and oceans, and enter data about prevailing winds, seasonal changes, levels of carbon dioxide, and many other variables. The computer models then predict how phenomena such as temperature, rainfall patterns, and sea levels will be affected.

However, the predictions may vary from one model to another, partly because different scientists use different equations to model physical processes. For example, one scientist might observe clouds that reflect more energy in the form of light than the clouds hold in as heat. Another scientist might make a different observation. Each scientist would model his or her observations using different equations. As a result, each scientist would come up with a different prediction about how much the climate would change and how rapidly the change would occur.

The construction of climate models is also complicated by the Earth's own feedback processes. For example, as the Earth warms, more water will evaporate from the oceans and more clouds will form. These clouds could reduce the amount of heat that reaches the ground, which would slow the warming trend. This is an example of a negative feedback process.

On the other hand, positive feedback could increase the rate of global warming. One effect of global warming is the partial melting of the polar icecaps, which is already happening in parts of Alaska. Ice reflects back most of the sunlight that shines on it rather than changing the sunlight into heat energy, as darker surfaces do. If the amount of ice near the poles decreases, global warming may speed up.

Computer models are becoming more reliable as more data are available and additional factors are taken into account. Scientists recently discovered, for instance, that warming at the Earth's surface might be reduced

the plants become coal, oil, or natural gas, which are fossil fuels. When fossil fuels are burned, they release the stored carbon as carbon dioxide. Millions of tons of carbon dioxide are poured into the atmosphere each year from power plants that burn coal or oil and from cars that burn gasoline.

The burning of living plants also releases carbon dioxide. This increases the carbon dioxide in the air in two ways. First, a burning plant gives off carbon dioxide. Second, when a living plant is burned, there is one less plant to remove carbon dioxide from the air by photosynthesis. As millions of trees are burned in tropical rain forests to clear the land for farming, the amount of carbon dioxide in the atmosphere increases.

GREENHOUSE GASES AND THE EARTH'S TEMPERATURE

Since greenhouse gases trap heat near the Earth's surface, many scientists think that more greenhouse gases in the atmosphere will

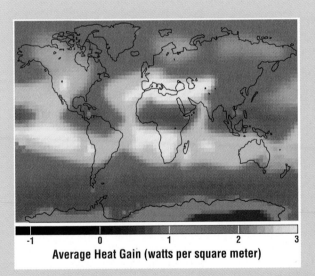

Average Heat Gain (watts per square meter)

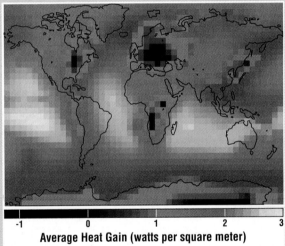

Average Heat Gain (watts per square meter)

These maps were developed from computer models. The one on the left shows the effect of greenhouse gases on the warming of the Earth before sulfur pollution was factored into the model. The map on the right shows how the addition of the sulfur-pollution variable changed the results.

by sulfur compounds in air pollution because particles formed by the sulfur compounds reflect sunlight back into space. This discovery could explain something that had previously puzzled scientists. Temperatures had been predicted to increase faster in the Northern Hemisphere than in the Southern Hemisphere. However, temperatures have actually been rising faster in the Southern Hemisphere. Some scientists think that the northern areas have not warmed as fast as the southern areas because the sulfur pollution is worse in the industrialized areas of the Northern Hemisphere. The change to one model as a result of this discovery is illustrated in the computer-generated maps above.

THINKING CRITICALLY

❶ *Identifying Relationships* What variables besides those mentioned in this Case Study might scientists consider as they construct their models of climatic change?

❷ *Analyzing Conclusions* Given that scientists use different estimates when constructing models, how should we evaluate their specific predictions related to global warming? Explain your reasoning.

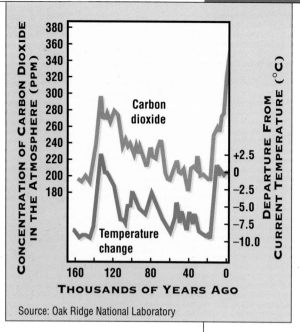

Source: Oak Ridge National Laboratory

Figure 7-14 **This graph shows the correlation between estimates of carbon dioxide levels in the troposphere and estimates of average surface temperatures of the Earth. The estimates were based on fossil evidence, rock strata, and samples of ice formed thousands of years ago.**

Figure 7-15 **Which of these greenhouse gases are affected by human activity?**

Some Major Greenhouse Gases	
Greenhouse Gas	**Main Sources**
Carbon dioxide	Coal, oil, natural gas, deforestation
Chlorofluorocarbons (CFCs)	Foams, aerosols, refrigerants, solvents
Methane	Wetlands, rice, fossil fuels, livestock
Nitrous oxide	Fossil fuels, fertilizers, deforestation

result in a warmer Earth. A comparison of carbon dioxide levels in the atmosphere and average global temperatures for the past 160,000 years supports that view. As you can see in Figure 7-14, when carbon dioxide levels rose, temperatures also rose.

Today we are releasing more carbon dioxide into the atmosphere than any other greenhouse gas. But we are also releasing other greenhouse gases—such as chlorofluorocarbons, methane, and nitrous oxide—in significant amounts. Figure 7-15 shows the sources of some major greenhouse gases.

Many scientists think that as a result of increasing greenhouse gases in our atmosphere, the average temperature of the Earth will increase by at least 2°C (about 4°F) by 2050. This predicted increase in temperature is called **global warming.**

A WARMER EARTH

The Earth's climate has changed dramatically in the past as the great ice ages came and went. Those changes, however, occurred over hundreds or thousands of years. Scientists are not sure how quickly the Earth will warm or how severe the effects will be. Different computer models give different answers to these questions, as discussed in the Case Study on pages 182–183.

Weather Patterns If the Earth heats up significantly, the oceans will absorb more heat energy, which may make hurricanes and typhoons more common. Some scientists are concerned that global warming will also cause a change in ocean current patterns. Such a change could significantly affect the world's weather. Some regions might have more rain than normal, while others might have less. Severe flooding could occur in some regions at the same time that droughts devastate other regions.

Agriculture Disruptions in weather patterns could hit farmers especially hard. The American Midwest, which includes some of the most productive farmland in the world, is one of the regions that might get hotter and drier. With increasing average temperatures in North America, the weather patterns that are best for farming would shift northward.

Sea Levels As polar regions warm, more icebergs may break loose from glaciers and melt in the sea. Sea levels would then rise, not only from melting ice but also because water expands as it warms. As a result of higher sea levels, some coastal areas might be covered with water.

How Much Carbon Dioxide Do You Send Into the Atmosphere?

If you want to figure your own monthly contribution of carbon dioxide to the atmosphere, begin by finding out how much electricity you use. Consult a recent family electric bill to find the number of kilowatt hours used in one month, and divide by the number of people in your household. If your house or water heater is heated with natural gas, do the same with the family gas bill. Using the odometer on the car, find out how many miles a month you drive or are driven somewhere. Then use the following figures for your calculations.

- Burning 1 gal. of gasoline produces 9 kg of carbon dioxide.
- Using one kilowatt hour of electricity from a coal-fired generating plant produces 1 kg of carbon dioxide.
- Burning 100 cubic feet of natural gas produces 5.5 kg of carbon dioxide.

When you have calculated your direct production of carbon dioxide, double it to account for the carbon dioxide produced in manufacturing the products you buy.

Figure 7-16 **Perform the calculations shown at left to get a rough estimate of the amount of carbon dioxide you send into the atmosphere.**

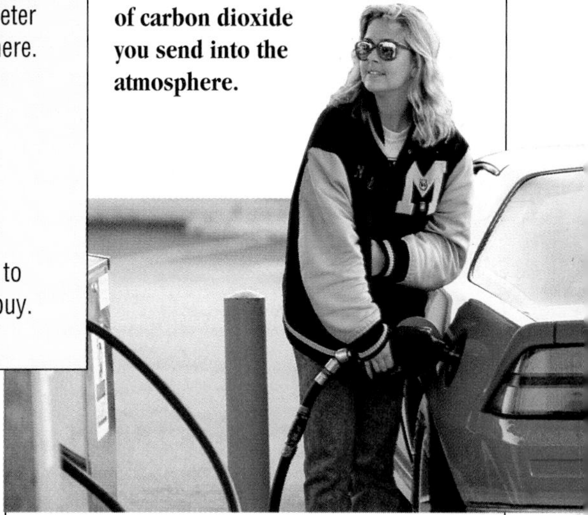

SLOWING THE TEMPERATURE CHANGE

What can be done to slow global warming? The use of fossil fuels could be reduced so that less carbon dioxide is released into the atmosphere. Additionally, the Earth's existing forests could be preserved, and more trees could be planted. The trees would remove carbon dioxide from the atmosphere.

But the act of planting trees is not enough by itself. In December 1997, representatives from 150 nations met in Kyoto, Japan, to debate international limits on greenhouse-gas emissions. The developed nations, including the United States, agreed to cut greenhouse-gas emissions by an average of 5 percent below 1990 levels.

Figure 7-17 **These volunteers are participating in Tree Week, an urban beautification program in Austin, Texas. The tree they plant will also remove carbon dioxide from the atmosphere.**

SECTION REVIEW

1. Why is the air warmer inside a greenhouse than outside it?
2. What are the two main causes of the increase in carbon dioxide levels in the atmosphere?
3. What evidence do scientists have that global warming is occuring?

THINKING CRITICALLY

4. *Analyzing Relationships* Some scientists predict that crop yields will increase in some parts of the world and decrease in others as a result of global warming. Name one factor that would account for this change.

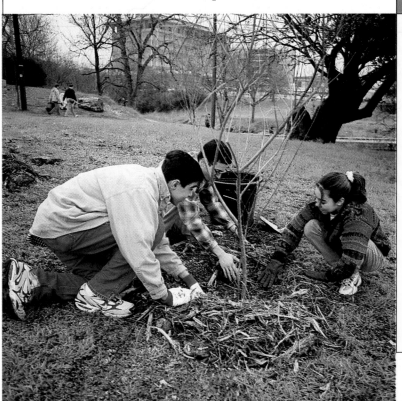

THE OZONE SHIELD

AFTER READING THIS SECTION YOU SHOULD BE ABLE TO

❶ explain how the ozone layer shields the Earth from much of the sun's harmful radiation.

❷ explain how CFCs are damaging the ozone layer.

❸ describe the damaging effects of excessive ultraviolet light.

SCI**LINKS**
NSTA
TOPIC: ozone shield
GO TO: www.scilinks.org
KEYWORD: HE186

Figure 7-18 The CFC molecule in this illustration contains one chlorine atom, which can destroy 10,000 ozone molecules.

The stratosphere contains the Earth's ozone shield. **Ozone** is a form of oxygen with molecules made of three oxygen atoms. Ozone in the stratosphere absorbs most of the ultraviolet (UV) light from the sun. UV light is very harmful to organisms because it can damage the genetic material in living cells. By shielding the Earth's surface from most of the sun's ultraviolet radiation, the ozone in the stratosphere acts like a sunscreen for the Earth and its inhabitants.

OZONE EATERS

During the 1970s, scientists began to worry that a class of human-made chemicals called **CFCs (chlorofluorocarbons)** might be damaging the ozone shield. For many years CFCs were thought to be miracle chemicals. They were nonpoisonous and nonflammable, and they didn't corrode metals. CFCs quickly became popular as coolants in refrigerators and air conditioners. They were also used as a gassy "fizz" in making plastic foams such as styrofoam and were used as a propellant in spray cans of everyday products such as deodorants, insecticides, and paint.

Breaking Apart CFCs At the Earth's surface, CFCs are chemically stable. They don't combine with other chemicals or break down into other substances. But CFC molecules can be broken apart high in the stratosphere, where UV radiation is absorbed. This is because UV radiation is a powerful energy source, powerful enough to break down CFC molecules.

Over a period of 10 to 20 years, CFC molecules released at the Earth's surface make their way into the stratosphere. If you study Figure 7-18, you will see how the CFCs destroy ozone in the stratosphere. CFC molecules contain from one to four chlorine atoms, and it is estimated that a single chlorine atom can destroy 10,000 ozone molecules.

1. **UV light causes the CFC to break down, releasing a chlorine atom.**

UV light

CFC molecule ($CCIF_3$)

breaks CFC into

One carbon atom and three fluorine atoms (CF_3)

Chlorine atom (Cl)

2. **The chlorine atom reacts with an ozone molecule to create an oxygen molecule and a chlorine monoxide molecule.**

Two oxygen molecules (O_2)

reacts with

Chlorine atom (Cl)

Ozone molecule (O_3)

creating

4. **The chlorine atom can then break up another ozone molecule.**

creating

Ozone molecule (O_3)

reacts with

Chlorine monoxide molecule (ClO)

3. **The chlorine monoxide molecule then reacts with another ozone molecule, creating two molecules of oxygen and one chlorine atom.**

Oxygen molecule (O_2)

CHAPTER 7 • ATMOSPHERE AND CLIMATE

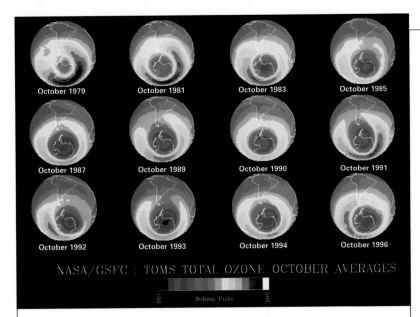

NASA/GSFC : TOMS TOTAL OZONE OCTOBER AVERAGES

Dobson Units

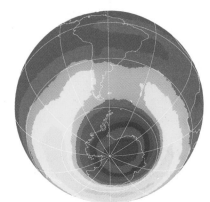

October 1997

Figure 7-19 In these satellite images (left and below), the Antarctic ozone hole appears purple. The ozone hole occurs during the Antarctic spring, when UV light breaks apart CFC molecules that have built up during the dark polar winters.

Susan Solomon has braved polar climates at both ends of the Earth to study the ozone layer. Find out more about her on pages 194–195.

Figure 7-20 Depletion of the ozone layer allows more ultraviolet (UV) radiation to reach the Earth's surface.

THE OZONE HOLE

In 1985, an article in the British scientific journal *Nature* reported the results of studies by scientists working at Halley Bay, on the coast of Antarctica. The studies revealed that the ozone layer above the South Pole had thinned by 50 to 98 percent. This was the first news of the now-famous "ozone hole."

After the results from the studies were published, NASA scientists reviewed data that had been sent back to Earth by the *Nimbus 7* weather satellite since its launch in 1978. They saw the first signs of ozone thinning in the data from 1979. Although the concentration of ozone fluctuates during the year, the data show a growing ozone hole, as shown in Figure 7-19. Ozone levels over the Arctic have decreased as well. In fact, March 1997 ozone levels over the Canadian Arctic were down to 45 percent below normal.

You read in Chapter 6 that ozone is being produced as air pollution, so you may be wondering why this ozone doesn't just float up to the stratosphere and repair the ozone hole. The answer is that ozone is very chemically reactive. Ozone produced by pollution breaks down or combines with other substances long before it can reach the stratosphere to replace ozone that is being destroyed.

The Effects of Ozone Thinning As the amount of ozone in the stratosphere decreases, more ultraviolet light is able to pass through the stratosphere and reach Earth's surface. (See Figure 7-20.) UV light is dangerous to living things because it damages DNA. UV light is a major cause of skin cancer and cataracts. High levels of UV light can kill one-celled organisms that live near the surface of the ocean. Their loss could disrupt ocean food chains and reduce fish harvests. In addition, a reduction in the number of microscopic photosynthesizers would further increase the amount of

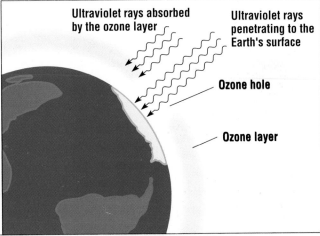

Ultraviolet rays absorbed by the ozone layer

Ultraviolet rays penetrating to the Earth's surface

Ozone hole

Ozone layer

187

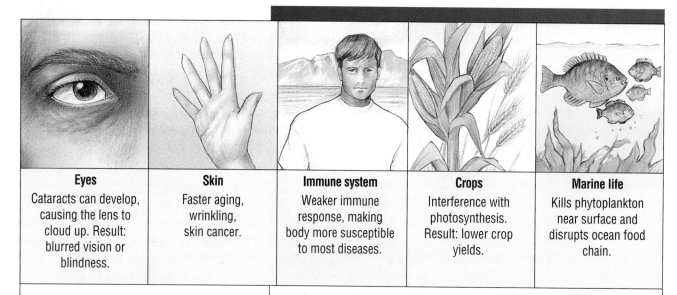

Eyes	Skin	Immune system	Crops	Marine life
Cataracts can develop, causing the lens to cloud up. Result: blurred vision or blindness.	Faster aging, wrinkling, skin cancer.	Weaker immune response, making body more susceptible to most diseases.	Interference with photosynthesis. Result: lower crop yields.	Kills phytoplankton near surface and disrupts ocean food chain.

Figure 7-21 This table shows some of the adverse effects of increased exposure to UV light as a result of the depletion of the ozone layer.

carbon dioxide in the atmosphere. Other damaging effects of excessive UV light are shown in Figure 7-21.

More UV light could be especially damaging for amphibians, such as toads and salamanders. Such animals lay eggs that lack shells in the shallow water of ponds and streams. Natural levels of UV light kill many eggs of some species by damaging exposed DNA. Higher UV levels might kill more eggs, putting amphibian populations at risk.

STOPPING THE OZONE EATERS

In 1987, a group of nations met in Canada and agreed to take action against ozone depletion. Under an agreement called the Montreal Protocol, nations agreed to sharply limit their production of CFCs. A second conference on the problem was held in Copenhagen, Denmark, in 1992. The 93 countries represented at the conference reached the following agreements.

- Industrialized countries agreed to eliminate most CFCs by 1995. The United States pledged to ban by 2000 all substances that pose a significant danger to the ozone layer.
- Industrialized countries also agreed to set up a fund to help developing countries switch to substitutes for CFCs.
- Other substances that destroy ozone were also banned.

After developed countries banned most uses of CFCs, chemical companies developed CFC replacements. Aerosol cans no longer use CFCs as propellants, and air conditioners are becoming CFC-free. For these reasons, many people consider ozone protection an international environmental success story. The battle to protect the ozone layer is not over, though, because some countries still make and use CFCs. Also, CFC molecules remain active in the stratosphere for decades. CFCs released thirty years ago are still destroying ozone today, so it will be many years before the ozone layer recovers.

SECTION REVIEW

❶ What is ozone? How does it act as a "sunscreen" for the Earth?

❷ What are the main sources of CFCs in our atmosphere?

THINKING CRITICALLY

❸ *Interpreting Graphics* Consult Figure 7-18 to answer the following question. Why is chlorine destructive to the ozone layer?

❹ *Recognizing Relationships* If the ozone layer gets significantly thinner during your lifetime, what changes might you need to make to your lifestyle?

HIGHLIGHTS

SUMMARY

- The atmosphere is a thin layer of gases that surrounds the Earth. This mixture of gases is called air.

- The oxygen in air is released by organisms that break apart water molecules during photosynthesis. The balance between photosynthesis and cellular respiration keeps the amount of carbon dioxide in the atmosphere constant.

- Climate is affected by latitude, wind and ocean currents, and local geography.

- Certain gases trap heat in the troposphere. This process, called the greenhouse effect,

keeps the Earth warm enough for life to exist.

- The burning of fossil fuels and the clearing of forests are causing a rapid rise in carbon dioxide levels in our atmosphere. Some scientists predict that this will increase the intensity of the greenhouse effect, causing changes in global weather patterns.

- Ozone in the stratosphere absorbs most of the UV light that comes to Earth. Ozone is destroyed by chlorine atoms released when chlorofluorocarbons (CFCs) are broken down.

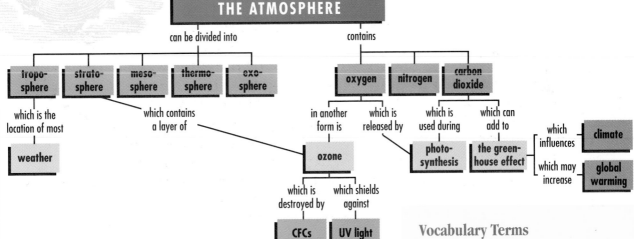

Vocabulary Terms

atmosphere (p. 173)

CFCs (chlorofluorocarbons) (p. 186)

climate (p. 176)

global warming (p. 184)

greenhouse effect (p. 180)

greenhouse gases (p. 181)

ozone (p. 186)

stratosphere (p. 175)

troposphere (p. 175)

weather (p. 176)

EcoLog

Now that you've studied this chapter, revise your answers to the questions you answered at the beginning of the chapter, based on what you have learned.

❶ Why is the warming of the Earth by carbon dioxide and other gases called "the greenhouse effect"?

❷ Why are some scientists concerned about the loss of ozone from the ozone layer?

REVIEW

UNDERSTANDING VOCABULARY

1. For each pair of terms, explain the differences in their meanings.
    a. weather
       climate
    b. atmosphere
       ozone
    c. greenhouse effect
       global warming
    d. troposphere
       stratosphere

RELATING CONCEPTS

2. Copy the unfinished concept map below onto a sheet of paper. Then complete the concept map by writing the correct word or phrase in each box containing a question mark.

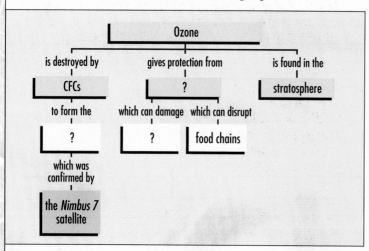

UNDERSTANDING CONCEPTS

Multiple Choice

3. The Earth's early atmosphere probably contained very little
    a. hydrogen.
    b. oxygen.
    c. methane.
    d. ammonia.

4. Today, 99% of the Earth's atmosphere is made up of
    a. hydrogen and oxygen.
    b. nitrogen and methane.
    c. oxygen and carbon dioxide.
    d. oxygen and nitrogen.

5. Carbon dioxide makes up about how much of the Earth's atmosphere?
    a. 0.03%
    b. 3.0%
    c. 10%
    d. 30%

6. Which is NOT a greenhouse gas?
    a. water vapor
    b. carbon dioxide
    c. methane
    d. nitrogen

7. At what time of year does carbon dioxide in the atmosphere decrease as a result of natural processes?
    a. summer
    b. fall
    c. winter
    d. The amount of carbon dioxide stays constant year-round.

8. How is climate related to weather?
    a. They are the same thing.
    b. Climate is the average weather in an area over a long period of time.
    c. Climate is simply the weather conditions at a particular time in a particular location.
    d. They have no relation to each other.

9. Which factor has the MOST influence on a region's climate?
    a. number of forests
    b. distance from the ocean
    c. number of mountain ranges
    d. distance from the equator

URBANIZATION

Until about the 1850s, most people lived in villages and worked the surrounding land. Those people who were not farmers managed the forests, worked in local mines or mills, or manufactured the necessities of life for the village.

Today, modern machinery and methods have made it possible for farms to be operated by fewer people. In addition, efficient transportation networks have reduced the need for manufacturers to locate near their customers. As a result, the number of jobs in the countryside has fallen, and people have moved to cities in search of work. The growth of cities as people move from rural to urban areas is known as **urbanization.** Urbanization occurred rapidly in developed countries between 1880 and 1950. Now it is occurring most rapidly in developing countries.

The Urban Crisis Not surprisingly, many countries have had trouble coping with their rapidly growing urban populations. People sometimes migrate to the cities faster than jobs become available for them and before an adequate infrastructure can be established to support them. **Infrastructure** is all of the things that a society builds for public use. Infrastructure includes roads, sewers, railroads, bridges, canals, fire and police stations, schools, libraries, hospitals, water mains, and power lines.

When more people live in a city than the city can support with jobs and infrastructure, living conditions deteriorate and unemployment increases. In developing countries, newcomers often create informal communities called squatter settlements on the edge of cities. The lack of an adequate infrastructure in overpopulated cities throughout the developed and developing world has become so widespread that the term **urban crisis** was coined to describe it. According to the United Nations, the crisis is so bad that almost one-fourth of the world's city dwellers could be homeless by the year 2020.

Figure 8-4 **A skyscraper could be viewed as a symbol of big-city life. It is only through advances in machinery and transportation that its existence is possible.**

Suburban Sprawl One consequence of the urban crisis is a phenomenon called suburban sprawl. **Suburban sprawl** is development, characterized by houses and strip shopping malls, that spreads out around cities. Generally, the suburbs offer more living space for less money, lower crime rates, and more privacy. With a car or two, a family can live in the suburbs and still work in the city. Since 1992, more Americans have been living in suburbs than in cities and the countryside combined.

Each year suburbs spread over another 1 million hectares (2.5 million acres) of land in the United States. Most of the development that California officials recorded in their land-use study was due to suburban sprawl. The Los Angeles area, shown in Figure 8-5, has the largest and fastest-growing area of suburban sprawl in the world. Houses, schools, roads, and shopping malls now cover land that once supported crops and native ecosystems.

Figure 8-5 **Suburban sprawl around Los Angeles, California**

LAND-USE PLANNING

When suburban sprawl began to take over the countryside surrounding Washington, D.C., in the 1960s, a commission was established to develop a growth plan for the region. The plan called for new cities about every 6.4 km (4 mi.) along a series of transportation corridors. These corridors would extend from the city like the spokes in a wheel, as seen in Figure 8-6.

The plan was called a "wedges-and-corridors" system because it integrated corridors of highly developed cities with wedges of non-urban, open spaces that allowed for recreation, agriculture, and the conservation of natural resources. In 1964 Montgomery County, Maryland, was the only county of those shown in Figure 8-6 to adopt the wedges-and-corridors plan. This plan helped county officials successfully anticipate and develop infrastructure for a population that grew dramatically in the next few decades.

As a result of the plan, Montgomery County has established itself as a leader in land-use planning. **Land-use planning** involves determining in advance where people will live, where they will locate their businesses, and where land will be protected for farming, wildlife, recreation, and other uses. Land-use planners also determine the best locations for roads, shopping malls, sewers, landfills, electrical lines, and other infrastructure.

Montgomery County had the insight to plan for future urban growth. But many other cities have been overwhelmed by rapid growth before they could develop land-use plans. What can be done to improve these cities? The use of mass transit, inner-city renovation, and protection of open spaces are a few of the many possible solutions.

Figure 8-6 **This plan integrates corridors of urban development with wedges of open spaces in an attempt to control suburban sprawl from the Washington, D.C., area. Montgomery County was the only county to actually follow through with this plan.**

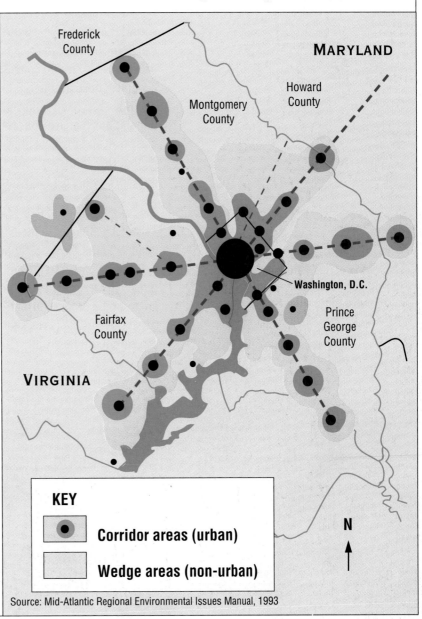

KEY

⬤ Corridor areas (urban)

▢ Wedge areas (non-urban)

N

Source: Mid-Atlantic Regional Environmental Issues Manual, 1993

SCI**LINKS**
NSTA

TOPIC: mass transit
GO TO: www.scilinks.org
KEYWORD: HE202

MASS TRANSPORTATION

Ask any urban dweller to name the number one annoyance of big-city life and the answer is likely to be "traffic." The roads of every major city in America are clogged with cars, most of which are carrying only one person. Because cars are so convenient, most Americans use them to travel everywhere. But this convenience has a cost. In 1993 the average American spent about $1,700 in gasoline and car-maintenance costs just to travel to and from work. This did not include the cost of parking, which can be steep in cities with limited parking space. By contrast, the average European spent half that amount to commute to work. Why the difference? Most Europeans use mass transit, which includes buses, subways, and trains.

Mass transit is an economical, efficient alternative to the automobile. It is energy-efficient and reduces highway congestion, air pollution, and the loss of land to roadways and parking lots. Cities served by mass transit can be more compact, reducing suburban sprawl. Furthermore, studies have shown that mass-transit systems can help revitalize decaying urban areas. With an efficient mass-transit system, traffic congestion is usually reduced and a city becomes more livable.

However, many suburban areas in the United States do not have populations that are concentrated enough to financially support mass transit. Efficient subway systems, such as those serving Washington, D.C., and New York City, are expensive to maintain and therefore require a large number of paying riders.

INNER-CITY RENOVATION

As more people leave the cities for the suburbs, businesses follow them. Without the large sums of money that the original businesses were contributing to the community, many city areas fall into disrepair. However, cities are now attempting to renovate run-down areas. Some of these urban-renewal projects have been very successful. Figure 8-7 shows the result of Baltimore's renovation of a deteriorated waterfront.

Figure 8-7 The successful renovation of this waterfront in Baltimore, Maryland, has encouraged other cities to invest in improving their urban centers.

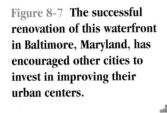

Figure 8-8 **Open spaces help make urban areas more livable.**

For the most part, the most successful urban-renewal projects have been those that use a combination of government grants, tax incentives, and other assistance to induce private citizens to renovate an area. A recent innovation of this type encourages residents in low-income housing projects to manage their own properties. These programs usually work well because, when planning, private citizens tend to understand the practical needs of their community better than a planner who is far removed from the community.

OPEN SPACES

As mentioned earlier, the "wedges" of open space that Montgomery County officials integrated into their land-use plans serve a valuable purpose. In fact, open spaces can help alleviate many of the problems experienced in crowded urban areas. Open spaces come in many forms, including parks, pools, stretches of bicycle and hiking trails, historical settings, gardens, and agricultural areas.

Open spaces have numerous benefits. They give people a place to escape the crowded, noisy conditions that can make big-city life so stressful. They can also be used for civic activities such as concerts, or simply for socializing. Open spaces serve valuable environmental functions as well. The greenery of open spaces absorbs carbon dioxide, produces oxygen, and filters out pollutants. Green spaces can even help keep a city cool in the summer.

Another important function of open spaces, especially those with vegetation, is to reduce drainage problems. Unlike cement, open spaces with grasses and soil can absorb water runoff from rain or melting snow. So by increasing the amount of open space in a city, flooding may be reduced.

SECTION REVIEW

❶ Explain why the amount of land that cities occupy is not a true reflection of the actual amount of land required to sustain them.

❷ In the last 150 years, many people have moved from small rural communities to huge urban centers. Why?

❸ What is the urban crisis? What might be done to relieve it?

THINKING CRITICALLY

❹ *Making Decisions* In your opinion, should laws limit suburban sprawl? Why or why not?

HOW WE USE LAND

AFTER READING THIS SECTION YOU SHOULD BE ABLE TO

❶ describe how humans use non-urban lands as natural resources.

❷ explain how logging, ranching, and mining activities affect the land.

❸ explain how lands can be logged, grazed, and mined sustainably.

As the human population grows, ever-increasing amounts of land and resources are needed to support it. Most of these resources come from the world's non-urban, or rural, lands.

Non-urban lands include forests from which we harvest timber for paper, furniture, and home construction. These lands also include rich grasslands that support livestock and can be used for farmland. Tremendous stores of mineral resources that power our engines and become part of our skyscrapers and electronic devices

Figure 8-9 This footbridge is part of the McKenzie River National Recreation Trail, in Willamette National Forest, Oregon. Non-urban lands such as this can provide a surprising number of uses to humans. Unfortunately, humans sometimes overuse and degrade these lands.

also come from non-urban lands. But as our population grows, non-urban land areas are put under greater stress. Often, the usefulness of these areas is even destroyed by overuse.

HARVESTING TREES

Trees are harvested to provide products we use every day, such as paper, furniture, and lumber and plywood for our homes. We all use enormous amounts of wood. The worldwide average is 1,800 cu. cm of wood per person each day but the average person in the United States uses 3.5 times this amount. This is the equivalent of each person in the United States cutting down a 30-m-tall tree every year.

Harvested trees also provide firewood for many people. In fact, about 1.5 billion people in developing countries depend on firewood as their major source of fuel.

In some places, it's not the trees but the forest land that is valuable—the trees are removed to make way for farming or ranching enterprises. In developing countries, poor city dwellers sometimes move into forested regions, cut down the trees on a small parcel of land, and farm or ranch the area. By building roads into the forests and then letting people claim property rights to land that they clear, governments offer many people hope for a better future. This is similar to what happened in the United States during the settlement period.

Deforestation Today forests around the world are being cleared at an alarming rate, and deforestation has become a serious environmental problem. **Deforestation** involves clearing trees from an area without replacing them. Today this situation is especially serious in tropical rain forests, which exist primarily in developing countries. Because the poor soil in tropical rain forests can usually support crops for only a short time, farmers must continuously move from one parcel of land to another, clearing additional forest with each move. The problem is made worse by the fact that human populations are growing so rapidly in developing countries.

There are many different methods of harvesting trees. Most methods cause damage to the forest, and some are more destructive than others. **Clear-cutting,** for example, is a process that involves removing all of the trees from a land area. The top illustration in Figure 8-11 shows a clear-cut area. Clear-cutting destroys wildlife

Figure 8-10 **Logging operations provide resources that are important in construction and manufacturing.**

Each year at least 2 million hectares (4.9 million acres) of forest are cut down worldwide.

habitats, increases soil erosion, and diminishes the beauty of forests. Clear-cutting is popular because it is the least expensive way for timber companies to harvest trees. In addition, clear-cutting requires very little road building to harvest a large number of trees.

The main alternative to clear-cutting is **selective cutting,** shown in the bottom illustration of Figure 8-11. Selective cutting involves cutting only middle-aged or mature trees. These trees are removed from the forest individually or in small groups, and the rest of the trees are left alone. With time, the harvested trees are naturally replaced by reseeding. Selective cutting has less of an impact on the forest environment than any other method of tree harvesting. However, selective cutting requires more roads to harvest a given amount of timber than does clear-cutting or other cutting methods. Roads are the primary cause of soil erosion associated with logging. If not properly controlled, both clear-cutting and selective cutting can increase soil erosion, damage wildlife habitats, and cause other environmental problems.

Reforestation When trees die or are removed from a forest, reforestation helps restore the area to its original condition. **Reforestation** is the process of replacing trees that have died or been cut down. This can happen naturally when seeds fall from nearby trees, or it can happen when humans plant seeds or seedlings.

Sometimes when humans harvest a large number of trees from an area, natural reforestation cannot occur. For example, if a very large area is clear-cut, there may be no way that the mature trees

Figure 8-11 Each of these methods of harvesting timber has benefits and drawbacks.

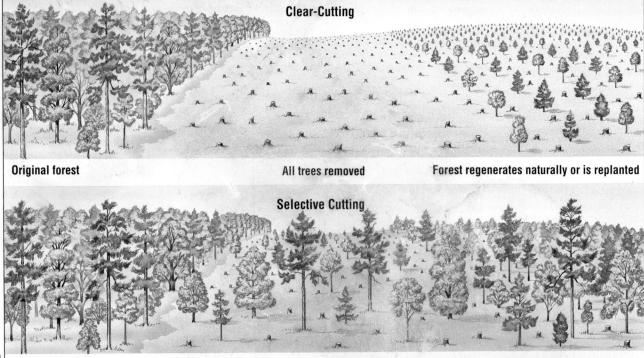

Clear-Cutting

Original forest   All trees removed   Forest regenerates naturally or is replanted

Selective Cutting

Original forest   Mature trees selectively cut   Forest regenerates naturally

bordering the area can provide seed for the natural regeneration of the entire area. In addition, reforestation may fail because tree seedlings cannot grow where clear-cutting has caused soil erosion or where the seedlings will not be shaded by other trees. Even when it is successful, reforestation is a slow process. It may take 20 to 50 years or more to regrow a forest.

Some governments require reforestation after timber is removed from public land. But worldwide, more than 90 percent of all timber comes from forests that are not managed by the government. This means that some countries are still chopping down original forest land and not replanting the trees. Reforestation is required on public land in the United States, but this law is often not enforced, and most of the country's forest land is privately owned. Several states now require private landowners to reforest after timber harvest.

Protecting Forests Many governments are currently working to improve reforestation efforts and promote less destructive harvesting methods. In addition, forest preserves established by government agencies, private conservation groups, and private citizens are appearing more frequently. Private organizations have also established effective tree-planting programs. These programs help guarantee the survival of forests. They also improve urban areas, where many trees are removed to make way for buildings and parking lots. The leader of one especially successful tree-planting organization is shown in Figure 8-12. It is important that these types of programs continue in order to protect forests and their many resources.

PLANT A TREE!

You can personally contribute to the reforestation effort simply by planting a tree. Find out how on pages 398–399.

Figure 8-12 **Wangari Maathai (below) is the founder of an organization in Nairobi, Kenya, called the Green Belt Movement. Her organization has helped over 50,000 people grow and plant more than 10 million tree seedlings.**

In the arid West it takes about 31 hectares (77 acres) of grazing land to raise one cow, while in the rest of the United States it takes an average of about 7 hectares (17.5 acres) to raise one cow.

RANCHING

Rangelands support grasses and shrubs that are used by ranchers for grazing animals such as cattle, sheep, and goats. Along with farmland (discussed in Chapter 9), rangeland is essential for maintaining the world's food supply. Some experts predict that current trends in population growth will necessitate a 40 percent increase in food production from rangeland between the years 1977 and 2030.

Problems on the Range Rangelands consist primarily of grasses and shrubs. Grasses are remarkably adaptable plants— they can live through droughts, freezes, fires, and years of animal grazing. This is because the growing point of grass is at the base of every leaf. So if the upper section of a leaf is damaged or cut, the leaf will grow back from its base. Shrubs are not as resistant to grazing as grasses are, but they also have numerous characteristics that help them survive grazing.

Another interesting feature of grass is its root system. As shown in Figure 8-13, the roots of grasses are fibrous, and they grow so densely that they form a matted tangle that extends several centimeters below the surface. This root system holds soil together, which prevents soil erosion.

Even though grass is adaptable, it does have limits. When too many animals graze in an area for too long, they damage the grass beyond its ability to recover and much of it dies. This is called **overgrazing.**

When an area is overgrazed, much of the grass is destroyed and the fibrous root system decays. Often, vast fields of grass turn into mere patches, and plants that are less appealing to grazers take over. The roots of these plants are less efficient at protecting the soil from wind and water erosion. If a prolonged drought plagues the overgrazed area before other plants can take over, the land may become so degraded that it can never recover, like the land shown in Figure 8-14. This process, called *desertification,*

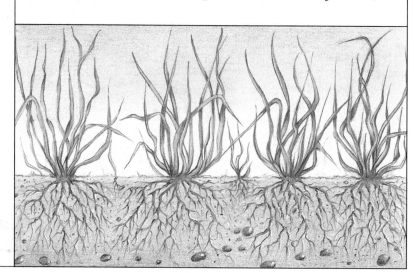

Figure 8-13 **The fibrous root system of grass helps prevent soil erosion.**

208

CHAPTER 8 • LAND

converts rangeland to wasteland. You will learn more about desertification in Chapter 9.

In some regions of the world, ranching has also contributed to the destruction of tropical forests. (See Figure 8-15.) In Brazil, an area of forest the size of South Carolina was cleared for cattle ranches between 1966 and 1978. In more recent years, however, government programs in Brazil have helped slow the rate of clearing.

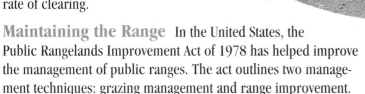

Maintaining the Range In the United States, the Public Rangelands Improvement Act of 1978 has helped improve the management of public ranges. The act outlines two management techniques: grazing management and range improvement.

Grazing management involves limiting animal herds to sizes the land can support. It also involves moving these herds in ways that will protect the plants that support them. Range improvement includes eliminating sagebrush and other weedy plants that invade overgrazed land, planting vegetation where soil is bare, fencing areas to let them recover from overgrazing, and digging enough small water holes to keep livestock from overgrazing the vegetation around a single watering area.

Figure 8-14 **Overgrazing led to the desertification of this Australian ranchland.**

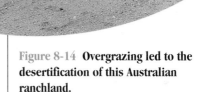

TOPIC: range management
GO TO: www.scilinks.org
KEYWORD: HE209

Figure 8-15 **Rain forest in South America was cleared for this ranching operation.**

Gold

Chromite

Sulfur

MINING

A surprising amount of land is used for mining minerals. A **mineral** is a solid substance that is found in nature and consists of a single element or compound. Minerals include common substances, such as salt, as well as rare ones, such as gold and silver. Minerals that are useful to humans are called **mineral resources.** For instance, iron, copper, aluminum, and other metals derived from minerals are used in cars, stereos, refrigerators, and buildings. We build with concrete, brick, and glass, which are also made from minerals. And many minerals go into paper, paint, plastics, chemicals, films, fertilizers, and a host of other products. Figure 8-16 shows some of the minerals that are important to industry.

Two common methods for extracting minerals from the Earth are open-pit mining and strip mining. In **open-pit mining,** machines are used to dig large holes in the ground and remove the **ore,** which is the mineral-containing rock. Sand, gravel, and building stone are also mined in this way. The copper mine shown in Figure 8-17 is an open-pit mine. In **strip mining,** huge bulldozers and other machines are used to clear away large strips of the Earth's surface. The rock phosphorite, which is a raw material used to make fertilizers and phosphate chemicals, is often mined in this way.

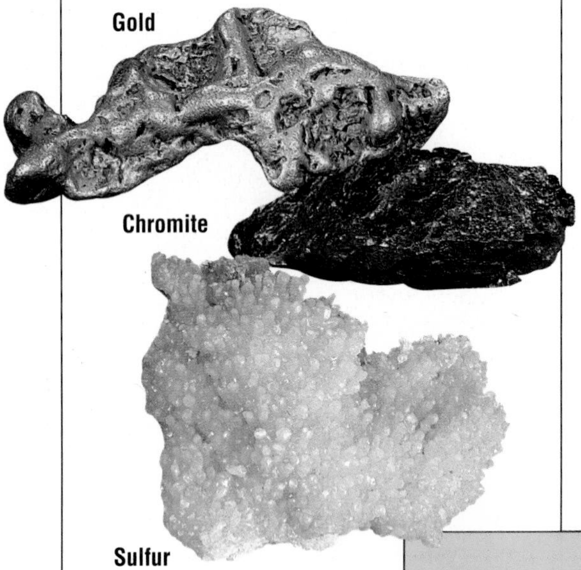

Figure 8-16 **This table identifies some of the most important minerals used in the manufacture of products.**

Some of the Minerals Most Important to Industry	
Minerals	**Some Uses**
Diamond	Industrial abrasives, jewelry
Chromite	Toolmaking, jet engines, stainless steel, pigments
Copper	Electrical wiring, metal alloys
Hematite	Steel making, jewelry, pigments
Halite	Flavoring (as table salt)
Gold	Jewelry, money, electronics
Platinum	Electroplating, jewelry, cancer therapies, catalyst in pollution control and fertilizer synthesis
Silver	Jewelry, photography
Sphalerite	Metal alloys, electroplating, batteries, paint
Sulfur	Papermaking, photography, food additives, paint, explosives, pesticides, pharmaceuticals, rayon
Graphite	Electronics, lubricants, nuclear reactor cores, pencil "lead"

The Effects of Mining As you might imagine, extracting minerals from the Earth causes environmental damage. The most obvious damage is the disruption of the land surface and the ugly piles of waste materials left behind. When large areas of natural vegetation are cleared, wildlife habitat is lost, and the area's natural ecosystem is disrupted.

Such large-scale removal of vegetation and rock can cause land erosion and even landslides. In addition, toxic substances left behind at a mining site can pollute the air and water. It also requires a tremendous amount of energy to extract and process minerals.

Mines in the United States collectively produce more waste than all American cities and towns combined. Some of the waste that remains after mineral processing is dangerously toxic. The open-pit copper mine pictured in Figure 8-17 produces 1,200 metric tons of

Figure 8-17 **This open-pit copper mine in Bingham, Utah, is wider than 35 football fields and more than twice as deep as the Empire State Building is high! It is the largest human-made hole, and out of it comes 227,000 metric tons (250,000 tons) of copper each year.**

Figure 8-18 **Mines, such as this one in Colorado, can leave the land polluted and heavily scarred.**

Figure 8-19 **Would you believe this area in West Virginia was once strip-mined for coal?**

SECTION REVIEW

❶ What is reforestation, and why is it important?

❷ How can grazing-management and range-improvement techniques help sustain rangelands?

❸ Name and describe two ways to decrease the impact of mining on the land.

THINKING CRITICALLY

❹ *Identifying Relationships* It is sometimes difficult to provide an economic justification for the environmental protection of our nation's lands (such as providing wildlife habitat). How might this difficulty affect decisions about land use?

waste material for every metric ton of copper metal produced. And every year the amount of waste increases as miners have to dig deeper and deeper to find the copper.

Responsible Mining One way to reduce damage from mining is to require mining companies to restore mined land to the condition it was in before mining began. This process is called **reclamation.** A successful reclamation project is shown in Figure 8-19. Environmental laws in the United States now require companies to reclaim mining sites on public land. Some states also have laws that require reclamation on private land.

Another way to reduce the destructive effects of mining is to reduce the need for more minerals. By recycling existing products made from minerals such as iron, copper, and aluminum, we not only save energy, water, and money, but also reduce the pollution caused by additional mining and processing operations.

mineral claims could still be made in wilderness areas until 1983. Many mining companies filed claims at the last minute to keep their mining operations in wilderness areas busy long into the future. And ranch animals, such as cattle, can still be seen in some wilderness areas today.

In addition, the negative effects of nearby grazing, logging, oil and gas drilling, factories, power plants, and urban areas often affect these regions. Some scenic views in wilderness areas, such as that shown in Figure 8-24, are obscured by air pollution more frequently each year.

Figure 8-24 **Pollution from nearby urban areas obscures the view of Grand Canyon National Park, in Arizona.**

Since 1872, over 1.4 million hectares (3.5 million acres) of public land have been sold to private owners. As of October 1992, mining companies, many of them foreign owned, have applied for patents to thousands of hectares of federal lands, which contain at least $91 billion worth of mineral deposits. Recent investigations by the General Accounting Office, the investigative arm of Congress, have shown many instances where these lands were patented for mining but were used instead for real-estate development.

It may seem clear that the Federal Mining Act of 1872 should be reformed. The situation is not that simple, however. Those in the mining industry argue that they need the special provisions of the act in order to remain profitable. They assert that patented land offers them the security they need to finance the opening of a mine and the purchasing of equipment. In addition, they maintain that the states have enacted sufficient environmental controls and thus the act need not be amended. Reforming the act, according to the mining industry, would lead to the loss of thousands of American mining jobs and might cause a shortage of affordable minerals and mineral-based products in the marketplace.

Cyanide seeping from an abandoned gold mine pollutes this Colorado stream.

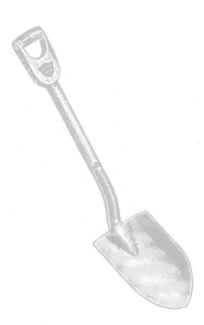

Figure 8-25 **These volunteers are reforesting land in California that was damaged by fires.**

"People Control" in Wilderness Areas

To protect wilderness from damage, limits have been set in some areas for the number of people who can hike or camp at any one time. Federal agencies now require people who want to use the most popular areas to apply for wilderness permits. A permit system enables the agencies to regulate the number of people inside national parks and other federal areas at any given time. Certain areas have also been designated as off-limits to camping, and an increasing number of wilderness rangers now patrol vulnerable areas. In addition, volunteer programs are now active in many wilderness areas. Volunteers help pick up trash and help build trails. New education programs, such as the Forest Service's Tread Lightly program, are also being implemented to help people better understand and reduce their impact on the natural world.

SECTION REVIEW

❶ What are the benefits and problems associated with using public land for multiple uses?

❷ How do you benefit from the nation's public lands? Give at least three examples.

THINKING CRITICALLY

❸ *Recognizing Relationships* Why do you suppose so many of the nation's public lands are in Western states?

❹ *Expressing Viewpoints* Some people suggest that the best way to care for our nation's land is to designate more land as wilderness. Do you agree or disagree? Explain your reasoning.

HIGHLIGHTS

SUMMARY

- Cities and surrounding suburbs have increased sharply in size in recent years as the population has grown and people have moved to the city from rural areas. Swelling urban populations threaten city infrastructures and burden the land.

- Many land-use practices cause damage to the land, reducing its value as a supplier of food and materials.

- The United States has millions of acres of public lands. "Multiple use" management allows these lands to be used for recreation, mining, and other purposes.

- Overuse and residual ranching and mining threaten the nation's wilderness lands.

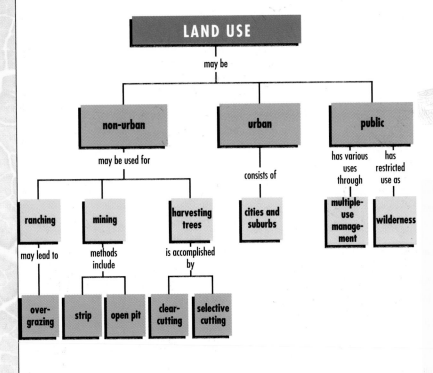

Vocabulary Terms

clear-cutting (p. 205)

deforestation (p. 205)

infrastructure (p. 199)

land-use planning (p. 201)

mineral (p. 210)

mineral resources (p. 210)

open-pit mining (p. 210)

ore (p. 210)

overgrazing (p. 208)

reclamation (p. 212)

reforestation (p. 206)

selective cutting (p. 206)

strip mining (p. 210)

suburban sprawl (p. 200)

urban crisis (p. 199)

urbanization (p. 199)

wilderness (p. 215)

Ecolog!

Now that you've studied this chapter, revise your answers to the questions you answered at the beginning of the chapter, based on what you have learned.

❶ Do you think your lifestyle affects the land in any way? Explain.

❷ Do you think humans should carefully plan how to use the land or simply let things work out as they will?

REVIEW

UNDERSTANDING VOCABULARY

1. Use the following terms in a sentence to show that you know what they mean.
   a. reclamation
   b. land-use planning
   c. suburban sprawl
   d. infrastructure

RELATING CONCEPTS

2. Copy the unfinished concept map below onto a sheet of paper. Then complete the concept map by writing the correct word or phrase in each box containing a question mark.

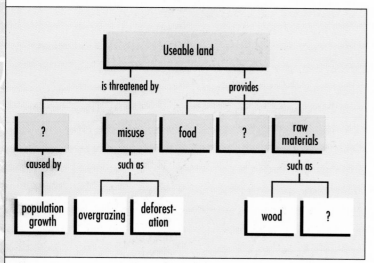

UNDERSTANDING CONCEPTS

Multiple Choice

3. Urbanization can best be described as
   a. the tendency for cities to develop large suburbs.
   b. the decline of the inner city as residents move to the suburbs.
   c. the revitalization of downtown areas that have fallen into decline.
   d. the growth of cities caused by the migration of people from rural areas to the cities.

4. What is the most common reason that people have moved to the city from the country?
   a. to escape war
   b. to search for jobs
   c. to seek higher environmental quality
   d. to find more spacious living accommodations

5. Which is NOT a part of the infrastructure?
   a. roads
   b. bridges
   c. restaurants
   d. power lines

6. What is a major advantage of mass transit over private vehicles?
   a. It reduces congestion on the roads.
   b. It is more convenient for most Americans.
   c. It uses energy more efficiently.
   d. both a and c

7. Selective cutting involves
   a. cutting all of the trees in a forest and then reseeding.
   b. cutting all of the trees of one species and leaving the rest.
   c. cutting the mature trees in a forest and leaving the rest.
   d. cutting the young trees in a forest and leaving the rest.

8. What is one advantage of clear-cutting?
   a. It is the cheapest way for companies to harvest trees.
   b. It enables the ecosystem to return rapidly to normal.
   c. It aerates the soil, allowing it to regenerate.
   d. It brings light to the heavily shaded plants of the forest floor.

9. Which choice best defines "wilderness"?
   a. any non-urban area
   b. any national park or monument
   c. any land protected from development and human impact
   d. any unspoiled area of more than 10,000 sq. km

FEEDING THE PEOPLE OF THE WORLD

AFTER READING THIS SECTION YOU SHOULD BE ABLE TO

❶ explain why providing adequate food for all of the world's people is so difficult.

❷ describe the advantages and disadvantages of the green revolution.

*E*thiopia, 1985: Thousands of people were starving. Lack of rain combined with soil degradation and war had caused a major crop failure for the second time in 15 years. Near the end of the year, the rains finally came and washed millions of tons of soil into the rivers. That year, another 15,000 sq. km (6,000 sq. mi.) were added to the North African desert.

Events like those in Ethiopia present a frightening picture of the problems associated with feeding the people of the world. Many people go hungry, but efforts to produce more food sometimes cause environmental damage, which in turn makes food production more difficult. In this chapter, you will learn why it is so difficult to feed all of the world's people, and about efforts to increase food production.

Figure 9-1 Harvesting rice in China

Major Nutrients in Human Foods		
Nutrient	**Function**	**Major Food Sources**
Carbohydrates	Supplies energy	Bread, cereals, potatoes, beans
Proteins	Used to build and maintain the body	Meat, fish, poultry, eggs, dairy products, beans
Lipids (fats and oils)	Used to build membranes and some hormones. Supplies energy and may also be stored and used later.	Butter, margarine, vegetable oils, animal fats

Figure 9-2 This table shows the three main types of nutrients. Humans also need vitamins and minerals to stay healthy.

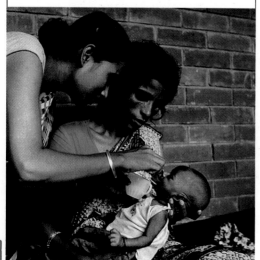

Figure 9-3 A relief worker in Bangladesh gives food to a starving baby.

WHAT PEOPLE EAT

Human beings must consume organic molecules produced by other living things in order to survive. The main types of organic molecules in all foods are carbohydrates, proteins, and lipids. In addition to these major nutrients, we need smaller amounts of vitamins and minerals to help our bodies function properly. The human body uses food both as a source of energy and as a source of materials for building and maintaining body tissues and structures. Figure 9-2 describes how the body uses each of the major nutrients and lists some common foods that contain them.

When people do not get enough to eat, they can become sick and even die. When starving people die, it is usually as a result of diseases that their bodies cannot fight. Underfed people lose resistance to diseases that normally do not threaten the lives of well-nourished people.

Even if people consume enough calories in the food they eat, they may still suffer from **malnutrition,** a condition caused by not consuming enough necessary nutrients. For example, a lack of protein in the diet can cause serious illnesses, especially in young children. These illnesses can cause brain damage if they are not cured quickly. The child shown in Figure 9-3 is receiving food that may prevent conditions caused by malnutrition.

WHY PEOPLE GO HUNGRY

Why are people starving? Because the world's population is increasing rapidly, more food is needed each year. As shown in Figure 9-4, world food production has been increasing for several decades, but the amount of food per person is no longer increasing. In other words, food production is not increasing as fast as the human population is. If everyone in the world today received an equal share of all the food produced, no one would have enough to stay strong and healthy.

However, the world's food is not divided equally. In many parts of the world, wealthy people have an abundance of food, while poor people have much less than they need. We often think of malnutrition as something that happens only in developing countries. But even in the United States many poor people suffer from malnutrition.

Starvation also results when food is available but cannot be transported to the people who need it. Transportation can be a problem when economic and political troubles cause trucking and railroad lines to break down. When there is war in a country, food donated by other countries may not reach the people who need it.

Droughts, or periods when rainfall is less than average, can contribute to starvation by causing crop failure. People can survive a crop failure if there is enough food saved from previous seasons and if there are effective systems for distributing that food. But if a drought is combined with war or inefficient transportation systems, the result can be famine. A **famine** is a food shortage so widespread that it causes malnutrition in many people.

THE GREEN REVOLUTION

In an effort to increase crop yields, new varieties of grain were introduced in Asian and Latin American countries between 1950 and 1970. These new varieties had a much greater **yield,** or amount produced per unit area, than the old varieties. The introduction of new grains and new farming techniques was called the "green revolution."

The green revolution allowed far more people to be adequately fed than was possible before. However, there were problems. The new varieties of grain did not grow well without the right kinds of fertilizers and pesticides, or without sufficient irrigation water. (See Figure 9-5 on the next page.) Many **subsistence farmers**—those who grow only enough food to feed their family—could not afford the necessary equipment and chemicals. Therefore, most of the green revolution's increase in food production was from large farms that grow food to be sold. These farms are now producing about as much food as they can be expected to produce.

Another drawback of the green revolution was that the use of large amounts of pesticides and fertilizers pollutes the

More than 2 billion people worldwide, mostly women and children, are malnourished. This is about 1 out of every 3 people on Earth.

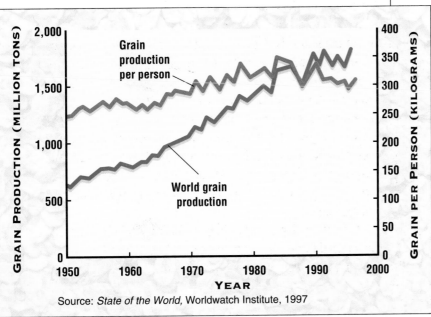

Source: *State of the World,* Worldwatch Institute, 1997

Figure 9-4 **Grains, which are nutritious and can be stored without refrigeration, make up most of the world's food. Since 1984, the amount of grain produced for each person on Earth has dropped slightly, indicating that world food production is not keeping up with population growth.**

229

Figure 9-5 **Many of the new varieties of grain introduced during the green revolution require more water and fertilizer than older varieties required. This corn crop in Guatemala is growing poorly because farmers cannot afford the crop's requirements.**

environment. Also, the necessary farm machinery consumes a great deal of energy, as does the manufacture of fertilizers and pesticides.

POLITICAL CHANGES

As Figure 9-6 suggests, making peace in a war-torn country is an important step toward supplying its people with enough food. Once the war ends, donated food can be distributed more effectively and people can begin to work the land again. They can also learn more sustainable farming techniques.

Figure 9-6 **In Somalia in 1993, soldiers had to make sure that warring factions didn't take food that was meant for starving people in the countryside.**

SECTION REVIEW

❶ Give two reasons why people might get too little to eat even in a country with plenty of food.

❷ Describe one benefit and one drawback of the green revolution.

THINKING CRITICALLY

❸ *Interpreting Graphics* Study the graph in Figure 9-4. World grain production was at an all-time high in the mid-1990s. Why was the amount of grain *per person* declining?

AGRICULTURE AND SOIL

AFTER READING THIS SECTION YOU SHOULD BE ABLE TO

❶ describe fertile soil.

❷ describe methods of preventing soil erosion.

❸ explain how irrigation can cause salinization.

❹ describe desertification and how it can be prevented.

❺ compare low-input and conventional farming.

The Earth has a limited amount of **arable land**—fertile land that can be plowed to grow crops. This amount is decreasing every year. As shown in Figure 9-7, the amount of arable land in the world will have decreased by about one-fifth from 1985 to 2000. About 150 million hectares (about 371 million acres) of farmland will be covered with houses, mines, roads, factories, and power plants. Another 135 million hectares (about 334 million acres) will become unusable for farming because the soil will be damaged.

The shortage of fertile agricultural land threatens our ability to feed the human population. In this section, you will learn how food is produced and how we can ensure that we have enough land to grow the crops we need in the years to come.

Figure 9-7 **This graph shows the amount of the land farmed in 1985 that experts estimate will be lost from production by 2000.**

FARMING

Some of the basic techniques used in farming—plowing, fertilization, irrigation, and pest control—began with the earliest farmers. People or animals pulled plows through the soil. Plowing the soil (cutting through it and turning it over) helps crops grow by mixing up soil nutrients, loosening soil particles, and uprooting weeds. Organic fertilizers, such as manure, were used to enrich the soil so that plants would grow strong and remain healthy. Fields were irrigated (supplied with water) by digging ditches for water to flow through. Weeds were removed by hand, and some plants were covered to keep out pests.

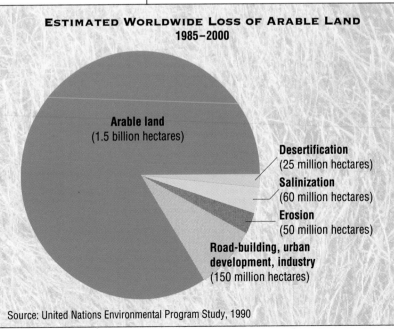

**ESTIMATED WORLDWIDE LOSS OF ARABLE LAND
1985–2000**

Arable land
(1.5 billion hectares)

Desertification
(25 million hectares)

Salinization
(60 million hectares)

Erosion
(50 million hectares)

Road-building, urban development, industry
(150 million hectares)

Source: United Nations Environmental Program Study, 1990

Figure 9-8 Since ancient times, farmers have used human and animal labor to grow crops. This Indonesian farmer uses oxen to plow his field, much like his ancestors did.

FIELD ACTIVITY

Determine the living components of a soil sample from your area. Obtain the following materials: a glass jar, a funnel, a piece of gauze, a magnifying glass, and a small soil sample. Place the funnel right side up in the glass jar. Put the soil sample on a piece of gauze inside the funnel. Leave the jar under a lamp overnight. The living organisms in the soil will move to the bottom of the jar to avoid the light. Use the magnifying glass to observe the kinds of organisms that inhabit the soil.

These ancient methods are still used today, as you can see in Figure 9-8. On large farms in industrialized countries, however, new methods are also used. Machinery is used to plow the soil and harvest crops. (See Figure 9-9.) Synthetic fertilizers, which are produced in factories, are used instead of manure and plant wastes. A variety of overhead sprinklers and drip systems are used for irrigation. And many different synthetic chemicals are used to kill pests.

FERTILE SOIL

Soil that can support the rapid growth of healthy plants is called **fertile soil.** Most plant roots grow in **topsoil,** the loose surface layer of soil. Fertile topsoil is composed of rock particles, water, air, and organic matter, such as dead plants, dead animals, and animal excrement. Living organisms also play an important role in fertile topsoil. Fungi, bacteria, and other microorganisms decompose the organic matter. Earthworms, insects, and other small animals help to break up the soil and let air and water into it. Figure 9-10 shows the large number of living organisms in fertile soil. As you can see in Figure 9-11, several other layers of soil lie under the topsoil. At the bottom is bedrock, which is solid rock.

Figure 9-9 In industrialized nations, machinery is used to do much of the work previously performed by humans and animals. This photograph shows the harvesting of lima beans in Quincy, Washington.

Most soil is formed from bedrock. (See Figure 9-12 on the next page.) Temperature changes and moisture cause the bedrock to crack and break apart, creating smaller and smaller particles. The combination of rock particles, water, air, decaying organic matter, and the action of living organisms forms the soil. It may take thousands of years to form a few centimeters of soil.

Number of Organisms in Average Farm Soil	
Organisms	**Quantity**
Insects	23 million per hectare
All arthropods (including insects)	725 million per hectare
Bacteria	2.5 billion per gram
Algae	50,000 per gram
Earthworms	6 million per hectare

Source: U.S. Department of Agriculture

Figure 9-10
Living organisms are crucial to maintaining the fertility of soil. The table at left shows the astounding number of organisms in farm soil.

Figure 9-11 **The diagram below shows the structure of soil. The number of soil layers and characteristics of the layers may be different in different types of soil.**

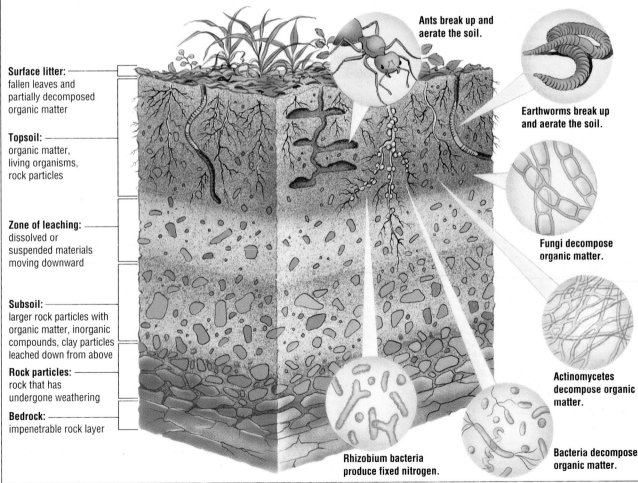

Surface litter:
fallen leaves and
partially decomposed
organic matter

Topsoil:
organic matter,
living organisms,
rock particles

Zone of leaching:
dissolved or
suspended materials
moving downward

Subsoil:
larger rock particles with
organic matter, inorganic
compounds, clay particles
leached down from above

Rock particles:
rock that has
undergone weathering

Bedrock:
impenetrable rock layer

Ants break up and
aerate the soil.

Earthworms break up
and aerate the soil.

Fungi decompose
organic matter.

Actinomycetes
decompose organic
matter.

Bacteria decompose
organic matter.

Rhizobium bacteria
produce fixed nitrogen.

233

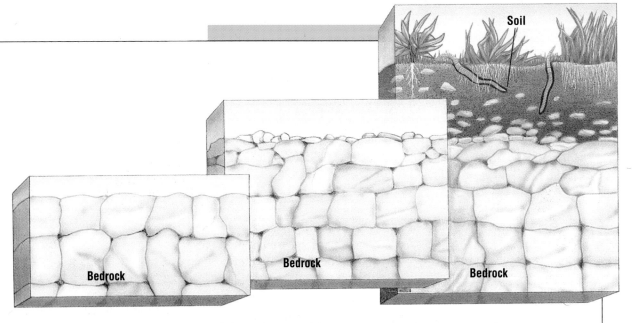

Figure 9-12 **The formation of fertile soil can take thousands of years. These diagrams show how weathering causes the bedrock to crack into rock particles. Soil also contains decaying organic matter and living organisms.**

Figure 9-13 **This map shows the extent of soil erosion around the world. Regions near deserts have been badly damaged because their thin topsoil is easily eroded.**

TOPSOIL EROSION: A GLOBAL PROBLEM

The soil that has taken so long to form is being lost to erosion at an alarming rate. **Erosion** is the wearing away of topsoil by wind and water. In the United States, about half of the topsoil has been lost to erosion in the past 200 years. Worldwide, it is estimated that about 11 percent of the soil has been eroded in the last 45 years. (See Figure 9-13.) Topsoil erosion is ranked as one of the most serious ecological problems we face. Without the valuable topsoil, crops cannot be grown to feed the world's people.

Certain farming practices can contribute to topsoil erosion. Plowing produces a loose surface layer of soil that is easily blown away by wind or washed away by rain. And harvesting may remove roots and other organic matter that hold soil together.

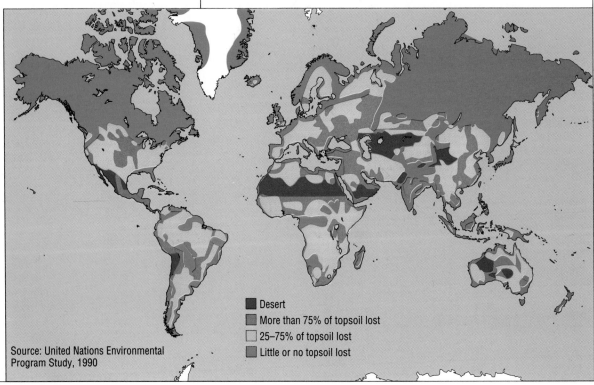

Source: United Nations Environmental Program Study, 1990

Desert

More than 75% of topsoil lost

25–75% of topsoil lost

Little or no topsoil lost

The clearing of forests to produce lumber also contributes to soil erosion. Trees and shrubs absorb large quantities of water. When they are cut down, the amount of water running off the surface of the soil increases, and more soil is carried away. Sometimes the soil washes away slowly, and sometimes large amounts wash away in landslides.

DESERTIFICATION

The loss of topsoil occurs all over the world, but it is especially severe in dry areas. Soil in these areas is easily destroyed because it is naturally thin. Soil fertility can deteriorate so much that the land becomes desertlike, a process called **desertification.** Worldwide, an area the size of Nebraska becomes desert each year.

An example of how desertification occurs is the Sahel region of northern Africa, shown in Figure 9-14. In the past, people in the drier part of the Sahel grazed animals, while those in the wetter part planted crops. The grazing animals were moved from place to place to find fresh grass and leaves. The cropland was planted for only four or five years at a time and then was allowed to lie fallow, or to "rest," for several years. These methods allowed the land to adequately support the people.

Today, an increased population has led to overuse of the land. Several crops a year may now be planted, and fallow periods may be shortened or eliminated, causing the soil

TOPIC: desertification
GO TO: www.scilinks.org
KEYWORD: HE235

Figure 9-14 **The map below shows the location of the Sahel region (in gold). The photograph shows how overuse of the land has led to desertification.**

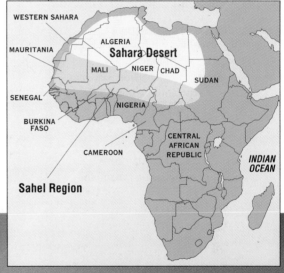

Figure 9-15 **The ridges formed by plowing in curves around the hill prevent topsoil from washing away. This is contour plowing, a way of preventing erosion. Leaving strips of vegetation in place also reduces erosion.**

to lose its fertility. More and more animals are put out to graze. Trees and shrubs are cut for use as fuel or animal feed until few plants are left to hold the soil in place or to trap any rain that falls. The topsoil in the Sahel is blowing away or being washed away by heavy rain. The land is becoming desert.

SOIL CONSERVATION

There are many ways of conserving topsoil and reducing erosion. One method is to pay attention to the slope of the land when planting. Contour plowing is plowing across the slope of a hill. The plow forms tiny ridges that help prevent the soil from washing down the hill. An even more effective technique is to leave strips of vegetation running across the hillside instead of plowing the entire slope, as shown in Figure 9-15. These strips catch soil and water that run down the hill. In very hilly areas, the best method of conserving topsoil may be not to farm the land at all but instead to use it as forest or grassland.

Using organic material instead of inorganic fertilizers can also help restore the soil. One type of organic material that can be used as fertilizer is compost. Compost is waste plant material that has been placed in piles and allowed to decompose. Animal manure can also be used as a fertilizer.

AQUACULTURE:

A DIFFERENT KIND OF FARMING

Seafood provides about 25 percent of the animal protein consumed by people in developing nations. But overfishing is reducing the catches of fish and shellfish from the world's oceans. One solution to the problem is aquaculture.

Aquaculture—raising fish, shellfish, crustaceans, or seaweeds in artificial environments—is hardly a new idea. It probably began in China about 4,000 years ago. Today, China

leads the world in using aquaculture to produce freshwater fish.

There are a number of different types of aquaculture operations. The most common is known as a "fish farm." Farm operations generally consist of many individual ponds, each containing fish at a specific stage of development. Clean water is circulated through the ponds, bringing in oxygen and sweeping away carbon dioxide and fecal wastes. The fish grow to maturity in the ponds and are then harvested.

Another type of aquaculture operation is known as a "ranch." In this method, fish such as salmon are raised until they reach a certain age and then are released. The fish migrate downstream to the ocean, where they live until adulthood. At maturity, the fish return to their birthplace to

reproduce. When they do so, they are captured and harvested.

Today, most of the catfish, crayfish, and rainbow trout and almost half of the shellfish consumed in the

Oyster farm in Washington State

Another method of soil conservation is to change the way the farmland is plowed, or tilled. In conventional farming, after a crop is harvested, the soil is plowed to turn it over and bury the remains of the harvested plants. Then it is raked before new seeds are planted. In **no-till farming,** shown in Figure 9-16, the seeds of the next crop are planted in slits that are cut into the soil, straight through the remains of the previous crop. The roots

Figure 9-16 In no-till farming, a special machine cuts a slit in the ground to plant seeds (left). As the new crop grows, remains of the old crop slowly decay (right). In these photos, soybeans are planted among the remains of old rye plants.

United States are products of aquaculture. Worldwide, about 23 percent of seafood comes from aquaculture.

Aquaculture is not without its drawbacks, however. If not managed properly, it can actually cause environmental problems. Large numbers of fish that are concentrated in a small space produce a great deal of waste matter, which can be a source of pollution. Also, large aquaculture operations can deplete local water supplies. One such operation in Texas used as much water as a city of 250,000 people, threatening the water supply of nearby San Antonio. Occasionally, sensitive wetlands are damaged or destroyed when large aquaculture operations are carved out of them. Fortunately, however, most aquaculture operations do not harm their surroundings.

Trout farm in Idaho

Aquaculture will probably continue to grow in importance as the world's population increases. While it cannot provide sustenance for the Earth's billions by itself, aquaculture may help to feed more people.

THINKING CRITICALLY

❶ *Analyzing Processes* What are the advantages of aquaculture compared with traditional fishing?

❷ *Inferring Relationships* Is aquaculture suitable for every part of the world? Why or why not?

of the first crop hold the soil in place while the new crop develops. And as the remains of the first crop decay, organic matter is added to the soil. No-till farming saves time compared with conventional cultivation. It can also reduce soil erosion to one-tenth of the amount caused by conventional methods.

SUSTAINABLE AGRICULTURE

How can we continue to feed the world's population without continuing to deplete the world's resources? One answer is low-input farming. **Low-input farming** is farming without using a lot of energy, pesticides, fertilizer, and water.

One kind of low-input farming is organic farming, that is, growing plants without any synthetic pesticides or inorganic fertilizers. Organic farmers keep the soil moist and fertile by adding manure, compost, and other organic matter, by keeping the soil planted at all times to avoid erosion, and by alternating different crops to reduce pest populations. In addition to protecting the environment, organic farming reduces the need for water, pesticides, and fertilizer.

Another promising method of increasing food production is aquaculture, described in the Case Study on pages 236–237. Aquaculture is "fish farming," raising fish in artificial environments.

PREVENTING SALINIZATION

The accumulation of salts in the soil is known as **salinization.** Although all soil naturally contains some salts, more salts are added when land is irrigated. This is because water for irrigation is taken from rivers or groundwater, which contain more salt than rainwater does. When land is irrigated, much of the water evaporates, leaving behind the salts it contained. Eventually, the soil may become so salty, like the land shown in Figure 9-17, that plants cannot grow in it.

Another way that irrigation can cause salinization is by causing the level of groundwater to rise. Once the groundwater comes within a few meters of the surface, it is drawn up through the soil by capillary action, in much the way water is drawn up by a sponge. When it reaches the surface, the groundwater evaporates and leaves its salts in the soil.

Soil salinization can be slowed by careful irrigation methods. For example, irrigation canals can be lined to prevent water from seeping into the soil and raising the groundwater level. Another technique is to water the soil heavily to wash out salts before seeds are planted. This helps protect young seedlings, which are more easily harmed by salt than are older plants.

Planting salt-tolerant crops, which absorb salts from the soil, can also slow salinization. If the soil is too salty to grow crops, planting salt-tolerant trees, as shown in Figure 9-18, can help

SCILINKS.
NSTA
TOPIC: sustainable agriculture
GO TO: www.scilinks.org
KEYWORD: HE238

Figure 9-17 **When irrigated land becomes salinized, it is difficult or impossible to farm.**

reclaim the land. Shade from the trees reduces the amount of water that evaporates from the soil surface. This slows the upward movement of groundwater. Tree roots penetrate the soil, allowing rainwater to sink in and wash out salts more rapidly. Fallen leaves improve the soil by adding organic matter. The water table can begin to fall within a year or two, although the complete restoration of salinized land takes decades.

Figure 9-18 **These Australian Girl Guides are planting trees to help reclaim former farmland that has become too salty to grow crops.**

OLD AND NEW FOODS

Researchers are beginning to rediscover ancient plants and investigate new varieties of plants. They hope to find plants that are better adapted to different climates and that can produce high yields without large amounts of fertilizer, pesticides, and water. For example, some researchers are studying amaranth, shown in Figure 9-19. Amaranth was a sacred food of the Aztecs. It can survive with little water, and it produces a grainlike fruit that is rich in protein.

Other researchers are studying plants that have not been widely used for food in the past but that may be useful because they can grow on poor soil. For example, a plant called glasswort, also shown in Figure 9-19, grows naturally in salt marshes. It can be grown on saline soils and can even be irrigated with salt water.

Figure 9-19 **These two plants, amaranth (left) and glasswort (below), may provide food for the future.**

SECTION REVIEW

① How do living organisms contribute to the fertility of the soil?

② How does irrigation cause the soil to become salty?

③ Why are the world's deserts expanding?

THINKING CRITICALLY

④ *Relating Concepts* Create a concept map about soil conservation using the following terms: contour plowing, no-till farming, organic farming, careful irrigation, soil erosion, nutrient depletion, and salinization.

⑤ *Interpreting Graphics* Examine the map in Figure 9-13. Propose one possible reason for the great amount of soil erosion in Central America.

239

PEST CONTROL

a

AFTER READING THIS SECTION YOU SHOULD BE ABLE TO

❶ explain why pest control is often necessary.

❷ explain how insects can become resistant to pesticides.

❸ describe alternatives to pesticides.

In North America, insects destroy about 13 percent of all crops. Crops in tropical climates suffer even greater insect damage because the insects grow and reproduce faster. In Kenya, for example, insects destroy 25 percent of the nation's crops. Worldwide, pests destroy about one-third of the world's potential food harvest. Clearly, pest damage must be controlled in order to feed the world's people.

As shown in Figure 9-20, insects are just one of several types of organisms that may be considered to be pests. A **pest** is any

d

Figure 9-20 Many kinds of organisms can be pests.

a. Tent caterpillars in cherry tree
b. Wasp on a grape
c. Weeds in a bean crop
d. Corn borer on an ear of corn
e. Hornworm eating a green tomato
f. Fungus on apricots
g. Brown rat in grain store

b

c

e

f

g

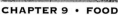

organism that occurs where you don't want it or in large enough numbers to cause damage.

Wild plants have more protection from pests than do crop plants. Wild plants grow scattered throughout a landscape, so pests have a harder time finding plants they can eat. Crop plants, however, are usually grown together in large fields, providing pests with a one-stop source of nutritious food. Wild plants are also protected from pests by a variety of pest predators that live on or near the plants. The wild plants themselves have evolved defenses to many pests, including the ability to repel pests with weapons such as poisonous plant fluids.

During the last 50 years, many new chemical **pesticides,** substances that kill pests, were invented. Some of the main types of pesticides are listed in Figure 9-21. The pesticides that kill insects, called insecticides, were so effective that farmers began to rely on them almost completely to protect their crops from insects.

Examples of Pesticides		
Pesticide	**Toxicity**	**Persistence**
Chlorinated Hydrocarbons		Persistent (half-life 2–5 years)*
Aldrin	Toxic	
DDT	Moderately toxic	
Lindane	Moderately toxic	
Organophosphates		Degradable (half-life 1–10 weeks)
Malathion	Toxic	
Parathion	Extremely toxic	
Carbamates		Degradable (half-life 1 week)
Carbaryl	Moderately toxic	
Zectran	Extremely toxic	

*The half-life of a pesticide is the time it takes for half of the quantity applied to break down.

Figure 9-21 **The table above shows some of the main types of pesticides developed in the last 50 years.**

Figure 9-22 **This field of pineapples in Hawaii is being sprayed with a pesticide.**

DRAWBACKS OF PESTICIDES

Unfortunately, the new pesticides affect a lot more than just the pests that they were designed to kill. They can also harm people and wildlife.

Figure 9-23 **This worker is wearing long sleeves, long pants, gloves, and a mask to protect himself while applying pesticides.**

Health Concerns Many pesticides can cause people to get sick. For example, the San Joaquin Valley, in California, is an area of fruit and vegetable farms with very high pesticide use. Cancer rates among children there are higher than the national average. Workers in pesticide factories may also become ill. And people living near these factories, like the people of Bhopal, India, may be endangered by accidental chemical leaks. (See Figure 9-24.)

Pollution and Persistence The problem of pesticides harming people and wildlife is especially serious because many pesticides are persistent. Persistent pesticides do not break down rapidly into harmless chemicals when they enter the environment. As a result, they accumulate in the water and soil.

One of the best known and most persistent pesticides is DDT. This pesticide was used in the 1940s to kill the mosquitoes that cause malaria and the lice that spread typhus, saving millions of lives. However, because DDT is very persistent, it gradually accumulated in bodies of water. It was then absorbed by fish, which

Figure 9-24 **This Union Carbide factory in Bhopal, India, made pesticides. In 1984 a cloud of deadly gas was accidentally released into the air. Thousands of people were killed or injured.**

were eaten by birds. Organisms high on the food chain, like fish-eating birds, are likely to have high levels of DDT in their bodies because they eat many smaller organisms whose bodies contain low levels of DDT. The DDT caused the birds to lay eggs with shells so thin that they broke when the birds sat on them. Penguins, pelicans, peregrine falcons, and eagles were endangered and even wiped out in some areas as a result. DDT was eventually banned in many places, including the United States. Although it remains in the environment, it has gradually dispersed, so most birds eat less of it. Many of the endangered birds have increased in number as a result.

Most persistent pesticides have been banned in the United States, but many of them will remain in the environment for years to come. About 60 different pesticides have been found in groundwater, sometimes making wells unusable.

Pesticide Resistance You might think that the most effective way to get rid of pests is to spray often with large amounts of pesticide. However, in the long run this approach usually makes the pest problem worse. Pest populations evolve **resistance,** the ability to tolerate a particular pesticide.

How does resistance evolve? A few insects out of many may happen to have a gene that protects them from a pesticide. (For example, they may be able to break down the pesticide into harmless substances.) These few insects survive spraying with the pesticide while most of the others are killed. The surviving insects pass on the gene to their offspring. With continued pesticide spraying, the resistant insects continue to reproduce and increase in number while the nonresistant ones die off. Eventually, the entire insect population is resistant to the pesticide. As shown in Figure 9-25, more than 500 species of insects have developed resistance to pesticides since the 1940s.

Did you know that you can get rid of household pests like ants and cockroaches without harmful chemicals? For more information, turn to pages 390–391.

Figure 9-25 **Pesticides have been widely used for about 55 years now. During that time, the number of insect species resistant to one or more insecticides has increased dramatically.**

BIOLOGICAL PEST CONTROL

Because resistance evolves rapidly, farmers and pest-control companies are using fewer pesticides. Some are turning to **biological pest control,** using living organisms or naturally produced chemicals to control pests. Biological pest control methods generally do not harm organisms other than the pests they are designed to control, and resistance takes much longer to evolve.

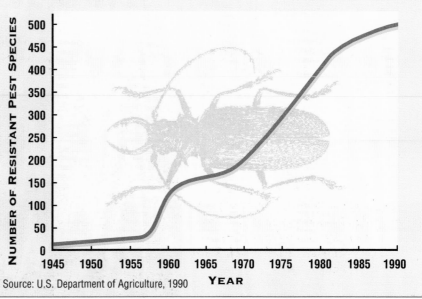

Source: U.S. Department of Agriculture, 1990

Figure 9-26 Gypsy moth caterpillars feed on the leaves of trees in the northeastern United States. Spraying with the bacterium *Bacillus thuringensis* can control outbreaks of the caterpillars.

❶ Why are pests more of a problem for cultivated plants than for wild plants?

❷ Why are persistent pesticides dangerous?

❸ How do insect populations evolve resistance to pesticides?

THINKING CRITICALLY

❹ *Inferring Relationships* Are pheromones a type of pesticide? Explain your reasoning.

❺ *Applying Ideas* What pesticides are used around your home? How could you reduce the amount of pesticides used at home?

Predators and Pathogens One type of biological control involves releasing a natural predator or parasite into the area where the pest lives. **Pathogens**—organisms that cause disease—can also be used to control pests biologically. One of the most common pest-control pathogens is the bacterium *Bacillus thuringensis,* often abbreviated *Bt.* This bacterium can kill the caterpillars of moths and butterflies as well as other insect larvae. Each strain of *Bt* attacks the larvae of a specific insect. *Bt* is often used to control gypsy moth caterpillars, such as those shown in Figure 9-26.

Plant Defenses Scientists and farmers crossbreed plant varieties to produce crops that have their own defenses, just as wild plants have. Examples of plant defenses include chemical compounds that repel pests and physical barriers, such as tougher skin. As you can see in the feature on pages 250 and 251, scientists use genetic engineering to develop crops with a variety of desirable traits.

Chemicals From Plants Another type of biological pest control also makes use of plants' defense chemicals. Several of these chemicals have been extracted from plants, such as the chrysanthemums shown in Figure 9-27, and are now sold as pesticides. These products are biodegradable, meaning that they are broken down into harmless substances by bacteria and other decomposers.

Disrupting Insect Breeding Pheromones, chemicals produced by one organism that affect the behavior of another, can also be used in pest control. For example, female moths find mates by releasing pheromones that attract males from miles away. By treating crops with pheromones, farmers can confuse the male insects and interfere with mating.

Another way to prevent insects from reproducing is to make it physically impossible for the males to reproduce. Male insects are treated with X rays to make them sterile and then are released. When they mate with females, the females produce eggs that do not develop.

Figure 9-27 The photograph below shows painted daisies, a type of chrysanthemum that grows in Rwanda. Extracts from the plants are used as pesticides.

BIODIVERSITY AT RISK

AFTER READING THIS SECTION YOU SHOULD BE ABLE TO

❶ explain how humans are causing extinctions of other species.

❷ explain why it is important that we preserve biodiversity.

The last dinosaurs died about 65 million years ago. Why? We don't know for sure, but one hypothesis is that a huge meteor crashed into the Earth. Another is that there was a dramatic increase in volcanic activity. In either case, it is possible that enough dust and ash were thrown into the atmosphere to block out much of the sunlight that normally reaches the Earth's surface. Without enough sunlight, many of the Earth's plants would have died. This would have led to the deaths of animals that ate plants and animals that fed on other animals. It is estimated that about half the species on Earth, including all the dinosaurs, became extinct during this time. As you learned in Chapter 2, a species is extinct when the last individual dies.

The dinosaurs' disappearance was part of a mass extinction, which is the extinction of many species during a relatively short period of time. Our planet has experienced several mass extinctions, as shown in Figure 10-1, each probably caused by a change in climate.

Figure 10-1 **The five mass extinctions indicated by ▾ were probably caused by changes in climate. This graph shows the effect on families (groups of related species) of marine organisms. Which mass extinction was the most destructive to marine organisms?**

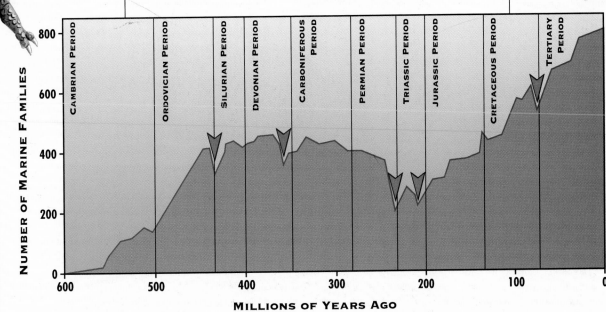

Many scientists think we are living during another mass extinction. They fear that by the year 2100, 25 percent or more of all species of plants and animals that were on Earth in 1900 will have become extinct. If a mass extinction is underway, it is being caused not by a natural change in climate but by the actions of humans. Humans weren't responsible for the dinosaurs' extinction—that was millions of years before our time. But we are now causing the extinction of thousands of other living things.

A WORLD RICH IN BIODIVERSITY

The term **biodiversity** refers to the number and variety of species on Earth. As shown in Figure 10-2, the number of species known to science is about 1.6 million, most of which are insects. The number of *known* species, however, is by no means close to the *actual* number of species on Earth. Although estimates vary, many scientists believe that there are about 13 million species now living on our planet.

In one study in Indonesia, British researchers counted the number of species of insects called hemipterans in a region of tropical rain forest. They found 1,690 species of hemipterans living on the ground there, but only 37 percent of these species had been known previously. This study and others point out that we still do not know about many of the species alive today.

HOW ARE HUMANS CAUSING EXTINCTIONS?

The human population of the world is increasing at a rate of about 220,000 people each *day*. Because the human population is growing so rapidly and changing the environment so dramatically, we are causing other species to become extinct at an accelerated rate.

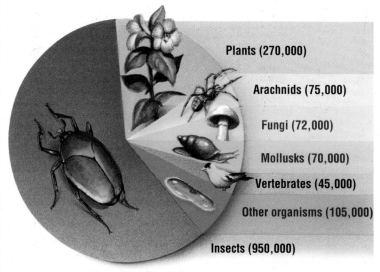

Plants (270,000)

Arachnids (75,000)

Fungi (72,000)

Mollusks (70,000)

Vertebrates (45,000)

Other organisms (105,000)

Insects (950,000)

Source: United Nations Global Biodiversity Assessment, 1996

Figure 10-2 This pie chart shows the number of species now known to exist, divided into major groups. Scientists estimate, however, that the actual number of species far exceeds the 1.6 million shown here. Perhaps as many as 8 million to 50 million species exist, most of them undiscovered.

In fact, scientists estimate that species are disappearing at least 1,000 times faster than at any other time in the last 65 million years. Evidence seems to suggest that this dramatic increase in extinctions has largely taken place during the last century.

Why is the increase in the human population so devastating to other species? As humans take up more and more space and deplete more resources, we destroy the habitats of other species. The most common cause of extinction today is the destruction of habitats by humans. Unregulated hunting and the introduction of nonnative species also contribute to extinctions.

Habitat Destruction As human populations grow, we use more land to build homes and harvest resources. When we take over land, we destroy the habitats of other species. It is estimated that habitat loss causes almost 75 percent of the extinctions now occurring. As you read in previous chapters, organisms are adapted to survive in a particular place under particular environmental conditions. When their habitats are destroyed, they die.

One large mammal in grave danger because of habitat loss is the Florida panther, a kind of cougar. The Florida panther is shown in Figure 10-3. Two hundred years ago, cougars (also called mountain lions) ranged from Alaska to South America. Cougars require a large range and protective cover for feeding and resting, as well as an adequate source of large prey, such as deer and elk. At one time the needs of the cougar were met in the forests of its original range. Today, much of the cougar's forest habitat has been destroyed or broken up into small patches by roads, canals, and fences. The only cougar population east of the Mississippi River is the Florida panther. Despite efforts to save the Florida panther, in 1994 only 30 to 50 remained in the wild, making the Florida panther one of the most endangered animals in North America.

Figure 10-3 **Only 30 to 50 Florida panthers remain in the wild. Almost all of the Florida panther's habitat was destroyed or fragmented by human development.**

Another animal endangered primarily by habitat loss is the whooping crane. The plight of the whooping crane is described in the Case Study below.

Most extinctions are occurring in tropical rain forests when the land is cleared for farming or cattle grazing. Biologists estimate that at least 50 percent of the world's species live in tropical rain forests, even though these forests cover only 7 percent of the Earth's land surface. Rain forests contain millions of species that have never been described, many of which may become extinct before we know much about them.

Figure 10-4 This Brazilian rain forest is being cleared by burning. Each minute, about 40 hectares (100 acres) of rain-forest habitat are eliminated from the face of the Earth.

Hunting Unregulated hunting can also lead to species extinction. In the early 1900s, for example, 2 billion American passenger pigeons were legally hunted to extinction in the United States.

Similarly, the American buffalo (also called bison) was nearly

WHOOPING CRANES:
REGAINING LOST GROUND?

Whooping cranes spend the winter at Aransas National Wildlife Refuge, in Texas.

Many years ago whooping cranes waded through wetlands and soared across prairies in Canada, the United States, and Mexico. The huge white birds, sometimes called whoopers, foraged for food while avoiding humans. But 200 years ago, a few early settlers wandered into the whoopers' habitat and discovered that the land was well suited for farming. A rush of settlers immediately descended upon the land—draining wetlands, uprooting vegetation, and cutting down trees to make room for crops and cattle. The birds were forced out.

As their habitat was destroyed, the whooping cranes kept moving their breeding grounds northward, until some of them ended up in a remote area of Canada. These were the lucky ones—beginning in 1922, the region was protected by the Canadian government as a national park.

From their breeding grounds in Canada, their annual journey south

became especially long. They had to fly up to 4,000 km (2,500 mi.) to their winter home. The birds rested each night during the migration, occasionally staying for a week or so at a single spot. But when the whooping cranes stopped to rest, farmers shot them because they fed on crops. Hunters found them easy targets because of their large size and spectacular white

be sold or traded. Anyone who violates this part of the law is subject to a substantial fine.

According to the third main provision of the Endangered Species Act, the federal government may not carry out any project that jeopardizes an endangered or threatened species. The Case Study on pages 264–265 describes a controversial case that was the direct result of this provision.

Under the fourth main provision of the Endangered Species Act, the U.S. Fish and Wildlife Service must prepare a recovery plan for each endangered and threatened species. The Fish and Wildlife Service has found that the most effective way to save most species is to protect their habitats. Simply putting a few individuals into zoos, aquariums, or greenhouses does very little to preserve a species. Why? For one thing, many animals will not breed in captivity, so their numbers continue to dwindle. Also, tiny captive populations are vulnerable to infectious diseases and genetic disorders caused by inbreeding.

Setting aside small plots of land for endangered or threatened species is usually not effective either. An endangered species living in a small area could be wiped out by a single grass fire. Some species require a large range to find adequate food, find a suitable mate, and rear their young. Therefore, protecting the habitats of endangered and threatened species may mean restricting human use of some areas.

Developers vs. Environmentalists? Plans to restrict human use of land to preserve species are sometimes controversial. Real-estate developers invest large sums of money in buying land and designing plans for houses and commercial buildings. Then they may discover that they cannot build on the land because it is the habitat of an endangered or threatened species.

The local community may have been looking forward to the jobs that the new development would create. The city government may have been counting on property and sales taxes to finance local improvements to sewer lines, schools, police forces, and fire protection. Many times, both the real-estate developers and the local residents are angry that all of these economic benefits are threatened by what appears to be an insignificant weed or bug.

Although battles between developers and environmentalists are widely publicized, in most cases compromises are eventually worked out. Usually neither the developers nor the environmentalists get everything they want, but both sides get something. There have been tens of thousands of these cases in the United States, but almost all were resolved by some kind of compromise.

Hawaii is home to more than one-third of the nation's endangered plant and animal species.

SC*L*INKS.

NSTA

TOPIC: Endangered Species Act
GO TO: www.scilinks.org
KEYWORD: HE263

WORLDWIDE EFFORTS TO PREVENT EXTINCTIONS

Several international organizations work to protect species on a worldwide basis. The World Wildlife Fund works to protect biodiversity, especially in tropical forests, by encouraging the sustainable use of resources. The Nature Conservancy currently manages a system of over 1,500 nature sanctuaries in the United States and other countries. Conservation International develops ecosystem conservation projects with partner organizations and local people in countries that are rich in biological diversity. Friends of the Earth is a group that lobbies governments and disseminates information to the public. Greenpeace International stages dramatic protests like the one in Figure 10-12 to help stop the destruction of rain forests and the killing of endangered animals.

At the governmental level, the International Union for the Conservation of Nature and Natural Resources (IUCN) is in the forefront of efforts to protect species and habitats. This organization is a collaboration of almost 200 governments and government agencies and over 700 private conservation organizations. The IUCN publishes data books that list species in danger of extinction around the world, advises governments of the most effective ways

A filmmaker was just doing his job for Conservation International when he was surrounded by machine guns and accused of being a terrorist. See pages 372–373 for an interview with him.

THE SNAIL DARTERS AND THE DAM

CASE STUDY

One of the first and most famous tests of the Endangered Species Act was the case of the Tellico Dam in Tennessee during the 1970s. The dam—a federal project—was being built on the Little Tennessee River to provide flood control and to generate hydroelectric power. Opponents had fought the dam for years, arguing that it was too expensive, that it was not really needed, and that it destroyed valuable farmland, forests, recreation areas,

and historic and archeological sites.

The project continued, however, until it was discovered that the habitat of a tiny fish called the snail darter would be destroyed by the dam. Opponents of the dam filed suit, and the courts ruled that the dam project was covered by the Endangered Species Act. Construction was halted even though the dam was 80 percent completed and had already cost taxpayers $50 million. Appeals went all the way to the U.S. Supreme Court.

The court ruled that under the provisions of the Endangered Species Act, construction of the dam must be stopped, no matter what the cost.

However, Congress then passed a law that granted certain exemptions to the Endangered

Efforts to protect the tiny fish shown at the upper right almost prevented the completion of the Tellico Dam (above), in Tennessee.

Figure 10-12 **These protesters are blocking the path of a Japanese whaling ship. Do you think this is an effective way to protect species?**

to manage their natural resources, and works with groups like the World Wildlife Fund to sponsor field projects around the globe. The projects range from attempting to halt poaching in Uganda to preserving the habitat of sea turtles on South American beaches.

Prevention of Poaching One offshoot of the IUCN is an international treaty, the Convention on International Trade in Endangered Species (CITES). CITES became well known for

Tellico Dam is on the Little Tennessee River in eastern Tennessee.

Species Act. One way a project could be exempted is if an Endangered Species Review Committee decided that the economic benefits outweighed the potential harm to an endangered species. Supporters of the Tellico Dam hoped that the committee would exempt the project under this provision. But instead, the committee ruled that the dam project was economically infeasible and

therefore could not be exempted.
    Was this the end of the story? No. Congress then passed a bill stating that the Tellico Dam project did not have to comply with the Endangered Species Act. The dam was finally completed. The snail darters were transplanted to nearby streams and now appear to be reproducing. Their status has been upgraded from endangered to threatened.

THINKING CRITICALLY

❶ *Making Decisions* Do you think the decision to halt the construction of the Tellico Dam was justified? Explain. Now answer the question again after considering the following scenarios.
  • Suppose the investment in the Tellico Dam had been $500 million, not $50 million.
  • Suppose that a type of beetle, rather than a fish, were endangered by the construction of the dam.

❷ *Making Decisions* Should money ever be a consideration in cases where a species may be endangered by human activity? Explain.

Figure 10-13 **After years of unsuccessful attempts to limit the sales of ivory, a total worldwide ban went into effect in 1989. What happened to the price of ivory after the ban? Why do you think the price of ivory climbed before 1989?**

Figure 10-14 **Before a complete ban on the sale of ivory in 1989, scenes like these were common.**

SECTION REVIEW

❶ What is the difference between an endangered species and a threatened species?

❷ Why can't some species survive on small plots of land?

THINKING CRITICALLY

❸ *Drawing Conclusions* Do you think it is reasonable for an expensive dam project to be stopped by the discovery of an endangered species that would be threatened by the dam? Why or why not?

❹ *Inferring Relationships* Why do you think a complete ban of ivory sales was so much more effective in reducing poaching than the limited ban was?

working to stop the slaughter of African elephants for their ivory tusks. Efforts during the 1970s and 1980s to limit the sale of ivory had little effect on the killing of elephants. In 1989, the members of CITES proposed a total worldwide ban on all sales, imports, and exports of ivory, hoping to put a stop to scenes like those in Figure 10-14.

Some conservationists were concerned that making ivory illegal would only *increase* the rate of poaching. They argued that illegal ivory, like illegal drugs, might become more expensive. Nevertheless, the sale of ivory was completely banned in 1989, and fears that the ban would increase poaching turned out to be unfounded. As you can see in Figure 10-13, the price of ivory fell steeply after the ban, and elephant poaching declined dramatically.

The Biodiversity Treaty One of the most ambitious efforts to tackle environmental issues on a worldwide scale was the United Nations Conference on Environment and Development, also known as the Earth Summit. More than 100 world leaders and 30,000 other participants met in Rio de Janeiro, Brazil, in 1992.

One of the agreements that came out of the Earth Summit was the Biodiversity Treaty, which encourages wealthier countries to give money to poorer countries for the protection of potentially valuable species. However, the treaty does not state exactly how this should be done. Arguing that it was too vague, former President George Bush decided not to sign the Biodiversity Treaty. One year later, however, newly elected President Bill Clinton signed the treaty.

THE FUTURE OF BIODIVERSITY

AFTER READING THIS SECTION YOU SHOULD BE ABLE TO

❶ describe how captive-breeding programs, botanical gardens, and germ-plasm banks help save species.

❷ explain the advantages of protecting entire ecosystems rather than individual species.

I t is possible to slow the loss of species, but to do so we must develop new approaches to conservation and a sensitivity to human needs around the globe. In this section you will read about methods of saving individual species as well as ways to protect entire ecosystems.

SAVING INDIVIDUAL SPECIES

In Section 10.2, you learned about attempts to save individual species through legislation such as the Endangered Species Act and anti-poaching laws. Additional ways to preserve individual species include captive-breeding programs, botanical gardens, and germ-plasm banks.

Captive-Breeding Programs Zoos and wild-animal parks can increase the population of an endangered or threatened species by establishing captive-breeding programs. Such programs involve breeding animals under carefully managed circumstances.

One well-known example of a captive-breeding program involves the California condor, shown in Figure 10-15. Condors feed mainly on dead animals and need vast areas in which to search for food. Habitat loss and poaching almost brought about

Figure 10-15 **California condors are slowly recovering, thanks to a captive-breeding program. The photograph at the left shows a release station where condors are being released into the wild.**

the extinction of the species. In 1986, when there were only nine California condors left in the wild, a captive-breeding program was established. Early results have been promising. By 1998, there were 39 condors in the wild and 93 in zoos and specialized captive-breeding centers. If all goes well, many more will be released in the next 10 years.

Botanical Gardens You may be surprised to know that botanical gardens, like the one shown in Figure 10-16, are storehouses of genetic diversity. Botanical gardens worldwide house around 90,000 species of plants. Even so, the gardens don't have the space or the funds to preserve most of the world's rare and threatened plants.

Germ-Plasm Banks Germ-plasm banks store germ plasm for future use in case species become critically endangered. Germ plasm is the genetic material contained within the reproductive (germ) cells of organisms. Plants may be stored as seeds, and animals may be stored as frozen sperm and eggs. The germ plasm is stored in refrigerated and humidity-controlled environments that allow the genetic material to survive for many years.

Figure 10-16 Botanical gardens are storehouses of genetic diversity. This botanical garden is in Queen Elizabeth Park, Vancouver, Canada.

THE ECOSYSTEM APPROACH

Recently, many conservationists have begun to concentrate on protecting entire ecosystems rather than individual species. There are two main reasons for this shift.

First, many more species are in danger of extinction than can possibly be placed on official lists. As you already read, biologists do not even know how many species actually exist on Earth today, let alone how many are endangered. By concentrating on entire ecosystems, we may be able to save most of the species in an ecosystem rather than just the ones that are on an endangered species list.

Second, the health of the entire biosphere depends on the preservation of individual ecosystems. Forest ecosystems, for example, clean the air by collecting small particles of air pollution on the leaves and needles of trees. Wetland ecosystems provide filtration that helps clean water supplies. The loss of these and other ecosystems can have damaging consequences throughout the biosphere.

To protect biodiversity worldwide, some conservationists suggest that at least 10 percent of the Earth's land be set aside as protected preserves. Primary consideration, they argue, should

Contra Costa wallflower

Marinkelle's sword-nosed bat

Milky stork

Lesser red panda

Gray's monitor

California Floristic Province

Hawaii

Colombian Chocó, Western Ecuador

Uplands of Western Amazonia

Ivory Coast

Tanzania

Western Ghats

Sri Lanka

Eastern Himalayas

Philippines

Northern Borneo

Atlantic Coast of Brazil

Central Chile

Cape Province

Madagascar

Peninsular Malaysia

New Caledonia

Southwestern Australia

Akiapolaau

Tassel-eared marmoset

Sumatran rhinoceros

Southern hairy-nosed wombat

be given to biodiversity "hot spots" around the world. Biodiversity hot spots are regions that contain unusually large numbers of species. Eighteen of these hot spots are shown in Figure 10-17.

As part of the effort to preserve ecosystems, ecologists are working to answer such questions as, How large does a protected preserve have to be to maintain a diversity of species? Questions like this often take years of research to answer. One research project in Brazil is designed to determine the minimum amount of land necessary to sustain a rain-forest habitat. (See Figure 10-18.) Research is expected to continue into the next century. Unfortunately, decisions must often be made before there is sufficient data.

Figure 10-17 **This map shows 18 areas that contain large numbers of species, many of which are in danger of extinction. Each of these "hot spots" is home to species that are found nowhere else.**

Figure 10-18 **Researchers in Brazil are trying to determine the minimum amount of land necessary to sustain a rain-forest habitat. This photograph shows a 1-hectare plot at the right and a 10-hectare plot in the center.**

Should the habitat of an owl species be preserved even if it means that people might lose their jobs? See pages 276–277.

SECTION REVIEW

❶ Which of the ways to save individual species may involve the preservation of only part of an organism?

❷ Why are some conservationists beginning to concentrate on protecting entire ecosystems rather than individual species?

THINKING CRITICALLY

❸ *Interpreting Graphics* The biodiversity hot spots shown in Figure 10-17 share several characteristics besides a great number of species. Look at the map, and name as many shared characteristics as you can.

WHAT ABOUT HUMAN NEEDS?

As much as we may want to protect this planet's biodiversity, we can't ignore the needs of the human inhabitants of the world. In the developed countries of the Northern Hemisphere, the desire to protect biological resources often comes into conflict with the need to protect people's jobs. Such a situation arose in the states of Washington and Oregon in the late 1980s. The U.S. Fish and Wildlife Service designated millions of hectares of forest in these states as protected habitat for the northern spotted owl, which is threatened with extinction. Some argued that people in the timber industry would lose their jobs as a result.

In the poorer nations of the world, the conflict between human needs and biodiversity may even be a matter of life or death. It is difficult to blame a parent who shoots an endangered animal so that a child won't starve, or one who clears part of a rain forest to grow crops that will support a family.

We must find ways to meet human needs and manage living resources at the same time. Preserving these resources will perhaps be the greatest challenge of the twenty-first century.

Figure 10-19 **Human needs must also be considered. This family cleared and burned land to plant a maize crop.**

HIGHLIGHTS

SUMMARY

- The term *biodiversity* refers to the number and variety of species on Earth. There are now an estimated 13 million species of living organisms.

- While extinction is a natural event, humans are accelerating the rate of extinction worldwide.

- The major causes of extinction today are habitat destruction, poaching, and the introduction of exotic species.

- One reason for concern about the accelerated rate of extinction is that the disappearance of a single species can disrupt an entire ecosystem. In addition, many species have practical value to humans as medicines and foods.

- The Endangered Species Act is designed to protect plant and animal species that are in danger of extinction.

- The Biodiversity Treaty is an international agreement that encourages wealthier countries of the world to give money to poorer countries for the protection of potentially valuable species.

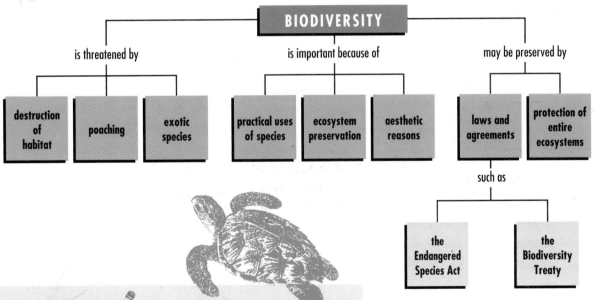

BIODIVERSITY

is threatened by

- destruction of habitat
- poaching
- exotic species

is important because of

- practical uses of species
- ecosystem preservation
- aesthetic reasons

may be preserved by

- laws and agreements
- protection of entire ecosystems

such as

- the Endangered Species Act
- the Biodiversity Treaty

EcoLog

Now that you've studied this chapter, revise your answers to the questions you answered at the beginning of the chapter, based on what you have learned.

❶ What is the major cause of extinction today?

❷ Do you think humans should try to prevent the extinction of other species? Explain your reasoning.

Vocabulary Terms

biodiversity (p. 254)

endangered species (p. 261)

Endangered Species Act (p. 261)

exotic species (p. 258)

poaching (p. 257)

threatened species (p. 261)

REVIEW

UNDERSTANDING VOCABULARY

1. For each pair of terms, explain the differences in their meanings.
   a. hunting
      poaching
   b. native species
      exotic species
   c. endangered species
      threatened species

RELATING CONCEPTS

2. Copy the unfinished concept map below onto a sheet of paper. Then complete the concept map by writing the correct word or phrase in each box containing a question mark.

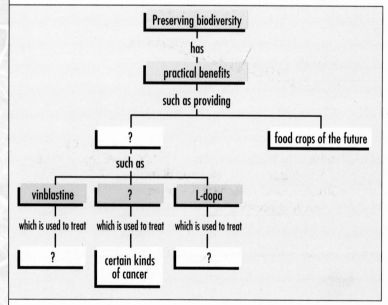

UNDERSTANDING CONCEPTS

Multiple Choice

3. A mass extinction is
   a. a rapid increase in biodiversity.
   b. caused by the introduction of exotic species.
   c. the extinction of many species in a short period of time.
   d. beneficial to the environment.

4. The term *biodiversity* refers to
   a. the variety of species on Earth.
   b. the large number of dinosaurs that became extinct.
   c. habitat destruction.
   d. the fact that 40 percent of prescription drugs come from living things.

5. Most of the species known to science today
   a. are large mammals.
   b. live in deserts.
   c. live in the richer countries of the world.
   d. are insects.

6. Some species are so important to the functioning of an ecosystem that they are called
   a. threatened species.
   b. keystone species.
   c. endangered species.
   d. extinct species.

7. When sea otters disappeared from the Pacific coast of North America,
   a. the area became overrun with kelp.
   b. the number of fish in the kelp beds increased.
   c. the number of sea urchins in the kelp beds increased.
   d. the area became overrun with brown seaweed.

8. Which is NOT true of the Endangered Species Act?
   a. Parts of an endangered animal, such as feathers or fur, may be traded or sold, but only if the animal is not killed.
   b. A species is considered endangered if it is expected to become extinct in the near future.
   c. The federal government cannot carry out a project that may jeopardize an endangered plant.
   d. A recovery plan is prepared for all threatened animals.

9. Because of efforts by the Convention on International Trade in Endangered Species (CITES),
    a. the poaching of elephants increased.
    b. the international trade of ivory was banned worldwide.
    c. the cost of ivory worldwide increased.
    d. a captive-breeding program for elephants was established.

10. By emphasizing the preservation of entire ecosystems,
    a. insect-resistant peaches can be developed.
    b. unknown species can be saved from extinction.
    c. the health of the biosphere will be jeopardized.
    d. biodiversity will be decreased.

11. Conflicts that arise in trying to preserve biodiversity include all of these EXCEPT
    a. short-term benefits versus long-term resources.
    b. job security versus the protection of biological resources.
    c. the cost of preserving animal species versus the cost of preserving plant species.
    d. balancing the needs of humans versus the needs of other species.

Short Answer

12. Why is legal hunting no longer a cause of extinctions in the United States today?

13. What are exotic species?

14. Why do biologists favor using an ecosystem approach to preserve biodiversity?

15. Describe three ways that preserving biodiversity can come into conflict with human needs and desires.

INTERPRETING GRAPHICS

16. The table below shows the number of vertebrate species on the Endangered Species List in early 1998. Figure the percentage for each vertebrate group, and then construct a pie chart that represents the data.

Mammals	58
Birds	75
Reptiles	14
Amphibians	9
Fish	67

THINKING CRITICALLY

17. **Comparing Processes** How is the present pattern of extinction different from the pattern of extinction in the past?

THEMES IN SCIENCE

18. **Evolution** Contrast the process of natural selection discussed in Chapter 2 with the forces that are causing the present mass extinction.

19. **Interacting Systems** How might the loss of huge tracts of forested land be related to the global climatic changes discussed in Chapter 7?

CROSS-DISCIPLINE CONNECTION

20. **Math** There are 1,587,000 species known to exist. Consult Figure 10-2, and figure the percentage that are insects.

21. **Geography** Obtain a list of the plants and animals that are endangered in your state. Find out where those species reside, and mark the locations on a map of your state. Research the effects of habitat loss on species in your county and in surrounding counties.

PORTFOLIO ACTIVITY

Do a special project about one endangered species of your choice. Consider using one of the following media to inform your classmates about your chosen species or to persuade them of the importance of saving the species.

- a poster
- an oral presentation
- a video

internetconnect

SCiLINKS   National Science Teachers Association
NSTA   On-Line Resources www.scilinks.org

When you see a SciLinks logo, visit the NSTA Web site and type in the keyword. There you will find current information relevant to that section or topic.

INVESTIGATION

BACKYARD DIVERSITY

When we think about biodiversity, we usually think about endangered species, dwindling habitats, and international efforts to protect large ecosystems. The wildlife and rare plants of the rain forests are important to protect, but you don't have to travel that far to see habitat destruction and struggle for survival. You can watch the drama in your own backyard every day of the year. In this activity you will investigate the factors that affect diversity among the insects in your own area.

BACKGROUND

You will survey two very different sites. One site will be an area that has been greatly affected by humans, and the other will be an area that has been less affected by humans. You are going to measure off a small area at each site and count the number and types of insects at each. You will also record the physical and biological features of each site.

First you will observe, gather information, and think about the factors that might affect insect diversity. Then you will propose a hypothesis and describe an experiment that would test it.

PREPARE

CAUTION: Before beginning your field study, review the safety guidelines on pages 409–412. Remember to approach all plants and animals with caution.

OBSERVE, RECORD, AND THINK

1. Choose two different sites for your survey. One should be an area that has been intensively managed by humans, such as a well-groomed lawn. The other should be an area that has been less affected by humans, such as a natural area or a vacant lot overgrown with weeds.

2. At Site 1, use the tape measure or meter stick, four stakes, and string to mark off a square plot 2 m × 2 m, as shown in the photograph at the upper right of the next page. This is your sample area.

3. In a table similar to Table A on the next page, record any features that you think might affect insects. Use the following list of features as a guide, adding any others you think of.

- **Maintenance** Is the area maintained? If so, interview the person who maintains it, and find out how often the site is watered, fertilized, treated with pesticides, and mowed.
- **Time Left Undisturbed** Estimate how long it has been since humans disturbed the site. For example, if the site is a well-tended lawn that was mowed one week ago, you would record "one week." If the site is a vacant lot that was mowed six months ago, you would write "six months."
- **Sunlight Exposure** How much of the area is exposed to sunlight?
- **Soil** Is the soil mostly sand, silt, or fine clay particles?
- **Rain** When was the last rain recorded for this area? How much rain was received?

MATERIALS

- **tape measure or meter stick**
- **4 stakes**
- **string (about 10 m)**
- **hand lens**
- **field guide to insects (optional)**
- **notebook**
- **pen or pencil**

- **Slope** Is the area flat or hilly?
- **Water Drainage** Is the water standing or pooling, or is the area well drained?
- **Vegetation Cover** How much of the soil is covered with vegetation? How much is exposed?

Table A		
Feature	**Site 1**	**Site 2**
Maintenance	Well-maintained yard. Owner of home says she waters the yard once a week and mows it about twice a month. Doesn't treat with pesticides or fertilizer.	Vacant lot. City maintenance mows the grass about once every summer, more often if people complain. Pesticides also applied about once a year. Lot is not watered or fertilized.
Time Left Undisturbed	One week (mowed one week ago)	Six months (mowed and treated with pesticides six months ago)
etc.	etc.	etc.

Table B		
	Site 1	**Site 2**
Number of Insects		
Number of Insect Types		

Place stakes at the corners of a 2 m × 2 m square area, and loop string around the stakes to mark the edges of your site.

4. In your notebook, create a blank table similar to Table B shown above.

5. Use the hand lens to inspect the sample area, and count the number of insects you see, being careful not to disturb the soil or the organisms. Record the number of insects in Table B. Then count the *types* of insects, and record that number in Table B.

6. Follow exactly the same procedure at Site 2, starting with step 2.

7. Examine the two tables, and think about what might be causing the difference (if any) between the two sites in the number and diversity of insects. In your notebook, jot down your hunch (your best guess) about what is causing the difference.

STATE A HYPOTHESIS

8. State your hunch in the form of a hypothesis.

DESIGN AN EXPERIMENT

9. Describe an experiment that could test your hypothesis.

Record the number of insects and the number of types of insects in your sample area.

INVESTIGATION

OWLS VS. LOGGERS

The northern spotted owl became the center of controversy in 1990 when the U.S. Fish and Wildlife Service listed the bird as a threatened species. To save the owl, scientists and federal agencies developed a recovery plan that designated millions of hectares of old-growth forest in Washington and Oregon as protected habitat. Because spotted owls nest in dead trees, their habitat is limited to old-growth forests. The controversy stems from the fact that under the recovery plan trees cannot be cut down in the owls' protected habitat, so the loggers' jobs are threatened. Read the following points of view, and then analyze the issue for yourself.

PEOPLE AND JOBS SHOULD COME FIRST

Loggers, sawmill workers, and residents of communities that depend almost entirely on logging for their livelihoods argue that the recovery plan will result in the loss of tens of thousands of jobs. Towns and counties stand to lose millions of dollars from logging revenues that now fund schools and other essential community services.

Many logging families have lived in the area for generations. They say that if they lose their jobs, they will have to move away in search of other work, struggle to find one of the scarce jobs in the area, or depend on welfare to survive. Doing any of these things to save one species of bird seems absurd to the loggers.

As for saving the forest itself, they argue that when forests are logged and then replanted with young trees, they are healthier and grow faster than the old forests. They also point out that trees do not live forever even when they are not cut down.

Eventually they will die from insects, disease, or fire. Why not make use of these resources rather than simply letting the trees fall to the ground and rot?

Furthermore, the loggers say, millions of hectares of old-growth forest will never be logged even without the plan. Some forest lands are already designated as parks and wilderness areas. Other forests are located in areas so inaccessible that it will never be profitable to cut them down.

Many loggers resent the fact that they are often portrayed as villains who destroy nature. They insist that they do not want to harm the forests. One of the reasons they want to keep their jobs is that they love going into the forest each day.

Logger at work in the Pacific Northwest

For A Forester Every Day Is Earth Day

Members of a logging community protest the owl recovery plan.

OWLS AND FORESTS SHOULD COME FIRST

Environmentalists argue that the spotted owl is a beautiful and gentle bird that deserves to live and to have its natural home protected. And more important, by protecting the owl, the old-growth forests will also be saved.

These forests, they insist, have a diversity of life that is not found in replanted, managed forests. If all of the old forests are logged, many species will become extinct because of habitat loss. It would take hundreds of years for the logged areas to recover the complexity of their ecosystems.

Environmentalists emphasize that these ecosystems do more than provide a home for plants and animals. They also reduce air pollution and soil erosion. And by reducing runoff from rains, the forests maintain water quality and protect the

The northern spotted owl

spawning grounds of fish.

Supporters of the recovery plan argue that historically, most logging jobs have been lost due to factors that have nothing to do with protecting the forest. Automation and advanced logging equipment produce more pulp and lumber with fewer workers. Also, logging companies in recent years have been shipping more lumber overseas for processing. This has led to a loss of jobs in the American lumber-processing industry.

Finally, they argue that change is coming to the logging industry no matter what. If logging is allowed to continue at the high rates of the past, all of the old trees will be gone in 50 years. Why not make adjustments now while there is still some old forest left?

Logs ready for processing

An old-growth forest that has been clear-cut

ANALYZE THE ISSUE

1. **Making Decisions**
   Based on the information you have, use the decision-making model presented in Chapter 1 to develop a recommendation for action in this case.

2. **Analyzing Relationships**
   What additional information would be helpful in developing a recommendation? How might a scientist obtain this information?

ENERGY

"The law of conservation of energy tells us that we can't get something for nothing, but we refuse to believe it."

ISAAC ASIMOV, AMERICAN SCIENCE WRITER

SECTION 11.1

FOSSIL FUELS TO ELECTRICITY

SECTION 11.2

NUCLEAR ENERGY

SECTION 11.3

A SUSTAINABLE ENERGY FUTURE

EcoLog

Before you read this chapter, take a few minutes to answer the following questions in your EcoLog.

❶ You flip on a light switch, and the lights instantly come on. Where does the electricity come from?

❷ What do you think our major source of energy will be 100 years from now? Explain your reasoning.

FOSSIL FUELS TO ELECTRICITY

AFTER READING THIS SECTION YOU SHOULD BE ABLE TO

❶ explain how fossil fuels are used to produce electricity.

❷ distinguish between renewable and nonrenewable resources.

❸ explain how our major sources of energy are dwindling.

It was a warm night in July. Twelve hundred feet above the streets of Manhattan in the World Trade Center restaurant, diners chatted quietly among themselves, stopping occasionally to admire the glittering New York City skyline. Then, without warning, all the lights in the restaurant went out. "Oh great," someone muttered. A waiter tripped in the darkness, sending a load of dishes crashing to the floor. "Hey, the elevator's out!" a woman shouted. "So is the rest of New York," replied the waiter, looking out the windows. The skyline was totally black against the night sky. All the lights of the city were out. And all over New York, people were stuck in elevators hundreds of feet in the air. A series of lightning strikes had knocked out several important power links to the city, which triggered automatic safety devices that shut down the entire power system.

Events like the 1977 blackout of New York City are newsworthy because they are so rare and because they underscore our dependence on electric energy. In this chapter you will learn how we get energy and how we use it to power our world. You'll also learn about some alternatives to our most important energy resources, which are dwindling rapidly.

Figure 11-1 The night the lights went out in New York City

ELECTRICITY: ENERGY ON DEMAND

Enormous amounts of electric energy—enough to meet the needs of thousands of people—can be transported through a wire the diameter of a quarter. You can use electricity to light up the night, cook dinner, heat a home, run a train, and much more. But what exactly is electricity?

Electricity is the flow of electrons, which are tiny charged particles that whirl around the nucleus of an atom. To generate electricity you simply have to set electrons in motion. One way to do this is to move an electrically conductive material such as a copper wire through a magnetic field. (See Figure 11-3.) In this example, the energy of the moving wire is converted into electricity. Of course, the amount of electricity produced in a single wire is very small. But imagine moving the equivalent of 100,000 wires through a magnetic field. This is what happens in a commercial electric generator.

An **electric generator** is simply a device for converting mechanical energy into electricity. The huge electric generators used in power plants require great amounts of energy to generate the electricity we use. Where does this energy come from? Most power plants use fossil fuels.

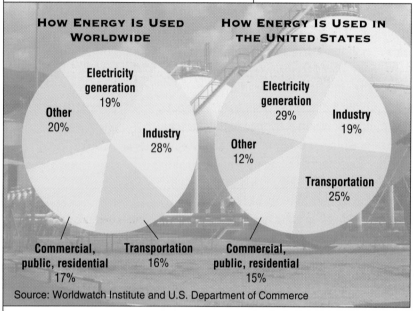

HOW ENERGY IS USED WORLDWIDE

Electricity generation 19%

Other 20%

Industry 28%

Commercial, public, residential 17%

Transportation 16%

HOW ENERGY IS USED IN THE UNITED STATES

Electricity generation 29%

Industry 19%

Other 12%

Transportation 25%

Commercial, public, residential 15%

Source: Worldwatch Institute and U.S. Department of Commerce

Figure 11-2 **A comparison of energy usage worldwide and in the United States**

Figure 11-3 **A very simple electric generator**

a. The wire at rest in the magnetic field produces no electricity.

b. Moving the wire through the lines of magnetic force sets electrons in the wire in motion, generating electricity.

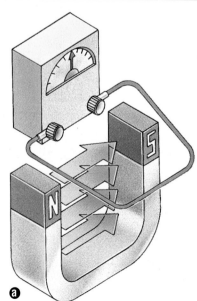

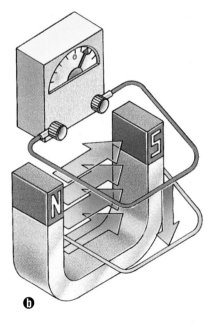

One gram of uranium-235 (^{235}U), the most common nuclear fuel, delivers about as much energy as 3.5 metric tons of coal. Well-designed reactors can run for years without having to be refueled or shut down for anything other than minor maintenance. Furthermore, nuclear energy does not produce gases such as carbon dioxide, which is an enormous advantage compared with fossil fuels. Many nations—especially those with meager fossil-fuel reserves—rely heavily on nuclear plants to meet their energy needs.

SO WHY AREN'T WE USING MORE NUCLEAR ENERGY?

The most serious disadvantage of nuclear energy is that it produces radioactive waste. At present, the United States has no facility for the permanent disposal of its commercial nuclear waste. Each nuclear power plant has its own temporary storage facilities.

Another disadvantage is that nuclear fuel is in relatively short supply. Estimates vary, but there may be only a 100- to 200-year supply of ^{235}U at current rates of consumption.

Nuclear energy is also extremely expensive. Nuclear power plants are very large and complex, with elaborate safety systems, so they are expensive to build. Minor problems in a nuclear facility can force weeks or months of costly downtime. All of these extra expenses are reflected in higher utility bills. It was mainly the expense of nuclear energy, along with the fear of nuclear accidents, that caused the worldwide slowdown in nuclear plant construction.

Safety Concerns The fission reaction creates radioactive products, many of which are very dangerous. If the reaction gets out of control, the enormous heat it generates may destroy the reactor building and spew the radioactive products into the air.

The former Soviet Union has experienced at least two major nuclear accidents. One occurred at a plant in the Ural Mountains in 1957, and the other occurred at Chernobyl in 1986. The details of the 1957 accident were kept secret, but the events at Chernobyl are well known.

Engineers at the Chernobyl nuclear power plant turned off most of the reactor's safety devices while they conducted an unauthorized test. This test caused massive explosions that demolished the reactor and the surrounding structure and blasted tons of hazardous materials high into the air. (See Figure 11-11.) Radioactivity contaminated thousands of square kilometers of land. Hundreds of firefighters and other workers died from radiation exposure, and thousands more may contract cancers as a result of their exposure to high levels of radiation.

The Chernobyl reactor was an obsolete type that, for safety reasons, is not used in the United States. In addition, the operators at Chernobyl violated basic safety guidelines.

ACTIVIST

Bob Geyer thinks the nuclear waste facility being built near his hometown might be dangerous. Find out what he's doing about it on pages 300–301.

Figure 11-10 **Each of these uranium fuel pellets contains the energy equivalence of about 1 metric ton of coal.**

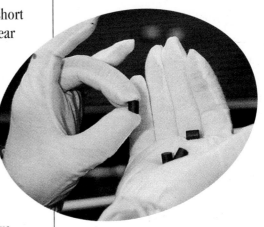

Figure 11-11 **This is how the Chernobyl plant looked shortly after the accident in 1986. The arrow points to the damaged reactor.**

Figure 11-12 **Experimental reactors such as this one at Princeton University have successfully achieved nuclear fusion for brief periods.**

In the United States, the most serious nuclear accident occurred in 1979 at the Three Mile Island nuclear power plant, in Pennsylvania. Human error, combined with blocked valves and broken pumps, was responsible for this accident. Fortunately, only a small amount of radioactive gas escaped the containment structure. Since the accident at Three Mile Island, the Nuclear Regulatory Commission has required more than 300 safety improvements to nuclear power plants.

NUCLEAR FUSION

One possible future energy source is nuclear fusion. **Nuclear fusion** occurs when lightweight atomic nuclei combine to form a heavier nucleus, releasing huge amounts of energy in the process. This is basically the opposite of nuclear fission, in which the nucleus of an atom is split apart. Figure 11-13 shows how fusion works. Nuclear fusion is the process that powers the stars, including our sun, and is a potentially safer energy source than nuclear fission.

Unfortunately, although the potential of fusion is great, so is the technical difficulty of achieving it. For fusion to occur, the atomic nuclei must be heated to extremely high temperatures (100,000,000°C, or 180,000,000°F), be maintained at very high concentrations, and be properly confined. Achieving all three of these conditions simultaneously is extremely difficult. The problem is so complex that discovering a solution may take decades—or may never happen.

Figure 11-13 **During nuclear fusion, the nuclei of two forms of hydrogen (deuterium and tritium) join to form helium, releasing huge amounts of energy.**

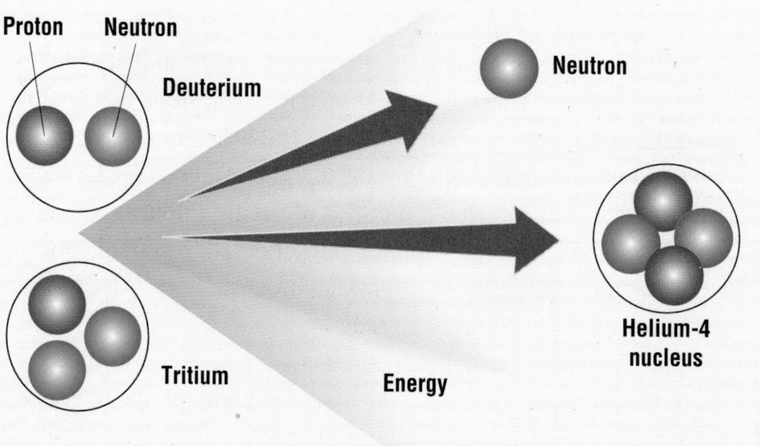

SECTION REVIEW

❶ How are a fossil-fuel-burning power plant and a nuclear power plant similar?

❷ Name two advantages and two disadvantages of nuclear power plants.

❸ Explain the difference between nuclear fission and nuclear fusion.

THINKING CRITICALLY

❹ *Making Decisions* Suppose the world had an unlimited supply of either nuclear fuels or fossil fuels. Use the decision-making model presented in Chapter 1 to decide which would be the better energy supply.

- skylights
- roof overhang
- insulation
- interior and exterior surface colors and finishes
- heat-absorbing materials, including rocks, tile, water containers, and soil
- air leakage around windows and doors

Sample hypothesis:
The greater the surface area of windows on the side of the home facing the sun, the more solar energy the home will collect and the more rapidly it will heat up.

Passive solar homes use the sun's clean, plentiful energy for inexpensive heating.

PERFORM AN EXPERIMENT TO TEST YOUR HYPOTHESIS

5. After your teacher has approved your hypothesis, design and build a new model to test your hypothesis.

6. Test your model, and record your results in a table like the one on the facing page.

ANALYZE YOUR RESULTS

7. Did your second model reach a higher internal temperature than your first model? How do you account for any differences in the effectiveness of your two models?

8. Compare your results with the results of other groups. Were their designs more efficient? If so, what did they do differently? If you could redesign your model yet again, what changes would you make?

9. If a passive solar heating system adds $5,000 to conventional home construction costs, the maintenance cost of the system is $25 per year, and the estimated savings on heating costs are $475 per year, how long will it take for the solar system to pay for itself?

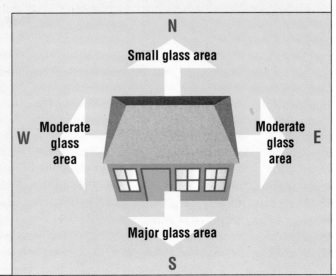

During winter in the Northern Hemisphere, the south side of a house receives almost three times more solar radiation than any other side. For this reason, passive solar windows usually face south.

ENVIRONMENTAL ACTIVIST

Bob Geyer is making a difference both on and off his job. As the planning manager for the mass-transit system in El Paso, Texas, Bob encourages his associates and the people of El Paso to take full advantage of alternative-fuel vehicles, car-pooling programs, and mass transit in general. In his spare time, Bob educates himself and others about issues and policies that affect the environment. When he learns of some action, activity, or company that he believes will threaten the environment, Bob doesn't hesitate—he acts.

If I saw something that bothered me, even back in high school or college, I would write a letter or speak out against it.

Q: *What environmental issue is most important to you right now?*

Bob: The Texas state government has selected Sierra Blanca, Texas, as a disposal site for low-level nuclear waste. This type of waste is still very toxic and could pose a serious threat to the people in the vicinity. And many of the people who live in Sierra Blanca are poor, undereducated, and basically ill prepared to fight against this sort of an environmental hazard.

Plus, the Sierra Blanca nuclear dump site is only 86 mi. from El Paso and 16 mi. from the Río Grande. I hate to think about the area becoming contaminated by nuclear waste. I grew up in El Paso, and I love it. In recent years I've seen the area plagued by all sorts of environmental problems—air pollution, uncontrolled development, and so on. I'll do whatever I can to get people to really think about the long-term consequences of actions such as the disposal of nuclear waste.

Q: *But nuclear waste has to go somewhere, right?*

Bob: Sure it does. It's not that I'm opposed to the storage of nuclear waste. And it's not that I just want it to go somewhere else. I just think the people in charge of finding disposal sites have an obligation to find the most appropriate sites. And "appropriateness" should be based mainly on physical and safety conditions. Plus, those in charge have the obligation to demonstrate to the community that the facility will be safe as long as it exists. Personally, I think that nuclear waste should be stored above ground and at the location where it is produced.

Bob Geyer points to the proposed nuclear dump site in Sierra Blanca, Texas.

Bob prefers that nuclear power plants store their spent fuel rods on-site, as this plant in Morris, Illinois, is doing.

Q: How did you become interested in the environment?

Bob: I guess I became an environmentalist as a kid when I went with my family on camping trips to the mountains of New Mexico. I really learned to appreciate nature during those trips, and I developed a real concern for what happened to the natural world. If I saw something that bothered me, even back in high school or college, I would write a letter or speak out against it. In the last year and a half or so, I really got going full steam into the environmental movement when I heard about the proposed nuclear dump site at Sierra Blanca.

Q: As an environmental activist, exactly what do you do?

Bob: I do what I can to raise people's consciousness about certain environmental issues. I write letters and organize and attend protests and marches. Recently I organized a visit from an author of a book

As an environmental activist, Bob reads about current environmental issues, writes letters to politicians and newspapers, and arranges for experts to speak to the El Paso community.

about nuclear energy. She spoke to various groups of influential people and really stirred up the community. This sort of activity is good because it helps people think about the long-term consequences of certain activities, such as the health consequences of radiation dumping.

Q: Do you ever feel overwhelmed by the number and complexity of environmental problems?

Bob: No. I have a great deal of experience with overwhelming odds. My wheelchair has given me a lot of experience dealing with difficult problems. What I have learned is that by working harder, you can change people's perceptions, which is often the hardest step in solving a problem. For 25 years I have been changing people's perceptions about what a person who uses a wheelchair can accomplish.

Q: Do you mind talking about your disability?

Bob: Not at all. I was in an automobile accident when I was a junior in college. The accident left me with a broken neck and a damaged spinal cord, and I've been using a wheelchair ever since.

I've also been an activist ever since. It all began when I realized that it was impossible to continue at the university I was attending because there were so many physical barriers to a person using a wheelchair. I had to transfer to another university, where I earned a bachelor's and a master's degree. I also became involved in making buildings and buses and other things more accessible to people with disabilities. We have come a long way since then, but we still have a long way to go. But I don't give up easily—I never have. So whether you're talking about fighting for the rights of people with disabilities or fighting to improve the environment, I don't intend to become easily discouraged.

WASTE

"Nothing can be forgotten, only left behind."

JOY HARJO
NATIVE AMERICAN POET

EcoLog

Before you read this chapter, take a few minutes to answer the following questions in your EcoLog.

1. Which one of the following materials do you think makes up the largest portion of household and business waste: plastic, glass, or paper?

2. What actions do you now take to limit the amount of waste you produce? What else could you do to limit the waste you produce?

SOLID WASTE: THE THROWAWAY SOCIETY

AFTER READING THIS SECTION YOU SHOULD BE ABLE TO

❶ define *solid waste*.

❷ explain how most municipal solid waste is disposed of.

It's lunchtime. You stop at a fast-food restaurant and buy a burger, fries, and a soda. Within minutes, the food is devoured, and you toss your trash into the nearest waste-basket. Figure 12-1 shows what might be in your trash: a paper bag, a polystyrene burger container, the cardboard carton that held the fries, a paper cup with a plastic cap, a plastic straw, a handful of paper napkins, and several little ketchup and mustard packets. Once it's gone, you probably don't give the trash a second thought. Why should you? It's gone. You threw it away. It's not your problem anymore. Wait a minute. Where exactly is *away*?

The trash from the wastebasket probably will be picked up by a collection service and taken to a landfill, where it will be dumped with thousands of tons of other trash and covered with a layer of dirt at the end of the day. That trash won't bother anyone anymore, will it? Maybe not, unless the landfill fills up next year and the city has nowhere to put the garbage anymore. Or what if rainwater runs down into the landfill, dissolves harmful chemicals such as paint thinner and nail-polish remover, and seeps into the groundwater? All of a sudden, *away* doesn't seem so simple anymore.

Now imagine multiplying the waste disposal problems that come with your lunch by the number of things that you and everyone else throw away each day. It adds up to enough waste to cause some

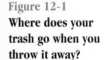

Figure 12-1
Where does your trash go when you throw it away?

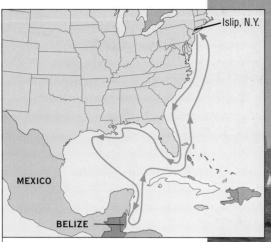

Figure 12-2 **The barge *Mobro* (right) from Islip, New York, sailed up and down the East Coast for five months looking for a place to dump its load of garbage. The map above shows its route.**

real crises. In 1987, the barge shown in Figure 12-2, loaded with garbage from the town of Islip, New York, sailed up and down the East Coast for more than five months in search of a dump. When no one would accept the garbage, it was finally incinerated (burned), and the ashes went back to Islip for burial.

Every year, Americans generate more than 10 billion tons of solid waste. **Solid waste** is any discarded material that is not a liquid or a gas. Solid waste includes everything from junk mail and coffee grounds to junked cars and the discarded trimmings from paper mills.

Many products today are designed to be used once and then thrown away. Partly as a result of this, the amount of waste each American produces each year has more than doubled since the 1960s. (See Figure 12-4.) Although Americans generate the most waste, other countries are also throwing away an increasing amount of trash. Every year, the amount of waste increases in every country.

Figure 12-3 **Few people are happy to have a waste-disposal facility near their home. These people from the Bronx, in New York City, are protesting an incinerator in their neighborhood.**

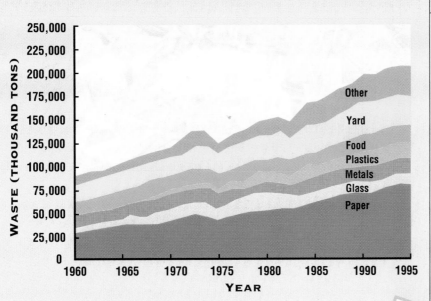

Source: U.S. Environmental Protection Agency, 1996

Figure 12-4 **This graph shows the total amount of municipal solid waste produced per year in the United States, as well as a breakdown of the major waste components.**

Figure 12-5 **The increase in waste is tied to an increasing dependence on disposable products. The 1955 *Life* magazine article shown below promoted the new products.**

ALL WASTES ARE NOT EQUAL

It isn't just the amount of waste that causes problems; it's also the *kind* of waste. There are two basic kinds of wastes: those made of biodegradable materials and those made of non-biodegradable materials. A **biodegradable material** is a material that can be broken down by living things into simpler chemicals that can be consumed by living things. Products made from natural materials are biodegradable. Examples of biodegradable products include news-papers, paper bags, cotton fibers, and leather. Many products made from synthetic materials are not biodegradable. Synthetic materials are made by com-bining chemicals to form compounds that do not exist in nature. Some examples of synthetic materi-als are polyester, nylon, and plastic.

Plastics illustrate how nonbiodegradable materials can cause problems. Plastics are made from petrochemicals (oil). They consist mainly of carbon and hydrogen, the same elements that make up most molecules found in living things. But in plastics, these ele-ments are put together in molecular chains not found in nature. Over millions of years, microorganisms have evolved ways to break down nearly all biological molecules. However, microorganisms have not developed ways to break down the molecular structures of plastics. Thus, when we throw away plastics, they may last for hundreds of years.

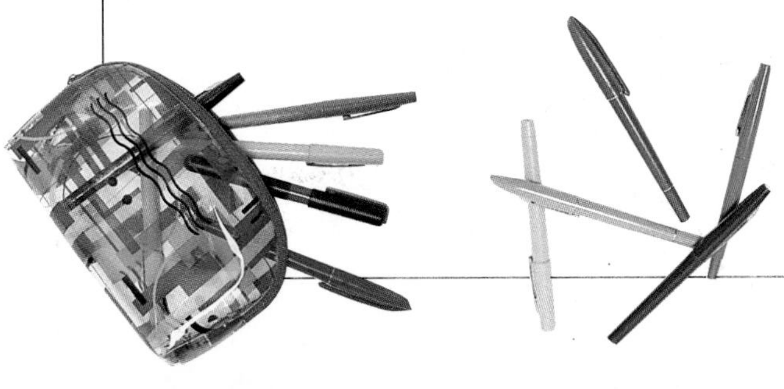

Figure 12-6 **Because of its versatility, plas-tic is used in an incredible variety of products. As a result,**

UNITED STATES SOLID WASTE
(Percentages by weight)

2%
Municipal solid waste

6%
Hazardous waste

26%
Mining waste

56%
Manufacturing waste

1%
Other waste

9%
Agricultural waste

Source: Office of Technology Assessment, 1992

Figure 12-7 This pie chart shows the composition of all solid waste generated in the United States. Municipal solid waste is mainly waste collected from homes and businesses.

Figure 12-8 Paper makes up the largest portion of municipal solid waste. How much of the waste shown in this chart could be recycled?

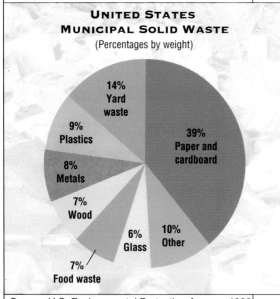

UNITED STATES MUNICIPAL SOLID WASTE
(Percentages by weight)

14%
Yard waste

9%
Plastics

8%
Metals

7%
Wood

7%
Food waste

6%
Glass

10%
Other

39%
Paper and cardboard

Source: U.S. Environmental Protection Agency, 1996

WHAT WE THROW AWAY

As shown in Figure 12-7, about 70 percent of the solid waste produced in the United States comes from manufacturing and mining. About 6 percent of the country's solid waste is considered hazardous. Hazardous waste contains dangerous chemicals and must be specially treated so that it will not contaminate the air, water, or soil. Hazardous waste will be discussed in Section 12.3.

The remaining 2 percent is **municipal solid waste,** the trash produced by households and businesses. Figure 12-8 shows the composition of municipal solid waste in the United States. As you can see, paper makes up a large part of our waste, partly because almost everything we buy comes in at least one layer of paper or cardboard packaging.

These figures may make you think that municipal waste is relatively unimportant. After all, it is only 2 percent of the total solid waste. Nevertheless, municipal waste is still a huge amount of waste—more than 200 million tons each year in the United States. That's enough to fill a bumper-to-bumper convoy of garbage trucks that would stretch around the Earth about six times. Furthermore, the amount of municipal waste that we produce is growing much faster than the amount of mining or agricultural waste. If every American reduced the amount of waste he or she produced by just a small amount, our total waste would be reduced by millions of pounds.

WHERE OUR TRASH GOES

Though most of our trash is sent to landfills and some is incinerated, over 25 percent of our trash is recycled. By comparison, in 1970 we recycled only 6.6 percent of our trash.

Landfills More than 50 percent of our waste ends up in landfills. A **landfill** is a waste-disposal facility where wastes are put in the ground and covered each day with a layer of dirt, plastic, or both. A modern landfill is pictured in

Where Our Trash Goes	
Waste-Disposal Method	**Percentage of Waste by Weight**
Stored in landfills	57
Recycled	27
Incinerated	16

Source: U.S. Environmental Protection Agency, 1996

Figure 12-9 Though more people are recycling, most of our waste still goes to landfills.

Figure 12-10. Landfills are safer than the open dumps of the past, which produced obnoxious smells and provided breeding grounds for flies and rats. Even so, many problems remain.

One problem with landfills is leachate. **Leachate** is water that contains toxic chemicals dissolved from wastes in a landfill. Leachate is formed when water seeps down through a landfill, dissolving chemicals from decomposing garbage along the way. Leachate may contain chemicals from paints, pesticides, cleansers, cans, batteries, and appliances. This poisonous "chemical soup" sometimes flows into groundwater supplies, making water from nearby wells unfit to drink.

Another problem with landfills is methane. As organic waste decomposes deep in the landfill, where there is no oxygen, it produces methane, a highly flammable gas. The methane may seep through the ground into basements of homes up to 300 m (1,000 ft.) from a landfill. If the methane is ignited by a spark, it can cause deadly explosions.

The Resource Conservation and Recovery Act (RCRA), passed in 1976 and amended and updated in 1984, requires that new landfills be built with safeguards to reduce pollution problems. New landfills must be lined with clay or a plastic liner and must have systems

TOPIC: landfills
GO TO: www.scilinks.org
KEYWORD: HE307

Figure 12-10 **New landfills, like the one in the photograph, are lined with clay or plastic and have a system for collecting and treating leachate. The landfill shown in the diagram generates electricity by burning the methane produced by decomposing garbage.**

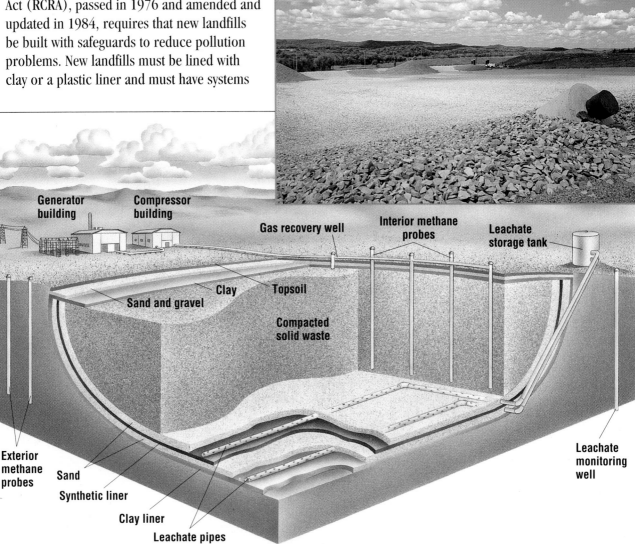

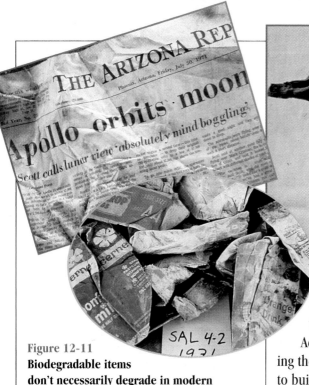

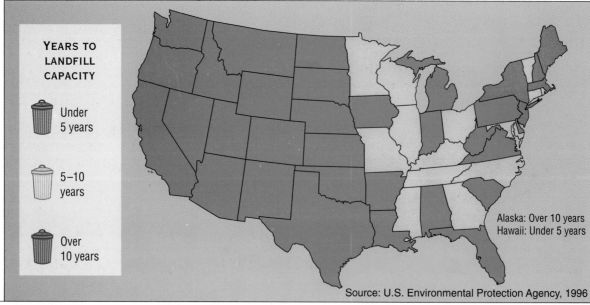

RIO SALADO Sample: 4-2   CORN
Context Date: 1971
Date Collected: June 1989

Figure 12-11
Biodegradable items don't necessarily degrade in modern landfills. The items shown in the three photographs above were put in a Tempe, Arizona, landfill in 1971 and removed in 1989.

SAL 4-2
1971

LANDFILL MANAGER

Being a landfill manager may sound like a dirty job, but it's a vitally important career. Find out more on pages 376–377.

for treating leachate. Vent pipes can be installed to carry methane out of the landfill, where it can be released into the air or burned to produce energy.

Adding these safeguards to landfills increases the cost of building them. In addition, it is getting harder to find acceptable places to build landfills. The landfills must be close enough to the city producing the waste, yet far enough from residents who object to having a landfill near their homes. Any solution is likely to be expensive, either because of the legal fees a city must pay to fight residents' objections or because of the cost of transporting garbage to a distant site. Because of the expense and hassle of building new landfills, most municipal solid waste is still being dumped in old, polluting landfills. But this cannot go on much longer. Many of the country's landfills are scheduled to fill up and close within the next 10 years. The U.S. Environmental Protection Agency (EPA) estimates that 20 states will be out of landfill space within 10 years. (See Figure 12-12.)

Figure 12-12 As this map shows, we are running out of places to bury our garbage.

YEARS TO LANDFILL CAPACITY

Under 5 years

5–10 years

Over 10 years

Alaska: Over 10 years
Hawaii: Under 5 years

Source: U.S. Environmental Protection Agency, 1996

CHAPTER 12 • WASTE

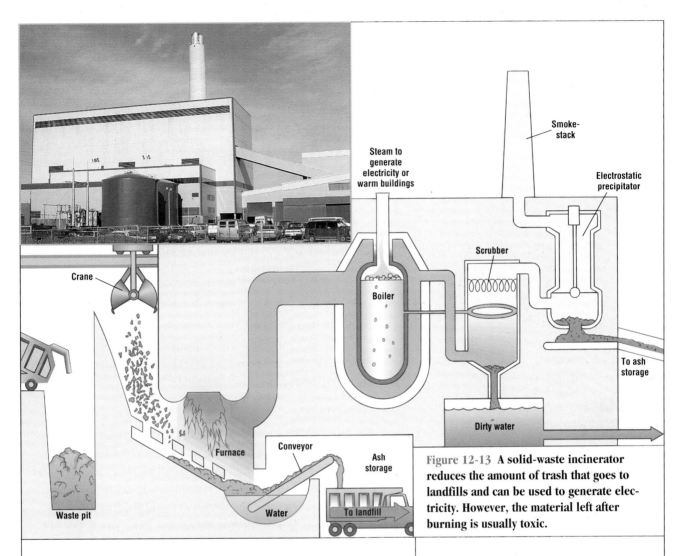

Figure 12-13 **A solid-waste incinerator reduces the amount of trash that goes to landfills and can be used to generate electricity. However, the material left after burning is usually toxic.**

Labels in figure: Smoke-stack; Steam to generate electricity or warm buildings; Electrostatic precipitator; Scrubber; Boiler; Crane; Furnace; Conveyor; Water; Ash storage; To landfill; Waste pit; Dirty water; To ash storage

Even if building new "state-of-the-art" landfills were easy, some problems would remain. The liners at the bottom of the landfills can't last forever, so eventually even the best-designed landfills can leak wastes into water supplies. And if we continue to bury our garbage this way for hundreds of years, the Earth will become overcrowded with closed landfills!

Incinerators   One option for reducing the amount of solid waste sent to landfills is to burn it in incinerators, as shown in Figure 12-13. Some incinerators have special equipment that uses the heat from burning waste to produce steam. The steam can be used to generate electricity. However, waste that is burned does not disappear. Some of it ends up in the air as polluting gases, and the rest is converted into ash that must be disposed of in a landfill. The amount of space needed in the landfill is reduced, but the material to be buried is more toxic. And even modern incinerators with specialized air-pollution control devices release small amounts of poisonous gases and particles of toxic heavy metals into the air. What's more, because incinerators need a certain amount of waste to keep operating, a community that builds an incinerator may not be as motivated to recycle or reduce its waste.

SECTION REVIEW

❶ Why do nonbiodegradable wastes cause waste-management problems?

❷ What is the difference between solid waste and municipal solid waste?

❸ Describe the structure of a landfill.

❹ What is one advantage of incinerating solid waste? What is one disadvantage?

THINKING CRITICALLY

❺ *Identifying Relationships* Name one nonbiodegradable product you use and a biodegradable substitute for it.

309

SOLID WASTE: OPTIONS FOR THE FUTURE

AFTER READING THIS SECTION YOU SHOULD BE ABLE TO

● describe three ways to reduce the amount of waste that goes to landfills and incinerators.

I f landfills and incinerators are expensive and polluting, what are some other options? This section examines three options for dealing with solid-waste problems—producing less waste, recycling, and changing the materials used in products.

PRODUCING LESS WASTE

If we produce less waste, we will reduce the expense and difficulty of collecting and disposing of it. Many ideas for reducing waste are simple common sense, like using both sides of a sheet of paper and not using unneeded bags, napkins, or utensils at stores and restaurants. You can also reduce the amount of trash you have to throw away by refusing to buy products with unnecessary packaging, like the product shown in Figure 12-14. By choosing products with as little packaging as possible, you also help influence manufacturers to create products with little packaging. Families with babies can reduce the amount of solid waste they produce by using washable cloth diapers instead of disposable ones.

Beverage manufacturers could use the kind of refillable bottles that were used in the past. Until about 1965, most bottled beverages were sold in bottles that were designed to be returned to stores when empty. They were then collected, washed, and refilled at bottling plants. Manufacturers could also reduce waste and conserve resources by redesigning products to use less material. A return to sturdy products that last longer and are designed to be easily repairable would both save resources and reduce waste-disposal problems.

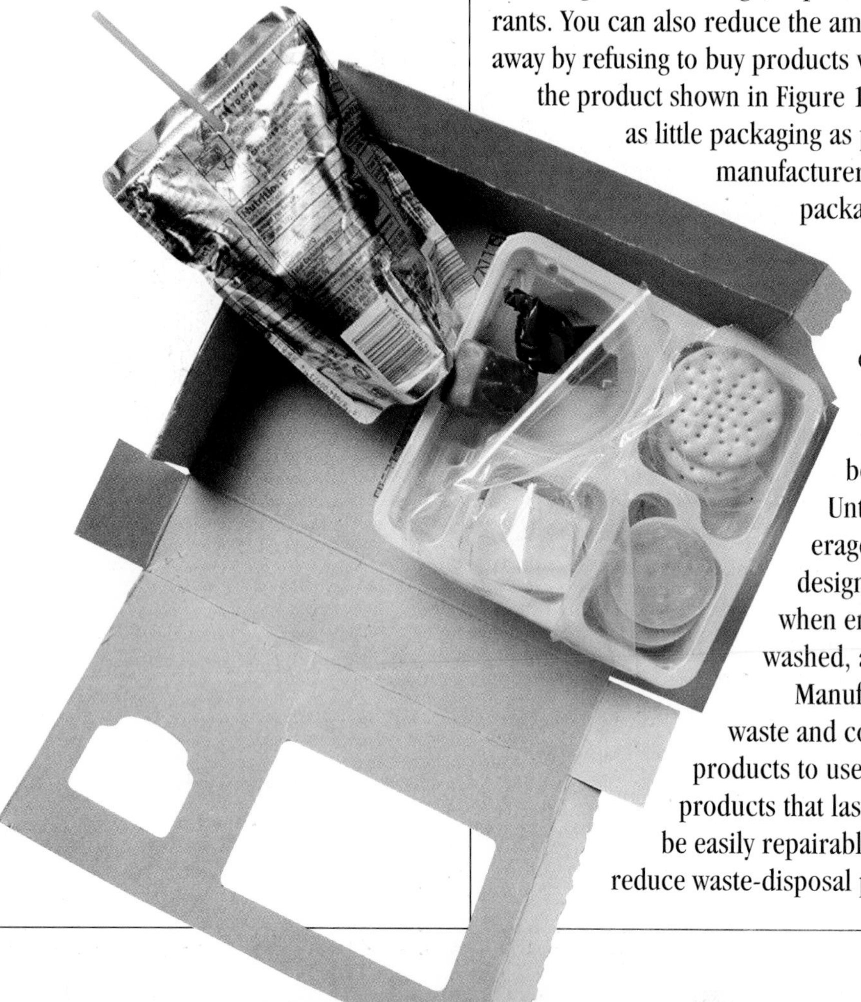

Figure 12-14 One way to reduce the amount of waste you produce is to avoid overpackaged products, like this one.

RECYCLING

In addition to reducing waste, we need to find ways to make the best possible use of all the materials we discard—to recycle as much as possible. Making products from recycled materials usually saves energy, water, and other resources. For example, it takes 95 percent less energy to produce aluminum from recycled aluminum than from ore. It takes about 75 percent less energy to make steel from scrap than from ore. And it takes about 70 percent less energy to make paper from recycled paper than from trees.

Figure 12-15 **Many cities now have recycling programs in which newspapers, cans, and bottles are picked up at the curb.**

When most people talk about recycling, they think of only the first step—bringing their bottles, cans, and newspapers to a recycling center or putting them at the curb in specially marked containers for city trucks to collect. However, as shown in Figure 12-16, recycling actually involves a series of activities, all of which must occur for recycling to work. First, the discarded materials must be collected and sorted by type. Next, each type of material must be taken to a facility where it can be cleaned and made ready to be used again. For example, glass is sorted by color and is crushed, and paper is sorted by type and made into a pulp with water. Then the materials are used to manufacture new products. Finally, buyers for these new products must be found.

Figure 12-16 **Recycling involves a series of activities, each of which must occur for recycling programs to work.**

"Buy Recycled" In the 1980s, so many cities and towns started recycling programs that many of them ended up with more recyclable materials, especially newspapers, than they could sell. The best solution to this problem starts with more people buying products made from recycled materials. Increasing the demand for these products encourages manufacturers to build facilities to make them. When such facilities are built, it becomes easier for communities to sell the materials that they collect from residents.

Composting Yard waste often makes up about 15 percent of a community's municipal solid waste. None of this waste really has to go to a landfill. Because it is biodegradable, yard waste can be allowed to decompose naturally in a compost pile. Many people also put fruit and vegetable trimmings and table scraps in their compost piles. The warm, moist, dark conditions inside a large pile of biodegradable material allow bacteria to grow and break down the waste rapidly. Eventually it becomes **compost**, a dark

PAPER OR PLASTIC?

Does the question "paper or plastic?" sound familiar? If you've ever stood in the checkout line of a grocery store, it probably does. Almost every grocery store today offers a choice between either paper or plastic bags for sacking grocery items. Many people make their choice based on convenience. But what is the best choice for someone who is concerned about the environment?

On the surface, it may seem that paper is the better choice. Paper comes from a renewable resource— trees—and is biodegradable. Plastic, on the other hand, comes from petroleum, which is usually considered a nonrenewable resource. In addition, plastic bags are not biodegradable.

Upon closer examination, however, the decision may not be as simple as it seems. Removing large numbers of trees from forests in order to manufacture paper can disrupt woodland ecosystems. Plus, a tremendous amount of energy is required to convert trees into pulp and then manufacture paper from the pulp.

In order to make the best decision about which product is better for the environment, the following factors should be considered.

- How much raw material, energy, and water is needed to manufacture each bag?
- What waste products will result from the manufacture of each bag, and what effect will those wastes have on water, the atmosphere, and land?
- Can recycled materials be used in the manufacture of the bag? If so, to what degree will the use of recycled materials reduce the amount of raw materials, energy, and water used and wastes produced in making the bag?
- How will the bag decompose, and what will the environmental impact be if it is incorrectly disposed of?

brown, crumbly material made from decomposed vegetable and animal materials. Compost is rich in the nutrients that help plants grow.

Some cities collect yard waste from homes and compost it at a large, central facility. Although most municipal (city-run) composting in the United States is limited to yard wastes, several European cities also collect and compost food wastes in municipal facilities. Composting can also be an effective way of handling waste from food-processing plants and restaurants, manure from animal feedlots, and municipal sewage sludge. If all such biodegradable wastes were composted, the amount of solid waste going to landfills could be greatly reduced.

CHANGING THE MATERIALS WE USE

Much waste could be eliminated by simply changing the materials used to package products. Single-serving drink boxes, for example, are made of a combination of foil, cardboard, and plastic. The

Compost

Conserve landfill space and make your own rich soil at the same time. Find out how on pages 394–395.

Although several studies have analyzed these factors, most have been conducted by parties with a vested interest, such as plastic or paper manufacturing companies. As you might expect, the studies done by plastic manufacturers conclude that plastic bags have the least environmental impact, while studies done by paper producers conclude that paper

A reusable canvas shopping bag may be the best response to the paper-or-plastic question.

bags have the least environmental impact. Often, these researchers fail to study all of the important factors listed previously.

But one thing is certain: the plastic-versus-paper debate has caused both industries to improve the way their products affect the environment. For example, paper bags recently outsold plastic bags because they were considered stronger, better for reusing or recycling, and less harmful in a landfill.

Then, new technology allowed the plastics industry to gain a larger market share. By incorporating recycled plastic into the bags, manufacturers improved the image of plastic bags.

Paper bag manufacturers responded to this increased competition by improving the quality of their recycled bags. This action again increased their sales.

The tug-of-war between the manufacturers of plastic and paper bags continues. And environmentally conscious people are still wondering which is better. Right now there

seems to be no single right answer. However, the following are environmentally sound options.

1. Carry your groceries in bags brought from home (paper, plastic, or canvas bags).

2. Choose a recycled bag, if available.

3. Choose the bag you are most likely to reuse in the future.

4. If you have only one or two small items, tell the checker you don't need a bag at all.

THINKING CRITICALLY

① *Identifying Relationships* Explain how environmentally conscious shoppers have helped improve paper and plastic bag manufacturing in this country.

② *Recognizing Relationships* Why should a person care which bag he or she is given at the grocery store?

Some Household Recyclables		
Product	**Primary Material**	**Recycled Products**
Newspapers 	Newsprint	Newsprint, cardboard, egg cartons, building materials 
Telephone books	Paper	Building materials
 Magazines and catalogs	Clay-coated paper	Building materials
Aluminum beverage cans 	Aluminum	 Beverage cans, lawn chairs, siding, cookware
 Steel food and beverage cans	Steel	Food and beverage cans, automobile parts, tools, construction materials 
Glass jars and bottles 	Glass	Glass jars and bottles
Plastic beverage containers	Plastic	Non-food containers, insulation, carpet yarn, textiles, fiberfill, scouring pads 
Plastic milk containers 	Plastic	 Non-food containers, toys, crates, plastic lumber

Figure 12-17 What happens to the products you recycle? They come back in the forms shown in the right-hand column.

SCiLINKS
NSTA

TOPIC: degradable plastics
GO TO: www.scilinks.org
KEYWORD: HE314

drink boxes are hard to recycle because there is no good way to separate the three different components. More of our waste could be recycled if such products were simply eliminated and all drinks came in recyclable glass or aluminum containers.

Degradable Plastics? As you read earlier, most plastics are not biodegradable. In order to make plastic products more appealing to people who are concerned about the environment, several companies have developed new kinds of plastics that they call "degradable." One type, called photodegradable plastic, is made so that when it is left in the sun for many weeks, it becomes weak and brittle and eventually breaks into pieces. Another type, usually called biodegradable by the manufacturers, is made by blending cornstarch and a special chemical agent into ordinary plastic. When this plastic is buried, the bacteria in the soil eat the cornstarch, leaving the plastic weakened because it is full of microscopic holes. The chemical agent then gradually causes the long plastic molecules to break into shorter molecules. These two effects combine to cause the plastic to eventually fall apart into small pieces.

The main problem with these "degradable" plastics is that although they do break apart and the organic portions can degrade, the plastic portions are just reduced to smaller pieces. This plastic

What You Can Do to Help With Waste Problems

1. Take your recyclable materials to a recycling center or put them out for curb-side collection.

2. Buy products made from recycled materials whenever possible.

3. At the grocery store, use durable cloth shopping bags instead of paper or plastic, or bring your old paper or plastic ones back and use them again.

4. Ask for "no bag, please" when buying just one or two items at a store.

5. When shopping, look for items sold with little or no packaging. Choose foods packaged in large quantities instead of many individually wrapped servings, and avoid products that have multiple layers of packaging (like a plastic-wrapped dish of noodles inside a plastic-wrapped cardboard box).

6. Don't take extra paper napkins, plastic utensils, or condiment packets when buying takeout food.

7. At meals, use washable cups, dishes, utensils, and cloth napkins instead of throwaways.

8. Keep a reusable cup or mug at school or work for beverages.

9. Use both sides of a sheet of paper when writing or photocopying.

10. Save unused pages from class notebooks for doing homework assignments or other writing.

11. Put dead leaves, weeds, and fruit and vegetable trimmings in a backyard compost pile instead of in the trash.

12. When mowing the lawn, leave grass clippings on the lawn to decompose naturally and add nutrients to the soil.

Figure 12-18 **Individuals can make a difference. Is there anything you could do to help with waste problems?**

does not go away but rather just gets spread around. Photodegradable plastic may help reduce the harm caused by plastic litter, because after many months of sitting on the ground or in the water it probably will break into pieces too small to strangle or choke most animals. However, neither type does much to reduce the amount of waste in landfills.

A few companies are developing new plastic-like materials from substances produced by living things, such as starch or a compound made by bacteria. (See Figure 12-19.) These materials are truly biodegradable, but very few products have been made from them so far.

Figure 12-19 **Packing material made from cornstarch is biodegradable.**

SECTION REVIEW

❶ Name four things you could do each day to produce less waste.

❷ What is the main drawback of photodegradable plastics? What is one potential benefit?

THINKING CRITICALLY

❸ *Analyzing Relationships* Describe how composting is a form of recycling.

315

HAZARDOUS WASTE

AFTER READING THIS SECTION YOU SHOULD BE ABLE TO

❶ define *hazardous waste.*

❷ explain how most hazardous waste is disposed of in the United States.

❸ explain the two best ways to deal with the hazardous-waste problem.

Many of the products we use today, from laundry soap to computers, are produced in modern factories using thousands of chemicals. Some of these chemicals are ingredients that become part of the products themselves, while others are used as cleansers or to make chemical reactions happen. Large quantities of the chemicals are often left as waste. Many of these chemicals are classified as **hazardous wastes,** which are wastes that are toxic or highly corrosive or that explode easily. Hazardous wastes may be solids, liquids, or gases. Some examples of hazardous wastes include the following substances.

• some dyes, cleansers, and solvents
• PCBs (polychlorinated biphenyls) used in insulating material, plastics, solvents, lubricants, and sealants
• toxic heavy metals, such as lead, mercury, cadmium, and zinc
• pesticides (discussed in Chapter 9)
• radioactive wastes (discussed in Chapter 11)

The methods used to dispose of hazardous wastes often are not as carefully thought out as the manufacturing processes that produced them. One case of careless hazardous-waste disposal with horrifying results occurred at Love Canal, in Niagara Falls, New York. The Case Study on pages 318–319 describes that situation.

The events at Love Canal shocked people into paying more attention to how hazardous wastes were being handled throughout the country. In thousands of other places, improperly stored or discarded wastes—like those shown in Figure 12-20—were leaking into the air, soil, and groundwater. Federal laws were passed to provide a system for cleaning up old waste sites and regulating future waste disposal.

Figure 12-20 A hazardous-waste site near Texas City, Texas

LAWS GOVERNING HAZARDOUS-WASTE DISPOSAL

The Resource Conservation and Recovery Act (RCRA) requires producers of hazardous waste to keep records of how their wastes are handled from the time they are made to the time they are placed in an approved disposal facility. If the wastes ever cause a problem in the future, the producer is legally responsible for cleaning them up. RCRA also requires all hazardous-waste treatment and disposal facilities to be built and operated according to standards that are designed to prevent the facilities from polluting the environment.

The Superfund Act Because the safe disposal of hazardous wastes is expensive, companies that produce hazardous wastes may be tempted to illegally dump them to save money. The Comprehensive Environmental Response, Compensation, and Liability Act of 1980, more commonly known as the Superfund Act, tried to discourage this by giving the Environmental Protection Agency (EPA) the right to sue the owners of hazardous-waste sites to make them pay for the cleanup. It also created a fund of money to pay for cleaning up abandoned hazardous-waste sites.

Cleaning up improperly discarded wastes is difficult and extremely expensive. At Love Canal alone, $275 million was spent to put a clay cap on the site, install a drain system and treatment plant to handle the leaking wastes, and relocate the residents. Now, more than 20 years after Love Canal was evacuated, many waste sites are still waiting to be cleaned up, as shown in Figure 12-21. Of the roughly 1,200 approved or proposed Superfund sites, cleanup has been completed at only 75. Even more discouraging is that much of the Superfund money has been spent on legal fees and administrative costs.

Figure 12-21 **This map shows the number of approved and proposed Superfund sites as of the spring of 1998. These sites represent some of the nation's most hazardous areas.**

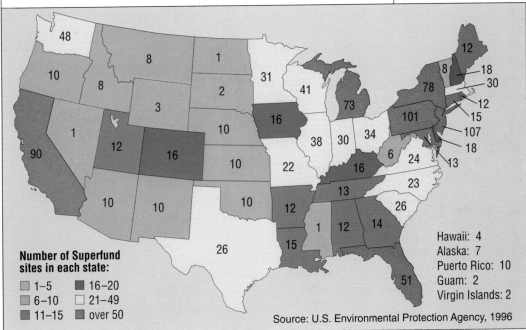

Number of Superfund sites in each state:
- 1–5
- 6–10
- 11–15
- 16–20
- 21–49
- over 50

Hawaii: 4
Alaska: 7
Puerto Rico: 10
Guam: 2
Virgin Islands: 2

Source: U.S. Environmental Protection Agency, 1996

HOW CAN WE MANAGE HAZARDOUS WASTES?

Each year, the United States produces about 280 million tons of hazardous waste, and this amount is growing each year. Unfortunately, the disposal techniques used today cannot guarantee that hazardous waste will not eventually pollute our air, food, or water.

Produce Less The best way to handle hazardous waste is to produce less of it. In recent years, many manufacturers have discovered that they can redesign manufacturing methods to produce less hazardous waste or none at all. For example, some manufacturers who used chemicals to clean metal parts have discovered that they can use tiny plastic beads instead. The beads, which "sandblast" the parts clean, can be reused several times and are not hazardous when discarded. Often, such techniques end up saving the manufacturers money in material costs as well as waste-disposal costs.

Reuse The second-best way to deal with hazardous waste is to find a way to reuse it. In the United States, more than 50 programs have been set up to help industries get in touch with other

LOVE CANAL: A TOXIC NIGHTMARE

To someone who has never heard of it, Love Canal may sound like a pleasant place for a picnic. But in the minds of those familiar with the abandoned canal site in Niagara Falls, New York, the area is synonymous with chemicals, disease, and loss.

It all began in 1942 when a chemical company purchased the area as a dump for toxic wastes. Over the next 11 years, the company buried almost 20,000 metric tons (22,000 tons) of hazardous chemicals in the canal. The chemicals were usually contained in steel barrels. At the time, disposing of chemical wastes in this way was legal. It was thought that the thick clay that lined the canal would prevent the wastes from escaping into the surrounding soil.

By 1953, the dump was full. It was covered with a cap of clay and soil and sold to the school board of Niagara Falls. The school board, ignoring warnings from the chemical company, built an elementary school on top of the canal. In addition, homes were built nearby, and roads and sewer lines were constructed across the site, which disturbed its clay cap and occasionally exposed barrels of waste.

The new homes drew many new residents, who were not warned about the nearby hazardous-waste dump.

By the late 1950s, problems started occurring. Children playing near the school were burned by chemicals they encountered. In

Families living near the chemical dump were evacuated in 1978.

companies that can use the materials that they normally throw away. For example, one company that has to throw away a cleaning solvent after one use can sell it to another company whose product (steel castings, for example) is not harmed by small amounts of contamination in the solvent.

Conversion Into Nonhazardous Substances Some types of wastes can be treated chemically to make them less hazardous. For example, lime (a base) can be added to acids to neutralize them, converting them into salts that are less harmful to the environment. Cyanides can be combined with oxygen to form carbon dioxide and nitrogen. In other cases, wastes can be treated biologically. Sludge from petroleum refineries, for example, may be converted by soil bacteria into less harmful substances.

Incineration Some toxic substances are disposed of by burning, often in specially designed incinerators. If properly designed and maintained, incinerators can be a safe means of waste disposal, but they face several problems. Incineration is generally the most expensive form of waste disposal. Incinerators need

SCI*LINKS*
NSTA
TOPIC: hazardous waste conversion
GO TO: www.scilinks.org
KEYWORD: HE319

the sixties and seventies the chemical leaks became more obvious. Residents near the former dump often noticed a strong odor in the air, especially after a rain. Puddles of chemicals appeared in their backyards. Thick, black sludge oozed into their basements. Worst of all, health problems such as asthma, dizziness, blurred vision, seizures, miscarriages, stillbirths, and birth defects were becoming more common among the residents.

Local, state, and federal officials began to take notice of the problems at Love Canal in the mid-seventies. Water-, soil-, and air-quality tests showed chemical contamination. In 1978, the governor of New York ordered the 235 families living closest to the chemical dump to evacuate. The state purchased their homes and paid for their relocation. In 1980, an additional 792 families were moved at taxpayers' expense.

Who was responsible for the Love Canal mess? Who should pay the $275 million in cleanup and relocation costs? The chemical company has denied all responsibility. Nevertheless, the company paid compensation to Love Canal residents in 1984. The amounts received ranged from $2,000 to $400,000. And in 1988, a federal judge ruled that the chemical company was indeed responsible for its wastes and would have to pay the cleanup bill.

Love Canal is now being redeveloped.

THINKING CRITICALLY

❶ *Evaluating Viewpoints* Who do you think should be held responsible for the Love Canal disaster? Why?

❷ *Comprehending Processes* Use the Love Canal situation to explain why we can never really throw anything away.

pollution-control devices and careful monitoring to avoid releasing hazardous gases and particles into the air. And even if perfectly safe incinerators existed, they would not solve all hazardous-waste disposal problems because not all wastes are burnable.

Land Disposal Most hazardous wastes produced in the United States are disposed of by some form of land disposal. One such method, illustrated in Figure 12-22, is **deep-well injection,** in which wastes are pumped deep into the ground, where they are absorbed into a dry layer of rock below the level of groundwater. Another common land-disposal facility is a **surface impoundment,** which is basically a pond with a sealed bottom. The wastes settle to the bottom of the pond while water evaporates and leaves room to add more wastes. Hazardous wastes in concentrated or solid form are often put in drums and buried in landfills similar to those used for ordinary solid waste but with extra precautions taken to prevent leakage.

In theory, all of these facilities, if properly designed and built, provide safe ways to dispose of hazardous wastes. In practice, however, it is possible for any of them to develop leaks, resulting in contamination of the air, soil, or groundwater. Contamination seems especially likely if you consider that the wastes may be left in these sites for hundreds of years—plenty of time for something to go wrong.

Although we talk about waste disposal, putting wastes into land-disposal facilities is really just long-term *storage,* because the wastes do not go away. Disposal of radioactive wastes from nuclear reactors is an especially difficult storage problem. The only way to make the wastes nonhazardous is to let them sit for thousands of years, allowing the radioactivity to decrease over time. Therefore, engineers search for disposal sites that probably will not be damaged by movements of the Earth or by groundwater for thousands of years.

Figure 12-22 **One method of hazardous-waste disposal is deep-well injection, in which hazardous wastes are pumped deep into the ground below the groundwater level.**

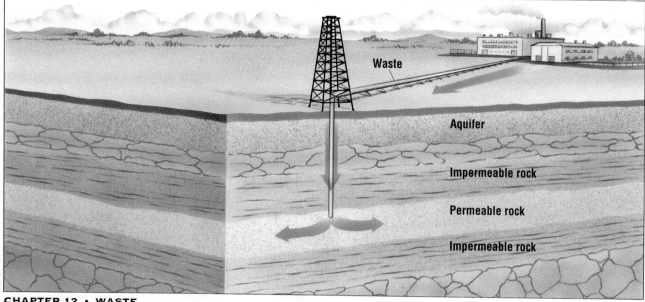

Waste

Aquifer

Impermeable rock

Permeable rock

Impermeable rock

DUMPING WASTE ON YOUR NEIGHBORS

Until recently, only local laws regulated waste disposal in the United States. Companies would often get rid of hazardous wastes by sending them to landfills in other states, especially the poorer southern states. In the 1980s, as southern populations grew, these states began to refuse hazardous wastes from other states. Now, hazardous waste is a worldwide problem. Industrialized countries sometimes ship hazardous wastes to developing countries, where laws governing the disposal of these wastes are less stringent. Some international agreements to control hazardous substances are now being made, and more such agreements are needed.

HAZARDOUS WASTES AT HOME

We usually think of hazardous-waste management as a problem that only big industries have to face. However, many hazardous chemicals, including house paint, pesticides, and batteries (which contain heavy metals) are used in homes, schools, and small businesses. People often do not realize that hazardous materials poured down the drain or put in the trash end up in sewage sludge and in solid-waste landfills, contaminating the environment.

To deal with this problem, more and more cities around the country have begun to provide collection for household hazardous wastes. Some collect materials only once or twice a year, while others have permanent facilities where residents can drop off their wastes. Trained workers sort the wastes, sending some materials for recycling and packing others into drums for disposal. Used batteries and motor oil are commonly recycled. Paint may be blended and used for city park maintenance or graffiti cleanup work, as shown in Figure 12-23.

An important benefit of such programs is that they make people more aware of which household wastes are hazardous, encouraging them to handle wastes properly and to look for ways to use less hazardous materials. For example, individuals can look for safer substitutes

Should radioactive waste travel across the country to a storage site deep underground? Turn to pages 328–329 for two points of view.

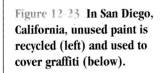

Figure 12-23 **In San Diego, California, unused paint is recycled (left) and used to cover graffiti (below).**

FIELD ACTIVITY

Find out how hazardous wastes are stored and disposed of in your own home. Prepare an inventory of hazardous household chemicals. Check for hazardous materials among cleansers, auto supplies, garden supplies, and wherever chemicals are stored in your home. Determine the proper disposal method for each product. Clearly mark each container with the safest disposal method for it.

SECTION REVIEW

❶ Define *hazardous waste*.

❷ What is the most common way to dispose of hazardous waste in the United States? What are two dangers of this method of disposal?

❸ Explain how the United States could produce less hazardous waste.

THINKING CRITICALLY

❹ *Evaluating Ideas* Suppose that a surface-impoundment site for hazardous waste is planned for your community. Would you oppose locating the site in your community? Explain your answer.

❺ *Applying Ideas* Suppose someone dumped leftover motor oil on a driveway. Could this disposal method contaminate the air, water, or soil? How?

Figure 12-24 **What can you do with your old, dirty motor oil? Take it to a service station or to a municipal oil-collection site, such as the one shown here.**

for toxic household chemicals, reduce the use of pesticides, and buy paints in the smallest quantities possible to avoid having to throw away leftovers.

What About Motor Oil? If you've ever changed the oil in your car yourself, you've probably wondered what to do with the old, dirty oil. Just pour it on the ground? Throw it in the trash? It may surprise you to find out that American backyard mechanics throw away about 700 million liters (185 million gal.) of used motor oil every year. This doesn't even include the oil discarded by service stations and auto-repair shops. The 1989 *Exxon Valdez* oil tanker spill polluted the environment with less than one-fifteenth the amount that individuals in the United States throw away each year.

Across the country, discarded oil is going down the drain, into landfills, and into the ground, where it can seep into groundwater or waterways. Just 2 L of old oil, which is less than half the amount in a car, can make 1 million L of fresh water undrinkable.

So what can people do with the oil? One option is to take it to a service station, where it will be turned in for recycling. Some cities have municipal oil-collection sites, and some even have pickup services for used oil. The cities recycle the used oil turned in by citizens. If you don't know what services your community provides, you can call your local city hall and find out.

Perhaps the fiercest outcry against the Yucca Mountain site comes from residents of Nevada. They fear that if tons of highly toxic waste are stored in one place, some of it might eventually leak out. Since some of this waste is so toxic that just a tiny speck could be lethal, even a small leak could result in a major environmental disaster.

Some people are concerned that the radioactive waste might leak into the groundwater underneath the facility. How might the radioactivity enter the water? The waste containers are expected to last 500 to 1,000 years. After that, the cavern that holds the containers will have to remain leakproof for 10,000 years. Opponents of the plan say that nobody can guarantee that the cavern will be leakproof for that long.

If radioactive waste were to leak out of the facility, it could contaminate the water in wells, springs, and streams. In time,

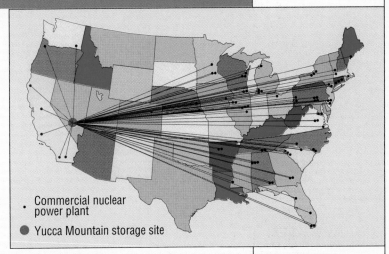

Commercial nuclear power plant

Yucca Mountain storage site

Preliminary plan for the Yucca Mountain nuclear-waste storage facility

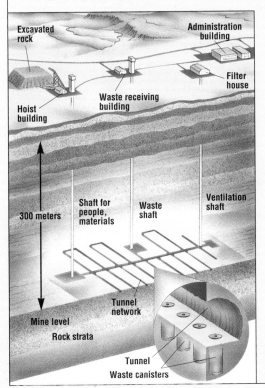

Excavated rock

Administration building

Filter house

Hoist building

Waste receiving building

300 meters

Shaft for people, materials

Waste shaft

Ventilation shaft

Mine level

Rock strata

Tunnel network

Tunnel

Waste canisters

the contamination could spread farther and farther from the site and into the biosphere.

Some people also worry that transporting nuclear waste across vast distances to Yucca Mountain is riskier than leaving the material near the facilities where it is produced. Any accident along the way could release radioactivity into the environment.

Most opponents of the Yucca Mountain site agree that current methods of storing nuclear waste are dangerous and should be improved. They suggest that by transferring the waste to solid steel and concrete containers, the waste could be safely stored at each nuclear power facility for 75 to 100 years. By that time, they suggest, more will be known about how to store the wastes safely for thousands of years.

This map shows the nuclear power plants around the country that are possible sources of nuclear waste for the Yucca Mountain facility.

ANALYZE THE ISSUE

1. ***Making Decisions*** Use the decision-making model presented in Chapter 1 to develop a recommendation for action in this case.

2. ***Analyzing Relationships*** Is there a nuclear power facility near your community? If so, did that affect your answer to question 1? Explain.

13

POPULATION GROWTH

"People are everywhere. Some people say there are too many of us, but no one wants to leave."

CHARLES M. SCHULZ
AMERICAN CARTOONIST

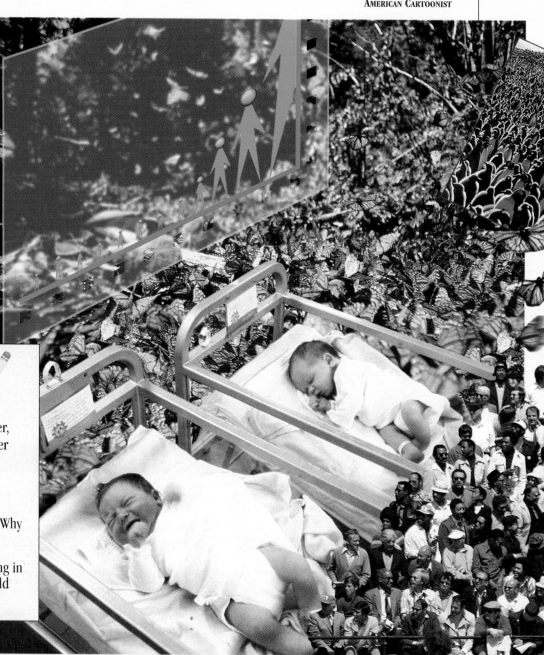

EcoLog

Before you read this chapter, take a few minutes to answer the following questions in your EcoLog.

❶ Could there ever be too many people on Earth? Why or why not?

❷ How could overcrowding in another part of the world affect you?

HOW POPULATIONS CHANGE IN SIZE

AFTER READING THIS SECTION YOU SHOULD BE ABLE TO

❶ describe the factors that affect a population's size.

❷ explain why populations grow.

❸ explain what limits a population's growth.

The Earth's human population has reached 6 billion and is climbing fast. It is estimated that there will be over 9 billion people alive by the middle of the twenty-first century. Many scientists think that the rapid growth of the human population is a fundamental cause of many environmental problems. To understand human population growth, you need to know something about the properties of populations of organisms in general.

As you read in Chapter 2, a population is a group of individuals of the same species living in a particular place. Birth and immigration (moving in) add individuals to a population. Death and emigration (moving out) subtract individuals. A population grows when the number of individuals added to the population is greater than the number of individuals subtracted, that is, when

$$\begin{matrix} \text{number of births} \\ + \\ \text{number of immigrants} \end{matrix} \quad > \quad \begin{matrix} \text{number of deaths} \\ + \\ \text{number of emigrants} \end{matrix}$$

Figure 13-1
It is estimated that the human population is growing at a rate of 94 million people per year.

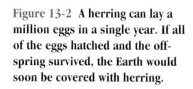

Figure 13-2 **A herring can lay a million eggs in a single year. If all of the eggs hatched and the offspring survived, the Earth would soon be covered with herring.**

On the other hand, a population will shrink if

$$\begin{array}{c}\text{number of deaths} \\ + \\ \text{number of emigrants}\end{array} > \begin{array}{c}\text{number of births} \\ + \\ \text{number of immigrants}\end{array}$$

HOW FAST CAN A POPULATION GROW?

Most organisms produce many more offspring than can survive to grow up and reproduce. For example, a herring may lay a million eggs a year. If all of the eggs hatched and survived, the entire surface of the Earth would be knee-deep in herring in just a short time. It is obvious that this is not what happens in normal

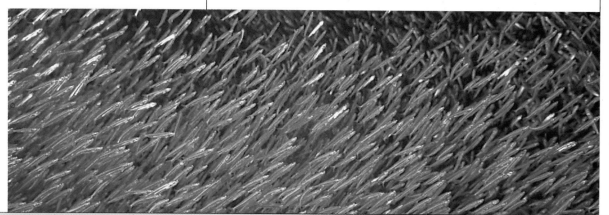

OVERSHOOTING THE CARRYING CAPACITY

disaster area, as the animals try to tear every last edible leaf from the trees and every blade of grass from the soil. The result is that the habitat's carrying capacity is reduced, and the population usually shrinks

substantially through emigration or starvation. The ecosystem and its carrying capacity may recover, but it may take hundreds of years.

A spectacular and well-studied example of a population exceeding

Reindeer were introduced to St. Paul Island, off the coast of Alaska, in 1911.

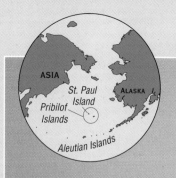

Carrying capacity is the maximum number of individuals an environment can support for a long period of time. When a population grows larger than the carrying capacity of the land, it uses up its resources faster than they are replenished. Environmental degradation is one obvious effect of exceeding the carrying capacity. An ecosystem in which starving animals are scrambling for food is an ecological

populations. However, in order to understand how populations work, we must first look at what would happen if there were no limits on the growth of a population.

Each population has a characteristic maximum growth rate. This maximum growth rate, also known as **biotic potential,** is the rate at which a population would grow if every new individual survived to adulthood and reproduced at its maximum capacity. Given these conditions, any population will grow exponentially, meaning that a larger number of individuals is added to the population in each generation, as shown in Figure 13-3. (The curved line showing exponential growth is called a J-curve because of its J shape.)

The biotic potential for the human population is estimated to be about 6 percent per year. If the human population were growing at this pace, it would double in size

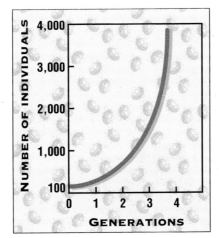

Figure 13-3 **If there are no limits to the growth of a population, the population will grow exponentially. Each generation will contain a larger number of individuals than the one before it. This kind of growth curve is called a J-curve.**

carrying capacity occurred in the Pribilof Islands off the coast of Alaska in the first half of the twentieth century. In 1911, 25 reindeer were introduced to St. Paul Island, a 41 sq. mi. island that is part of the Pribilofs. The reindeer were introduced to replace the native caribou, which had been hunted to extinction.

The population of reindeer on Saint Paul Island between 1910 and 1950

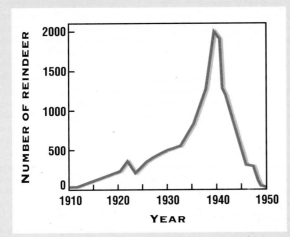

Scientists monitored the size of the introduced population for the next 39 years.

The reindeer found the small island very suitable. As you can see in the graph below, the reindeer population soared. There were 2,046 individuals in 1938—that translates to an average annual growth rate of 16 percent.

The large population quickly overgrazed and trampled the island's food supply of lichens (the multicolored, flaky growths you see on trees and rocks). Lichens grow slowly in the cold climate of the Pribilofs, so the reindeer's food supply could not recover from overconsumption. Short of food and

unable to leave the island, the reindeer starved. By 1950, only eight reindeer were left on St. Paul Island. The reindeer population did not die out, however. It began to grow again after 1950 and has now reached a size of about 800.

THINKING CRITICALLY

❶ *Interpreting Graphics* Compare the graph at left with Figure 13-3. How are the two graphs similar? How are they different?

❷ *Inferring Relationships* Suppose predators had also been introduced to St. Paul Island. How might their presence have changed the outcome of the reindeer introduction? Explain your reasoning.

FIELD ACTIVITY

To understand exponential growth, calculate the following. Suppose you have a flask containing one bacterium that divides into two at the end of one hour. If at the end of each succeeding hour, each bacterium divides, how many bacteria will be present at the end of 24 hours? Graph your results.

in just under 12 years. And the biotic potential for humans is small compared with the rates for many other organisms. For rats, the biotic potential is 1.5 percent *per day*—a population of rats living in a warehouse could double in size in only 47 days. Bacteria are probably the champion reproducers. Given perfect conditions, the growth rate of certain kinds of bacteria is 250 percent *per hour!* That means each bacterium divides more than once an hour.

WHAT LIMITS POPULATION GROWTH?

Given a population's biotic potential, you might expect it to keep growing indefinitely. However, this rarely happens. For example, if beetles reproduced at their biotic potential, they would soon overrun us. Why aren't we skating on beetles? What limits population size?

To answer these questions, consider that habitats contain limited supplies of food, water, shelter, and other resources needed for living. As a population grows, its members consume greater amounts of these resources. The resources that limit the growth of a population are called **limiting**

Figure 13-4 **The plants above are competing for light and space. The barn owl and the deer compete for food with other members of their populations.**

resources. Limiting resources for animals include food, water, shelter, and nesting sites. For plants, water, sunlight, and certain mineral nutrients are limiting resources.

When a population increases, more and more individuals must compete for the limiting resources. Crowding increases their exposure to predators, parasites, and diseases. As survival becomes more difficult, population growth slows as the birth rate drops and the death rate rises. The combined effect of all of the factors that limit population growth is called **environmental resistance.** Think of environmental resistance as a force opposing biotic potential. As a population naturally increases, environmental resistance acts to slow its growth much as friction slows a car and limits its speed.

The population eventually ceases to grow as it reaches, and often exceeds, a size known as its **carrying capacity.** The carrying capacity is the maximum population size an environment can support for a long period of time. A population may increase beyond its carrying capacity, but it cannot stay at the increased size for very long. In nature, populations tend to fluctuate above and below the carrying capacity in response to environmental changes, such as the seasons. Figure 13-5 shows the change in a population's size over time. (The curved portion of the line that shows a population approaching its carrying capacity is called an S-curve.) Carrying capacities can also change over time as the environment changes.

SCI
LINKS
NSTA
TOPIC: environmental resistance
GO TO: www.scilinks.org
KEYWORD: HE335

Figure 13-5 **This graph shows the growth of a population over time. At first the population increases according to its biotic potential. Environmental resistance slows the population's growth as it approaches its carrying capacity. Changes in weather and other natural forces cause the population to continue fluctuating over time.**

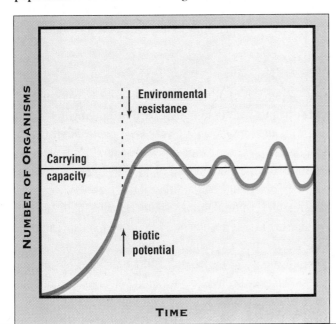

SECTION REVIEW

❶ What factors limit the growth of populations?

❷ Why can't a population increase indefinitely?

❸ What factors could cause the carrying capacity of the environment to increase or decrease?

THINKING CRITICALLY

❹ *Relating Concepts* Make a concept map using the following terms: population growth, population shrinkage, birth, death, immigration, and emigration.

❺ *Analyzing Processes* What are some reasons the human population does not reach the size it could given its biotic potential?

A GROWING HUMAN POPULATION

AFTER READING THIS SECTION YOU SHOULD BE ABLE TO

1 describe how the size of the human population has changed.

2 identify the factors that led to changes in the human population.

3 describe the stages of population growth.

Like a single ecosystem, the entire Earth also has a carrying capacity. However, no one knows the Earth's carrying capacity for the human population. Remember that carrying capacity is the maximum number of individuals an environment can support for a long period of time. Many scientists think that the Earth can support between 4 billion and 16 billion people. However, the carrying capacity for humans is very difficult to measure given changes in technology and society, such as the increase in food production that accompanied the green revolution. And the fact that humans are able to reflect on and consciously determine how many offspring we have affects how quickly our population will grow. Many scientists expect the world's human population to stabilize around 10 billion. But how will this larger population affect air, water, soil, biodiversity, and human health?

Though we can only estimate the future effects of population growth, we have been able to trace past population growth. Studying the patterns of the past may help us plan for the future.

FROM HUNTING AND GATHERING TO AGRICULTURE

For about 99 percent of our history, all humans were **hunter-gatherers,** people who obtain their food by hunting, fishing, and gathering wild plant foods. Today, very few people survive in this way. Most hunter-gatherer groups moved around from place to place, following game animals and plant foods that were available only in certain places at certain times of the year.

Hunter-gatherer populations usually remain small. Most hunter-gatherers live in groups of 25 to 50 people, spread widely across the landscape. It is estimated that there were only about 1 million individuals on Earth when all people lived by hunting and gathering. (This may seem like a lot until you consider that the population of Detroit is now about 1 million.)

Then about 10,000 years ago, people began to raise animals and grow crops instead of relying on wild animals and plants for their subsistence. This change from hunting and gathering to agriculture had such dramatic results that it is often called an **agricultural revolution.** Agriculture probably did not originate in just one area. People probably began raising animals and cultivating plants in many different places at about the same time. But once it started, agriculture spread all over the face of the globe.

Agriculture allowed people to produce more food than they could by gathering wild plants. In other words, farming increased the carrying capacity of the land. Agriculture also led to food storing because, unlike hunters and gatherers, agriculturists stayed in one place year-round. Farmers stored food supplies to help them survive cold winters or dry summers.

The human population began to grow, partly because more food was available. Also, larger families are advantageous to people who practice agriculture. Children can help out on a farm even when they are very young. A family with many healthy children could plant more crops and raise more animals than could a small family.

At first the population grew slowly, as you can see in Figure 13-7. It took almost 10,000 years—until about A.D. 1800—for the human population to reach 1 billion.

Figure 13-6 A large family was advantageous to farmers because the children could help with the work. The more children a family had, the more food they could produce.

The Earth's human population is increasing by 149 people each minute, 8,956 each hour, 214,934 each day, and 78 million each year.

Figure 13-7 **After growing slowly for thousands of years, the human population began a period of rapid growth in the 1800s.**

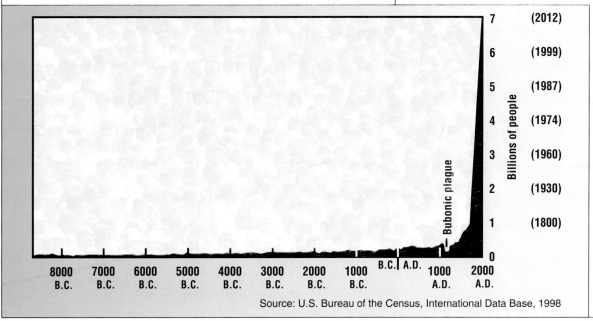

Billions of people	
7	(2012)
6	(1999)
5	(1987)
4	(1974)
3	(1960)
2	(1930)
1	(1800)
0	

Bubonic plague

8000 B.C. 7000 B.C. 6000 B.C. 5000 B.C. 4000 B.C. 3000 B.C. 2000 B.C. 1000 B.C. B.C. | A.D. 1000 A.D. 2000 A.D.

Source: U.S. Bureau of the Census, International Data Base, 1998

Number of Years to Add 1 Billion People		
	Year	Years to add
First billion	1800	all of human history
Second	1930	130
Third	1960	30
Fourth	1975	15
Fifth	1987	12
Projected		
Sixth	1999	12
Seventh	2012	13
Eighth	2026	14

Figure 13-8 **What is the projected population size for 2012?**

THE POPULATION CONTINUES TO GROW

After thousands of years of slow growth, the population doubled between 1800 and 1930, as shown in Figure 13-8. By 1975 the human population of Earth was 4 billion, and just 12 years later it had reached 5 billion. Why did the human population grow so quickly?

The answer is quite simple: people started living longer. Because of improvements in sanitation, nutrition, and medical care, more people survived childhood and grew up to have children of their own.

THE DEMOGRAPHIC TRANSITION

As we enter the twenty-first century, the human population is still growing rapidly. However, it may surprise you to learn that population growth is starting to slow. The reason is that birth rates have decreased in the developed countries and in some developing countries in Latin America and Asia. Frank Notestein, a scientist in the

THE STORIES BEHIND THE STATISTICS

Demographers often use mathematical formulas to predict population changes, but demography actually has more to do with understanding human behavior. Many complicated and interrelated factors influence people's choices about how many children to have and when to have them.

Take the people in the United States, for example. Hidden behind the demographic data found in census reports are the reflections of war and peace, economic boom and bust, and social change. Between the lines of

the dry statistics are the stories of how the lives of average Americans have been affected by the changes of the past century.

As America moved from the nineteenth into the twentieth century, the numbers reflect a phenomenal rise in the number of people coming to America from other countries. Almost 9 million immigrants came to America between 1900 and 1910, accounting for more than 50 percent of the growth in the population.

After the stock market crash of 1929, the United States was plunged into the Great Depression. Unemployment skyrocketed and millions of once-comfortable families found themselves in poverty. Many young people, convinced that the economy would soon improve, decided to wait a few years before marrying. And married couples

Since the first Europeans arrived, immigrants from all over the world have been eager to come to the United States to live.

CHAPTER 13

HIGHLIGHTS

SUMMARY

- Each population has a characteristic biotic potential. The biotic potential of a population represents the greatest growth possible if all members of the population reproduce at maximum capacity.

- If there are no limits to the growth of a population, it will grow exponentially. Factors such as scarce resources and disease provide environmental resistance, preventing populations from growing at their biotic potential.

- Carrying capacity is the maximum population a habitat can support indefinitely. A population that exceeds carrying capacity for long periods degrades its environment and reduces future carrying capacity.

- The transition from hunting and gathering to farming initiated the agricultural revolution, which allowed the human population to increase. Industrialization has led to further population increases by lowering the death rate.

- Today, the human population is growing at different rates in different parts of the world. The theory of demographic transition predicts that human populations will grow rapidly with increased industrialization, but will later stabilize as birth rates fall.

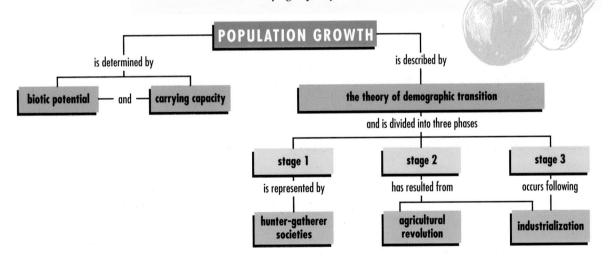

POPULATION GROWTH

is determined by

biotic potential — and — **carrying capacity**

is described by

the theory of demographic transition

and is divided into three phases

stage 1

is represented by

hunter-gatherer societies

stage 2

has resulted from

agricultural revolution

stage 3

occurs following

industrialization

EcoLog

Now that you've studied this chapter, revise your answers to the questions you answered at the beginning of the chapter, based on what you have learned.

❶ Could there ever be too many people on Earth? Why or why not?

❷ How could overcrowding in another part of the world affect you?

Vocabulary Terms

agricultural revolution (p. 337)

biotic potential (p. 333)

carrying capacity (p. 335)

environmental refugees (p. 345)

environmental resistance (p. 335)

hunter-gatherers (p. 336)

limiting resources (p. 335)

REVIEW

UNDERSTANDING VOCABULARY

1. For each pair of terms, explain the difference in their meanings.
   a. carrying capacity
      biotic potential
   b. environmental refugees
      hunter-gatherers
   c. demographic transition
      agricultural revolution

RELATING CONCEPTS

2. Copy the unfinished concept map below onto a sheet of paper. Then complete the concept map by writing the correct word or phrase in each box containing a question mark.

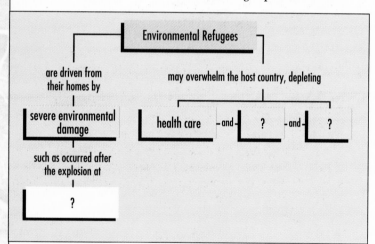

UNDERSTANDING CONCEPTS

Multiple Choice

3. Which of the following would cause a population to grow quickly?
   a. Many offspring are produced from each pregnancy.
   b. Reproduction usually occurs more than once in life.
   c. Members of the population begin to reproduce at a young age.
   d. Any of these factors would cause a population to grow quickly.

4. A population is most likely to grow explosively
   a. if the species is a very common one in the area.
   b. when a species moves into a new area of suitable habitat.
   c. after a natural disaster such as a flood.
   d. if there are few individuals of that species in the area to begin with.

5. A population will degrade its environment if
   a. the population stays above carrying capacity for a long period of time.
   b. it must share resources with many other species.
   c. it moves frequently from one habitat to another.
   d. it has a high biotic potential.

6. It took 130 years for the Earth's human population to double from 1 billion to 2 billion. How long did it take for the population to double again to 4 billion?
   a. 100 years
   b. 75 years
   c. 45 years
   d. 25 years

7. What was the most important factor leading to the explosive growth of the human population during the last 200 years?
   a. an increase in birth rates
   b. a decrease in death rates
   c. birth rates increased while death rates decreased
   d. a decrease in the number of people living in poverty

8. Because birth rates have begun to fall, demographers expect that the human population of the Earth will
   a. soon stabilize at the level it is today—about 6 billion.
   b. begin to decrease until it is only half the current population by the end of the twenty-first century.

c. continue to increase for a short time and then decrease to current levels by the end of the twenty-first century.

d. stabilize somewhere around 10 billion.

9. The cholera outbreak in Lima, Peru, was caused by

a. the inability to provide clean water for such a rapidly growing urban population.

b. inadequate medical care.

c. widespread malnutrition.

d. a population explosion of rats and disease-carrying insects.

10. Refugees from Somalia are considered environmental refugees because

a. they are fleeing war.

b. they are searching for food.

c. they are leaving an environmentally damaged homeland.

d. they are depleting the health-care system of their host country.

Short Answer

11. Explain how established species may be affected when a new species moves into an ecosystem.

12. If a population exceeds the carrying capacity of its habitat, what are the likely results?

13. How did our ancestors' lives change as a result of the agricultural revolution?

14. According to the theory of demographic transition, why do birth rates fall during the third stage?

15. Give two reasons why rapid population growth in rural areas results in the explosive growth of big cities in many countries.

INTERPRETING GRAPHICS

16. **Examine the table below.** It shows the numbers of people in different age groups in two populations that are now the same size. Make a bar graph of this data. From your graph, predict which population will grow the fastest. Explain the reason for your answer.

	0–10	11–20	21–30	31–40	41–50	51–60	61–70	71–80	81+
Population 1	500	700	1100	1800	1600	1100	600	200	100
Population 2	300	200	500	800	1200	1500	1300	1200	700

THINKING CRITICALLY

17. *Predicting Outcomes* Describe what you think life would be like for the average person over the next 50 years in a country that is now entering the third stage of demographic transition.

THEMES IN SCIENCE

18. *Patterns of Change* Explain why populations grow exponentially under ideal conditions.

CROSS-DISCIPLINE CONNECTION

19. *Health* Viruses are the cause of many infectious diseases. The common cold, for instance, can be caused by an assortment of different viruses. These viruses can be passed along in many different ways. For example, when someone with a cold coughs, the tiny droplets that are coughed out carry the cold viruses. These droplets, which float easily on air currents, can infect someone else if they are inhaled. Why do you think viral diseases spread more easily in an overpopulated area? What could be done to help slow the spread of such viruses?

PORTFOLIO ACTIVITY

At the library, find the *Demographic Yearbook/Annuaire démographique* published by the United Nations Department of Economic and Social Development, Statistical Division. Obtain copies for every other year going back 20 years (10 in all). For one continent, compile total population figures for each country, and then use the data to make a graph for each country. Using an encyclopedia, add the current average yearly income for each country to its graph. Then mount all of your graphs on a poster, and share the results of your research with your class.

 internetconnect

SCiLINKS. National Science Teachers Association
NSTA On-Line Resources **www.scilinks.org**

When you see a SciLinks logo, visit the NSTA Web site and type in the keyword. There you will find current information relevant to that section or topic.

INVESTIGATION

WHAT CAUSES A POPULATION EXPLOSION?

Can you predict the future? If you were a demographer, you might be asked to do so. Demographers try to determine how a population is changing, how it is likely to change in the future, and what factors will affect the rate of change. For example, both the number of children per family and the age at which people have children affect the rate of population growth. But which has a greater effect?

To explore this question, you will use population pyramids, like those shown below. These graphs show the distribution of age groups in a population at one point in time. The number of people in each age group is represented by a horizontal bar, with the bar on the bottom representing the youngest group.

MATERIALS

- notebook
- graph paper
- pen or pencil
- straightedge or ruler
- colored pencils or markers
- calculator

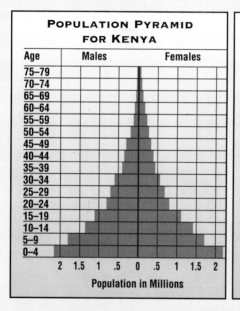

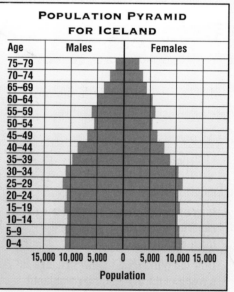

The population pyramid for Kenya, on the left, is typical of a rapidly growing population. Because there are so many young people, the number of women of child-bearing age will continue to increase each year, and so will the number of babies born. The population pyramid for Iceland, on the right, shows that about the same number of children have been born each year for the past 35 years. If current trends continue, the number of women of child-bearing age will stay about the same, and the population of Iceland will grow very little.

BACKGROUND

In this Investigation you will calculate future population trends for an imaginary city. To compare how different factors may affect population growth, different groups of students will do calculations using different assumptions. For simplicity, assume the following:

- In each age group, exactly half the population is male and half is female.
- Each woman has all of her children during a five-year period of her life.

- Everyone who is born lives to the age of 80 and then dies.
- No one moves into or out of the city.

PREDICT POPULATION CHANGES

1. Your teacher will divide the class into four groups. Each group will project population growth using different assumptions, as follows:
   - Group A will assume that each woman gives birth to five children when she is between 15 and 19 years old.
   - Group B will assume that each woman gives birth to five children when she is between 25 and 29 years old.
   - Group C will assume that each woman gives birth to two children when she is between 15 and 19 years old.
   - Group D will assume that each woman gives birth to two children when she is between 25 and 29 years old.

2. The table at right shows the 1995 population of our imaginary city. Use the data in the table to make an age-structure histogram for the city.

3. Make a table similar to the one shown, adding columns for the years 2000, 2005, and every fifth year until the year 2050.

4. Calculate the number of 0- to 4-year-olds in the year 2000. To do this, first determine how many women will have children between 1995 and 2000. (Hint: Remember that half the population in each age group is female.) Multiply that number by the number of children that each woman has.

5. Fill in the rest of the column for the year 2000, calculating the number of people in each age group older than 5 by "moving up" the population from 1995. For example, the number of 5- to 9-year-olds in 2000 will equal the number of 0- to 4-year-olds in 1995; the number of 10- to 14-year-olds in 2000 will equal the number of 5- to 9-year-olds in 1995; and so on.

6. Repeat the process described in steps 4 and 5 ten times to complete the table through the year 2050.

7. Add up the total population for each year. Plot these figures on a line graph.

8. Make a population pyramid for the population in 2050 from your table.

Age Group	1995 Population
75–79	500
70–74	600
65–69	700
60–64	800
55–59	900
50–54	1,000
45–49	1,250
40–44	1,500
35–39	2,000
30–34	2,500
25–29	3,000
20–24	4,000
15–19	5,000
10–14	6,500
5–9	8,000
0–4	10,000
Total	48,250

Most families in Kenya have many children, contributing to rapid population growth.

INTERPRET YOUR PREDICTIONS

9. Compare your graphs with those made by the other three groups. Which factor had a bigger effect on population growth, the number of children each woman had or the age at which women had children?

10. Did any of the graphs show no growth in population? Explain these results.

Families in Iceland, a country with a stable population, tend to be small.

351

Should POPULATION GROWTH Be Limited?

I n 1650 the human population was growing by 0.3 percent each year, doubling every 250 years. The Industrial Revolution raised standards of living, and medical advances increased life spans and reduced infant deaths. By 1970 there were 3.6 billion people, and the population was growing by 2.1 percent each year, doubling every 30 years. Today, the world's population is about 6 billion and could reach 10 to 14 billion in the twenty-first century. Some people believe that population growth must be limited to avoid exceeding the Earth's carrying capacity. But other people object, citing cultural, political, and economic reasons. Following are two points of view:

HUMAN POPULATION GROWTH MUST BE LIMITED

Like all organisms, humans depend on the Earth for food, water, shelter, and space. As the human population grows, people use more and more of the Earth's resources to fulfill these needs. Supporters of population control believe this has serious consequences for the Earth and for people.

Some people believe that uncontrolled population growth has stretched the Earth's resources to their limits. Most of the land suitable for farming has already been cultivated; little more land remains that could be used to grow more food. Forests around the world are being destroyed at an alarming rate to provide lumber and to clear land for agriculture. Overfishing has seriously depleted the number of fish in some marine fisheries. And water disputes will erupt as more and more rivers are diverted for irrigation and dams, thereby depleting the water supply of people in other areas.

Advocates of population control argue that the poorest countries in the world are those with the fastest-growing populations.

Controlling population growth would promote economic development in these countries, leading to a better standard of living for the citizens. If population growth continues unchecked, people in these countries will never have enough food, jobs, or education to go around.

Already, many people around the world do not get enough food or clean water to thrive, and starvation is a significant cause of death in some developing countries. Although population growth is only one factor in the world's food supply problems, the countries with the highest birth rates also experience the worst food shortages. Supporters of population control say that limiting growth will help ease food supply problems, allowing these countries to work toward a brighter economic future.

Population growth is contributing to a rapid depletion of the Earth's resources. For example, overfishing has reduced the annual catch in some marine fisheries.

Almost every bit of available space is taken in this area of Jodhpur, in northwestern India. Some people fear that if population growth is not limited, we may exceed the Earth's carrying capacity.

NO LIMITS SHOULD BE PLACED ON HUMAN POPULATION GROWTH

Population control is often opposed because of cultural values. In some societies, a higher value is placed on male children than on female children, so parents strive to have as many sons as possible. Such social pressure keeps birth rates high. Also, many countries lack social programs such as unemployment compensation or retirement plans. Parents rely on children to contribute to family earnings and to support them when they grow old. More children can earn more money and provide more support.

Religious values also may influence opinions about population control. Members of different religions have different average birth rates. Followers of some faiths think that birth control is immoral because they believe only God should determine the number of children that are meant to be born.

Other people believe population-control policies violate personal rights.

This agricultural scientist studies new strains of food crops. Some people believe that population control is unnecessary because technological advances, such as agricultural improvements, will solve the problems of a growing population.

These opponents point to a population-control measure that was used in China in the 1980s. The Chinese government offered couples incentives such as cash and good medical care if they pledged to have only one child. Penalties were given and the incentives taken away if a second child was born. Birth rates declined, but critics claim that the program inhibited freedom of choice. They believe that civil rights will suffer further if these policies are adopted elsewhere.

Some people oppose population control because they fear that a decrease in their country's population will slow economic growth and weaken the country's cultural identity. Other opponents of population control suggest that people are the world's greatest resource—more people will contribute more technological advances in agriculture and resource recycling that will lead to a higher standard of living for everyone, no matter how large the population.

This young boy is selling pastries on a street in Ho Chi Minh City, Vietnam. Children in some countries contribute to family earnings, so more children can mean a higher family income.

ANALYZE THE ISSUE

1. ***Making Decisions*** Using the decision-making model presented in Chapter 1, decide whether population growth should be limited. Explain your reasoning.

2. ***Analyzing Relationships*** China now uses education instead of penalties and incentives to try to lower the country's birth rate. Do you think this will be a more successful method? Why or why not?

353

TOWARD A SUSTAINABLE FUTURE

"Act, act, act. You can't just watch."

ANGELES SERRANO
COMMUNITY ACTIVIST, THE PHILIPPINES

SECTION 14.1

INTERNATIONAL COOPERATION

SECTION 14.2

ENVIRONMENTAL POLICIES IN THE UNITED STATES

EcoLog

Before you read this chapter, take a few minutes to answer the following questions in your EcoLog.

❶ What do you think the world will be like in 50 years? What could you do now to contribute to the kind of future you want?

❷ At which level of government—national, state, or local—can individual citizens have the most influence on environmental policies? Why?

INTERNATIONAL COOPERATION

AFTER READING THIS SECTION YOU SHOULD BE ABLE TO

❶ describe the results of the Earth Summit.

❷ describe international agreements relating to the environment.

The goals of environmental science go beyond understanding how we interact with the environment. They also include developing ways of living that permit humans and other species to survive and prosper into the future. This is what we call a sustainable future. A sustainable future can be achieved only if we can find ways to preserve and expand our environmental resources.

The solutions to our environmental problems require both individual and group action. Throughout this book, you have read about ways that individuals can help solve environmental problems. But what about group action? In this chapter you will learn how people can work together to help create a sustainable future. Cooperation is necessary at international, national, and local levels. The Case Study on pages 356–357 describes one example of international cooperation—the effort to regulate whale hunting.

THE EARTH SUMMIT: PROMISE AND PROBLEMS

Rio de Janeiro, Brazil, was the site of the 1992 Earth Summit, sponsored by the United Nations Conference on Environment and Development. For 12 days, hundreds of government officials (including 118 heads of state) worked together to hammer out international agreements. Thousands of environmentalists

Figure 14-1 **International cooperation is required to save species such as the orangutan.**

and indigenous people from around the world also gathered to share ideas and to influence the governmental proceedings. More than 9,000 reporters—the largest gathering of media in history—covered the proceedings.

The Earth Summit yielded some positive results. For example, Agenda 21 was passed. Agenda 21 is a blueprint for protecting the environment and promoting sustainable development. It includes an agreement by industrialized nations to help developing countries become industrialized without degrading the environment. However, Agenda 21 is nonbinding, which means that it cannot be enforced. Nations are very protective of their right to manage their own affairs. Consequently, binding agreements did not fare as well at the Earth Summit. The Earth Summit did, however, focus attention on global environmental issues and pave the way for future agreements.

A WHALE OF AN INTERNATIONAL CONTROVERSY

CASE STUDY

One species of whale, the blue whale, is the largest animal ever known to inhabit the Earth—bigger than even the dinosaurs. Blue whales reach lengths of up to 27.4 m (90 ft.) and weights as great as 136,000 kg (150 tons). Unfortunately, these enormous whales and other whale species have been hunted almost to the point of extinction. A look at the history of agreements between nations to regulate whale hunting illustrates both the problems and successes of international cooperation.

In 1949 the International Whaling Commission (IWC) voted to limit commercial whaling vessels to operations within a nation's territorial waters. However, France objected and invoked the IWC's "opting out" provision to ignore the ruling. Under this provision, any member nation can opt out of an IWC decision within 90 days. France was the first among many nations to use this loophole, which hampers the IWC's ability to enforce its own regulations. Over the years, member nations have frequently opted out of IWC attempts to protect threatened whale species.

The 1949 agreement also established a method of calculating the permitted quota of whales that could be killed. However, this method did not control whaling by species—a nation could "harvest" its quota by

The blue whale, the largest animal in the world, is also among the most hunted by whalers.

United States Departments and Agencies, and Environmental Laws They Enforce

Department of Agriculture
Soil Conservation Service
- Soil and Water Conservation Act

U.S. Forest Service—controls logging of national forests while protecting wildlife and forest ecosystems
- National Forests Management Act

Department of Commerce
National Oceanic and Atmospheric Administration
National Marine Fisheries Service
- Marine Mammal Protection Act

Environmental Protection Agency—responsible for research, setting guidelines, and enforcing regulations on numerous environmental issues
- National Environmental Policy Act
- Water Quality Act
- Safe Drinking Water Act
- Clean Water Act
- Clean Air Act
- Solid Waste Disposal Act
- Resource Conservation and Recovery Act
- Waste Reduction Act
- Toxic Substances Control Act
- Superfund (Comprehensive Environmental Response, Compensation, and Liability Act)
- Federal Insecticide, Fungicide, and Rodenticide Control Act

Department of Energy
- National Energy Act
- Public Utilities Regulatory Policies Act
- Electric Consumers Protection Act

Department of the Interior
- Wild and Scenic Rivers Act (with Department of Agriculture)

U.S. Fish and Wildlife Service
- Endangered Species Act
- National Wildlife Refuge System Act
- Alaska National Interest Lands Conservation Act (with Bureau of Land Management and U.S. Forest Service)
- Species Conservation Act
- Fish and Wildlife Improvement Act
- Fish and Wildlife Conservation Act

Bureau of Land Management—responsible for wilderness and other land management acts on land it controls
- Federal Land Policy and Management Act
- Taylor Grazing Act

National Park Service—manages nation's national parks
Bureau of Mines, Land Management, and Reclamation
- Surface Mining Control and Reclamation Act

Department of Justice—handles lawsuits involving federal environmental laws

Department of Transportation—responsible for jet noise, mass transit, pollution via transportation
- Quiet Communities Act

ENVIRONMENTAL IMPACT STATEMENTS

One of the laws listed in Figure 14-6 is the National Environmental Policy Act. This act led to the requirement that nearly all federal agencies file an **environmental impact statement (EIS)** for any proposed legislation or project that would have a significant effect on the quality of the environment. Environmental impact statements are also known as environmental assessments. Proposals for the construction of dams, highways, airports, and any other projects the federal government controls or subsidizes must be evaluated by an EIS.

An EIS states the need for a project, its environmental impact, and how such an impact can be minimized. After an EIS for a project is drafted, it must be available to the public for at least 90 days before the project begins. The public must have at least 45 days to comment on the project, and citizens' comments must be taken into account when the final EIS is written. Hundreds of plans for projects have been modified as a result of public and government reaction to these environmental assessments.

Environmental impact statements often do not work as their designers intended, however. An individual, business, or government agency planning a project may hire its own environmental

Figure 14-6 This table identifies federal departments, agencies, and environmental laws. Which department or agency has the major responsibility for preventing water pollution?

In a 1995 Gallup Poll, 63 percent of respondents said that they consider themselves environmentalists.

361

Figure 14-7 **Plans for construction of Two Forks Dam on the Platte River, southwest of Denver, Colorado, were modified as a result of an environmental impact statement. The Platte River is a crucial stop for migrating cranes, including these sandhill cranes.**

consulting firm to prepare the EIS. Because the consulting firm is paid by the interested party, it may be biased in presenting the data. However, independent environmental organizations may carefully review EISs and challenge the conclusions in court.

INFLUENCING NATIONAL POLICY

How can you influence national environmental policies? One way is to write or telephone your U.S. representative and senators and let them know what you think about proposed policies and laws. Another way to influence environmental policy is to join organizations that lobby Congress. Environmental organizations with large memberships can hire lobbyists to make sure that their points of view are heard.

It is sometimes difficult to keep up with proposed environmental laws. Citizens too often find out about environmental legislation after it has already been signed into law. One way to keep up with proposed legislation is to consult the *Environment and Energy Weekly,* published by the Environmental and Energy Study Institute. The bulletin lists all upcoming environmental and energy legislation in Congress. The same organization publishes the *Briefing Book on Environmental Issues and Legislation,* an annual summary of environmental legislation with quarterly updates. These publications may be found in the library.

STATE ENVIRONMENTAL POLICIES

The federal government may pass laws that set certain environmental standards, but these are generally considered minimum standards. Individual states are usually free to pass laws that set higher standards. For example, air pollution in California is so bad that the state has set very stringent air quality standards that far exceed federal guidelines.

Most states have one or more departments responsible for enforcing environmental laws. These departments often hold public hearings on proposed projects that may affect the environment in a community. You can influence state policy by expressing your views at these hearings and by contacting your state representative or the appropriate department in your state government.

FIELD ACTIVITY

Write a letter to your senator or representative about an environmental issue. Choose an issue you care about, and research it thoroughly. Go to the library and read all you can about the issue in books, magazines, and newspapers. In your letter, first state your position on the issue, and then offer facts to support your position. Be polite and respectful, and make sure to include your return address at the top of the letter.

LOCAL COMMUNITIES

Local governments have a significant impact on the environment. In most states, local governments and planning and zoning boards determine the type of development that will be allowed in their area. Consequently, local governments make decisions about issues such as the preservation or destruction of habitat, and human population density. Local governments also regulate recycling, sewage treatment, water quality, and other important concerns.

Government at the local level is often more responsive to citizen input than any other level of government—especially when citizens organize around an issue. People who are active in local government can have an immediate, tangible impact on their communities.

One common obstacle to local influence, however, is lack of coordination among neighboring communities. For example, your community may decide to limit commercial development. But if a neighboring community permits construction of a huge mall, traffic may become intolerable as shoppers drive through your town to the mall. In some states, different communities are trying to work together to preserve the environment. Communities along the Hudson River in New York, for instance, are cooperating to create a "greenway" of open space that will stretch hundreds of miles along the river. (See Figure 14-10 on the next page.)

Figure 14-8 **Anyone can express an opinion on environmental issues at state and local public hearings.**

Do you want to contribute to a healthier environment? Why not start in the grocery store? Find out how on pages 392–393.

Figure 14-9 **Your opinion can make a difference in whether your community looks like the one shown at left or the one shown above.**

363

Figure 14-10 **Because hundreds of communities and planning boards along the Hudson River worked together, the Hudson Valley Greenway will improve the quality of life for all residents of the region.**

SECTION REVIEW

1. What influence can an environmental impact statement have on the construction of a federal project? How can citizens influence an environmental impact statement?

2. At what level of government can individual citizens have the most influence? Explain your reasoning.

THINKING CRITICALLY

3. *Relating Concepts* Make a concept map showing how local governments can affect the environment. Include at least the following terms: local governments, habitat, population density, recycling, sewage treatment, and water quality.

4. *Expressing Viewpoints* Do you think people alive today have any obligation to future generations? Explain your answer.

INTO THE FUTURE

You have now learned about many ways we interact with and affect the environment. Since the first Earth Day, in 1970, we have discovered a great deal about pollution, atmospheric circulation, and the functioning of ecosystems.

Because our environmental knowledge has developed so rapidly, we have not had enough time to answer many important questions. For example, we are unsure how many species become extinct each year and how much a doubling of atmospheric carbon dioxide will raise the Earth's temperature. However, we do know enough to recognize environmental problems and to suggest possible solutions.

Ultimately, we must consider a range of values before we make complex decisions affecting the environment. These include environmental values, economic values, educational values, and so on. Science alone cannot answer questions such as, Should we set aside a nature reserve? or Should we require cars to be more energy-efficient? However, we can use scientific methods and knowledge to point the way toward decisions that protect the Earth. Every day, your actions contribute to the future of our planet. It is still within our power to build a sustainable future, a future in which the environment is not destroyed and all people have a decent standard of living.

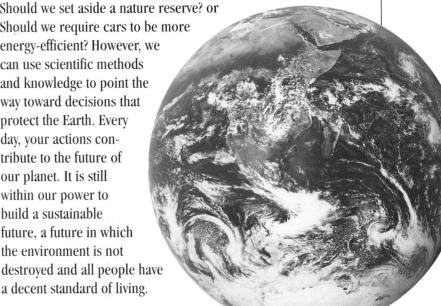

HIGHLIGHTS

SUMMARY

- The goals of environmental science are to study how we interact with the environment and to explore ways we can live sustainably.

- The 1992 Earth Summit, attended by representatives from most of the world's nations, was intended to develop world-wide environmental policy and foster solutions to current environmental problems.

- The United States government has established a set of environmental rules and regulations to govern environmental quality. For example, all major federally funded projects must be accompanied by an Environmental Impact Statement.

- States and communities can set their own environmental standards. These are usually more rigorous than federal standards.

- Citizens can influence environmental policy at all levels. The biggest barrier to influencing policy is lack of coordination.

- Much damage has been done to the environment, but much progress has also been made. With concerted action, a sustainable future is possible.

ENVIRONMENTAL POLICY

may be

| international | national | statewide | community level |

defined by

commissions	the Earth Summit	federal laws and regulations	state laws and regulations	local laws and regulations
such as the	highlighted different needs of	require an	which citizens influence by attending	can be influenced by
IWC	wealthy and poor nations	environmental impact statement	public hearings	citizen coalitions

for most

federally funded projects affecting the environment

Ecolog

Now that you've studied this chapter, revise your answers to the questions you answered at the beginning of the chapter, based on what you have learned.

❶ What do you think the world will be like in 50 years? What could you do now to contribute to the kind of future you want?

❷ At which level of government—national, state, or local—can individual citizens have the most influence on environmental policies? Why?

Vocabulary Terms

Environmental Impact Statement (EIS)
(p. 361)

REVIEW

UNDERSTANDING VOCABULARY

1. Explain what an environmental impact statement is and how it works.

RELATING CONCEPTS

2. Copy the unfinished concept map below onto a sheet of paper. Then complete the concept map by writing the correct word or phrase in each box containing a question mark.

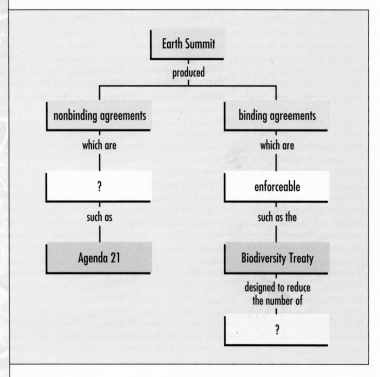

UNDERSTANDING CONCEPTS

Multiple Choice

3. The Earth Summit was
   a. designed to force all nations of the world to submit to an international environmental policy.
   b. intended to help diverse nations develop common environmental policy guidelines.
   c. a corporate convention.
   d. a complete failure as an instrument of policy.

4. At the Earth Summit, rich and poor nations
   a. agreed that their needs were exactly the same.
   b. agreed to disagree.
   c. realized that their needs were different.
   d. could not reach agreement on any matters of substance.

5. Most of the agreements drawn up at the Earth Summit
   a. became international law.
   b. were nonbinding.
   c. will be administered by the United Nations.
   d. will expire after five years.

6. The function of an environmental impact statement is
   a. to clarify the effect that a project would have on the environment.
   b. to generate a record of the ongoing impact to the environment of existing structures.
   c. to satisfy international legal requirements.
   d. to limit development to a bare minimum.

7. State and local environmental regulations
   a. are generally less strict than federal standards.
   b. are generally more strict than federal standards.
   c. may be more or less strict than federal standards.
   d. are nonexistent; all environmental regulation takes place at the federal level.

8. Environmental impact statements
   a. must be filled out by anyone carrying out any project that has any effect on the environment.
   b. are filled out for both the state and federal governments.
   c. are filled out for nearly all federally funded projects that have significant effects on the environment.
   d. are no longer required.

9. Air pollution standards set by California are

   a. much more stringent than federal requirements.

   b. much less stringent than federal requirements.

   c. nonbinding.

   d. a model for the rest of the nation.

10. The Environmental Impact Statement process is intended to

   a. evaluate the potential environmental impact of proposed projects.

   b. give the public an opportunity to comment on the project.

   c. provide the government with biased data.

   d. both a and b

11. Local governments do not regulate

   a. recycling.

   b. sewage treatment.

   c. water quality.

   d. the filing of environmental impact statements.

12. Environmental science can

   a. provide us with decisions about the environment.

   b. point the way toward decisions that protect our planet.

   c. point the way toward decisions that infect the Earth.

   d. tell us whether we should protect an area of land.

Short Answer

13. Why are gatherings such as the Earth Summit necessary?

14. Why are state environmental regulations no less stringent than federal regulations?

15. Why might there be fundamental disagreements between rich and poor nations regarding environmental policy?

16. What are some ways in which citizens can influence environmental policy?

INTERPRETING GRAPHICS

17. **Examine the graphs below.** They show that federal money is not spent exactly as citizens think it should be spent. Propose an explanation for this.

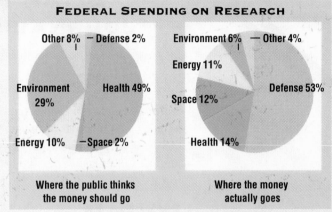

FEDERAL SPENDING ON RESEARCH

Other 8% — Defense 2%
Environment 29%
Health 49%
Energy 10% — Space 2%

Where the public thinks the money should go

Environment 6% — Other 4%
Energy 11%
Space 12%
Defense 53%
Health 14%

Where the money actually goes

THINKING CRITICALLY

18. *Communicating Ideas* One major barrier to achieving significant environmental reform is lack of enforcement. Nations cannot be held responsible in any real way for their environmental abuses because they won't give up sovereignty to a higher governing body. How might you convince skeptical nations to give up sovereignty in this matter?

THEMES IN SCIENCE

19. *Scale and Structure* A favorite expression of the environmental movement is "Think globally, act locally." Explain how action on a local scale can end up having global impact.

CROSS-DISCIPLINE CONNECTION

20. *Biology and History* The developed nations have urged developing nations to take better care of their resources. Developing nations have responded that they are just doing what the developed nations did in the past. How valid is this claim? Do a little research to find out.

PORTFOLIO ACTIVITY

Write a proposal for the creation of a new governing body that would have the responsibility of monitoring and enforcing a uniform environmental policy for all of the world's nations. Describe the agency's responsibilities and characteristics, and the skills needed by its officials to do the job. Describe also the methods the agency would use to monitor and enforce environmental policy.

 internetconnect

SCLINKS™ National Science Teachers Association
NSTA On-Line Resources **www.scilinks.org**

When you see a SciLinks logo, visit the NSTA Web site and type in the keyword. There you will find current information relevant to that section or topic.

INVESTIGATION

BE AN ENVIRONMENTAL JOURNALIST

In almost all cases, governmental agencies take public opinion into account before passing environmental legislation. The debates are reported by the media in newspapers and magazines as well as on television and radio. In addition, concerned individuals and groups often try to win support for their side of the debate through advertisements of their own. Sometimes the truth gets stretched a little, but usually there are valid arguments on each side of an environmental issue. An environmental journalist investigates these issues thoroughly and reports on what he or she has learned.

BACKGROUND

In this activity, you will find out what environmental legislation is currently being considered by your federal, state, county, or local government. After picking a topic that concerns you, you will research the progress of the pending legislation, taking care to identify biases in your sources of information. By investigating both sides of the issue, you will be able to write an educated and informative report on what you have found.

BE AN INVESTIGATIVE REPORTER

1. Look through several newspapers, magazines, and other publications to find out what environmental issues are being considered by legislators at various levels of government. If a computerized database is available at your school or local library, use it to quickly locate articles by topic or keyword. When you find a relevant article, summarize it briefly in your notebook, stating what the issue is about, who is involved in the controversy, and where you read about it.

MATERIALS

- back issues of newspapers and magazines
- tape
- scissors
- notebook
- pen or pencil

The general public depends on articles from magazines and newspapers to learn about environmental issues and legislation.

Student Group Seeks Broader Agenda for Environmental Movement

PROTECTING BIODIVERSITY

BY BRUCE BABBITT

Government to Study Quality of Indoor Air

River report finds toxic chemicals

2. Choose an issue that is important to you, and spend two or three days researching it thoroughly. You may be able to read current newspaper and magazine articles to learn more, but you will probably have to visit your school or local library to find back issues for further information. The library may also have books or other publications that relate to the environmental issue you choose.

ANALYZE YOUR FINDINGS

3. When you find a source, answer the following questions about it:

- Who is the author, and what type of source is it (magazine, pamphlet, etc.)?
- Does the source present both sides of the issue? If not, which side is the author arguing for?
- What are the main points that the source makes?
- Does any of the information conflict with other sources that you have read?
- What logical flaws do you find in the arguments people give?
- What biases (either information omitted or information presented in a misleading way) do you find in the research sources? Explain how the way an issue is reported may affect public opinion about it.

LET THE WORLD KNOW

4. Write a newspaper article about your issue. Include information about the people and organizations that are involved, the legislation, and the various opinions expressed by the public. Write your report as if it were a feature article in a newspaper, using headlines and, if possible, pictures with captions.
At the end of your article you may present your own opinion, but in the rest of the article, you should try to be as unbiased as possible.

5. Let your classmates read your article. Discuss the issues with them, and answer any questions they may have. Are their opinions the same as yours?

EXPLORE FURTHER

6. The League of Conservation Voters tracks the voting record of members of Congress on all federal environmental legislation. If you are interested, you may contact the League to get a summary record of how your representative and senators voted on various environmental laws. If possible, you may want to telephone your representative and find out his or her opinions on specific environmental issues. Contact the League of Conservation Voters by calling 202-785-8683 or by writing to the League at 1707 L Street, NW, Suite 750, Washington, D.C. 20036.

Environmental legislation often dictates how land may be used, whether for commercial and residential development, for recreation, or as a wilderness refuge.

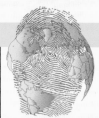

Making a DIFFERENCE

building toward THE FUTURE

To Michael Reynolds, a house is not just a home, and old tires and empty soda cans are not just trash. For more than 25 years, this Taos, New Mexico, architect has been designing and building energy-efficient houses out of automobile tires, cans, and other discarded items. These houses, which Michael now calls "Earthships," not only provide a comfortable, affordable place for people to live but also contribute to a sustainable future for our planet.

To Michael, an Earthship is not just a home—it's also a lifestyle.

In 1970 a television report about the growing number of beverage cans littering the streets and fields of America started Michael thinking about ways that trash could be used to build houses. Through many years of experimentation, he found that sturdy walls could be built by packing soil into old tires, stacking the tires like bricks, and covering them with cement or adobe, a heavy clay often used in buildings in the Southwest. Michael had this design tested by structural engineers to ensure that the walls would meet or surpass any existing building code requirements. One engineer even commented that the design could be used to construct dams!

The tire-stack design is used for three of the outside walls of an Earthship. These walls are approximately 1 m (3 ft.) thick, and this large mass causes the walls to act like a battery, storing energy from the sun and releasing it when needed. Also, the base of the Earthship is built below the frost line (the deepest level to which the ground freezes). Below this line, the ground maintains a constant temperature—around 15°C (59°F)—and walls anchored below the frost line

Earthships often look more like natural land formations than like houses.

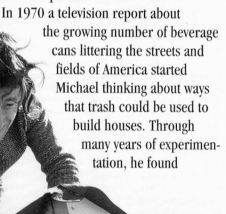

Michael Reynolds uses discarded materials, such as used soda cans, to construct environmentally friendly houses.

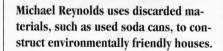

usually stay at that temperature, too. The fourth wall, which faces south, is constructed completely of glass to capture as much sunlight as possible. In the winter, the tire-stack walls hold in the sun's warmth; in the summer, cool air enters through windows in the front while warm air escapes through a skylight in the back.

Even the soil that is excavated for the site is used to build the house. Some of the soil is pounded into the tires to construct the walls, and the remaining soil is piled against the outside of these walls and on top of the roof (constructed of beams) for further insulation. The most suitable location for this design is a south-facing slope, where the Earthship can simply be "carved" out of the hill. Often, Earthships look more like natural formations of land than houses.

Inside, walls between rooms are constructed by embedding empty beverage cans into mortar or mud. If these walls are covered with cement and then painted with latex paint or some other durable finish, they look just like walls constructed with conventional materials. Other inside surfaces, including stairs and even bathtubs, can be built using the beverage-can technique. Because the cans are so lightweight, this method can even be used to create dynamic interior structures such as arches and domes.

Earthships are typically built to obtain electricity from photovoltaic cells that convert sunlight to electricity. All household water is supplied by rainwater that is collected on the roof. Wastewater from sinks, tubs, and the laundry room is recycled to nourish plants in the greenhouse, which can provide a sustainable source of food. With these features, Earthship inhabitants use fewer of the Earth's resources and often have *no* utility bills.

Because Earthships are kinder to the environment and less expensive to buy and maintain, more and more people are choosing them instead of conventional homes. Over 1000 Earthships have already been built, most of them in the Southwest. However, the design can be used anywhere. In fact, Earthships have been built in Florida, Vermont, Canada, Mexico, Bolivia, and Japan. Wetter environments simply require that the house be built entirely above the ground and use more cans and tires.

More tires in the design certainly wouldn't be a problem. According to the Environmental Protection Agency, more than 250 million tires are discarded in this country every year. But most landfills do not accept tires because of their tendency to rise to the surface even when the landfill is covered over. Tire dealers usually pay to have used tires hauled away to stockpile areas, where they sit indefinitely. Earthships provide one way to diminish the stockpiles.

A greenhouse, built along the Earthship's southern glass wall, can provide residents with a sustainable food source.

The tire-stack design of the outer walls accounts for much of the Earthship's energy efficiency. These tire stacks will be covered with cement or adobe for a finished exterior.

Michael enthusiastically shares his Earthship concept with others. He has published manuals with complete instructions for building an Earthship, and he leads seminars for prospective builders. Architecture students often study with him and learn his techniques. And he has established three self-sustaining communities of Earthships in the mountains near Taos. To Michael, an Earthship is not just a home— it's also a lifestyle. His dedication to designing Earth-friendly homes is a result of his commitment to "reducing the stress involved in living on the Earth, for both humans and the planet."

ENVIRONMENTAL FILMMAKER

Haroldo Castro considers himself a "citizen of the planet." It's easy to see why: he was born in Italy to a Brazilian father and a French mother, he was educated in France, he speaks five languages, and he has visited more than 80 countries. Furthermore, Haroldo has devoted his life to improving the planet's well-being. He has accomplished this by taking photographs, writing books and articles, and producing award-winning video documentaries. Haroldo works for Conservation International (CI), an environmental organization that establishes partnerships with countries all over the world to develop and implement ecosystem conservation projects.

> ▸The military thought we were terrorist guerrillas and surrounded us with machine guns. I think you might call that a crisis situation!

▶ **What do you do at CI?**

Haroldo: I am the International Communications Project Director. What I do is make documentaries and take photographs of CI's conservation projects. These videos and photos are designed to teach people how to better interact with their local environment. Most of our work is done in countries with tropical rain forests, such as those in Latin America, Asia, and Africa.

▶ **Can you describe one of your documentaries?**

Haroldo: Sure. We made a documentary in Guatemala about products that local people can sustainably harvest from the northern tropical forests.

After one year of production, we completed a half-hour documentary called *Between Two Futures.* CI then distributed the video to government officials, environmental organizations, university professors, and teachers. We also encouraged its broadcast on TV channels in Guatemala and other Latin American countries.

The film has been a real success story. I think our ability to be culturally sensitive to the Guatemalan people contributed in large part to the film's success. Each of us who worked on the project had a Latin American background.

Haroldo Castro (left) directing a video crew in Rio de Janeiro, Brazil

We worked closely with the Guatemalan people; we had a Guatemalan narrator and we used only Guatemalan music. If you are trying to deliver an important message to people of a different culture, it's important to step into their shoes and deliver it from their point of view.

▶ **What is your educational background and experience?**

Haroldo: Although I do have a degree in economics, my best education and training has definitely come from traveling and other real-life experiences. I learn by studying the diverse cultures around the world.

Once I spent two years traveling around Latin America by van; another time I drove from Europe to India in six months. These experiences are my education. When my friends say that it is necessary to have a master's or doctor's degree to gain respect, I respond by saying that I have a Ph.D. in "Travelology." That's a degree I think my real-world experience on the road has earned me.

▶ **Do you ever have to deal with crisis situations?**

Haroldo: [laughter] If there is *not* a crisis when I'm traveling, I'm worried—it usually means there will be a disaster later! Anyone who travels a lot has to deal with crises, such as getting sick on local food or getting robbed. I've had equipment stolen from Lebanon to Peru!

I would like to tell you a story. Two years ago we were working in a remote rain-forest region of Mexico for 10 days. When we were ready to leave, we boarded a small plane and set out for the nearest commercial airport, only to learn that it had been closed. We were forced to go to a nearby military airport instead.

When we landed and began to unload our large boxes of equipment, the military personnel got very nervous. We looked pretty grungy—unshaven and covered with mud. It was obvious that we'd been in the rain forest awhile. They thought we were terrorist guerrillas and surrounded us with machine guns. For three hours we pleaded our case, and finally they let us go. I think you might call that a crisis situation!

▶ **If a high school student were to ask you what he or she could do to help the environment, what would your answer be?**

Haroldo: I would say . . . Learn all you can, appreciate the world around you, and follow your passion. If you like photography, go out and take pictures of things that leave you with good and bad impressions. If you like gardening, start experimenting with seedlings. Whatever your interest, my advice is, *just go for it!*

Haroldo Castro filming slash-and-burn agriculture (left)

For Haroldo, capturing on film images like this Guatemalan girl holding a hummingbird allows him to recall rich travel experiences.

MORE ON THIS CAREER

Many government offices, publishers, and environmental organizations have in-house communications departments for producing films or photographs. Have a librarian help you make a list of such places, and then call them for more information and for possible volunteer or internship ideas.

While you're at the library, look through *The Guide to International Film and Video Festivals* for any mention of environmental film festivals in your area. Haroldo recommends attending a film festival if at all possible. "Doing so," he says, "would give you the invaluable opportunity to see some of the best films produced and to talk to the people who made them." If you can't find the guide or would like further information, contact the **Association of Independent Video & Filmmakers** at 304 Hudson Street, 6th Floor, New York, NY 10013.

RESEARCH WILDLIFE BIOLOGIST

Many people imagine wildlife biologists wrestling large game animals to the ground, slapping radio collars around their necks, and then creeping through the forest for weeks on end to study the creatures. According to Mariko Yamasaki, research wildlife biologist for the U.S. Department of Agriculture, Forest Service, there's a lot more to wildlife biology than that. To Mariko, "nature is fascinating on many, many levels, from the tiniest ant all the way up to charismatic animals such as bears and wolves. We have to get away from the notion that animals with feathers or fur and big brown eyes are more important than slimy, scaly creatures with beady eyes. All organisms have a role—we must be sure that their contribution to the big picture is recognized."

To Mariko Yamasaki, every creature, no matter how small or seemingly insignificant, has an important role in this biosphere. Below, she is searching for salamanders in the wild. Above, she and an associate are examining a salamander under a microscope.

▶ **What is your educational background and experience?**

Mariko: My background is basically a long and colorful stringing together of different experiences. I have bachelor's degrees in anthropology and zoology and a master's degree in natural resources (specific to wildlife). By the time I got out of school in the late 1970s, I came up against a surprising attitude—people in my home state really couldn't conceive of having female biologists supervising in the field. So I looked outside my home state. I ended up studying bald eagles for the Bureau of Land Management out West. This sort of snowballed into a permanent appointment in Washington as a wildlife biologist for the Bureau of Land Management. Today I work at the Northeastern Forest Experiment Station, where I do research in forested lands that cover a 200 mi. radius, including parts of Maine and New Hampshire.

▶ **What organisms are you studying in the field right now?**

Mariko: I'm studying small mammals, such as mice, shrews, voles, and squirrels. My colleagues and I also study insectivorous bats, migratory birds, and terrestrial salamanders. These are animals that we know something about, such as their basic biology, but we don't know how they respond to forest management. We're looking at these critters to get a sense of how they fit into the bigger picture.

▶ **What types of questions are you trying to answer about these animals?**

Mariko: One question my colleagues and I are trying to answer right now is how terrestrial salamanders respond to "even-aged management" of northern hardwoods. Even-aged management involves harvesting a large area

> ## We have to get away from the notion that animals with feathers or fur and big brown eyes are more important than slimy, scaly creatures with beady eyes.

of trees whose ages are within 20 years of each other. Foresters often use even-aged management because it is an efficient means of harvesting large amounts of timber at one time. My hypothesis is that when a large area of trees has been harvested, the ground temperature might change because the area is suddenly exposed to direct sunlight. This might affect the population and distribution of terrestrial salamanders in a negative way. I use the data I gather to make recommendations to forest managers about how they can manage tracts of forest to best support the needs of salamanders and other wildlife.

▶ **Do you work with other people a lot?**

Mariko: There's an old stereotype that a wildlife biologist leads a solitary life studying nature. This simply isn't true—it's important to know how to work with people and how to understand and deal with a variety of viewpoints. There is rarely a day that I sit alone in my office. But I will say that a wildlife biologist does have some control over the matter—generally, you can work with people as much or as little as you want.

▶ **Do you ever have to deal with crisis situations?**

Mariko: Not really, but I do see a lot of controversy, particularly related to wildlife and the use of natural resources. My work has often become the object of heated debate. Some people will support my findings wholeheartedly, while others call them worthless. There are any number of ways of dealing with this kind of pressure. I've found that it's real important to get my information together and analyze it as thoroughly as possible so that I can really stand behind what I'm saying. It's also important to realize that everyone is entitled to an opinion.

Mariko wants to know if the way in which trees are harvested from forested areas like this one affects the survival of terrestrial salamanders.

▶ **What are the most interesting or exciting aspects of your work?**

Mariko: Oh heavens! Being out and observing the natural world. Being able to test hypotheses. Being up real early on a bird survey. It's never the same twice. I also enjoy discovering something new—there's nothing any more special than that. There's a lot out there! The scale of things to observe and study is mind-boggling.

▶ **What advice might you give to someone who is searching for a career?**

Mariko: I think it's important to do something you are really interested in. My career, just like anybody else's, is not always a bed of roses. But if you really care about what you do, you can get beyond the problems and complications inherent to any job. It's also important to think that you've got something to contribute. I think that I can help contribute to the way people view wildlife, and that's important to me.

This group of community leaders, politicians, and scientists is discussing how best to use the natural resources of a forested region in Maine.

▶ MORE ON THIS CAREER

If you are interested in learning more about a career in wildlife biology, contact **The Wildlife Society,** 5410 Grosvenor Lane, Bethesda, MD 20814-2197 or the **American Institute of Biological Sciences,** 144 Eye Street NW, Suite 200, Washington, D.C. 20005.

375

LANDFILL MANAGER

Do you think careers associated with waste are dirty, uninspiring, and of little value? After listening to James Bailey describe his work for a few minutes, it's obvious that this common impression is far from accurate. James manages two landfills in Atlanta, Georgia, and he and his team of employees are dedicated to protecting the area's environment and the quality of life for Atlanta's citizens.

> **I often tell students that what I do for a living is play in the dirt—which is properly disposed-of waste!**

Above, James Bailey is doing management planning in his Atlanta office. Below, he is inspecting a landfill site to make sure that waste has been converted to a harmless dirtlike substance.

▶ **What does your daily work involve?**
James: I often tell students that what I do for a living is play in the dirt—which is properly disposed-of waste! You see, it's my job to make sure that waste is converted into a harmless dirtlike substance and that it does not contain dangerous levels of pollutants. To do this I review a lot of reports, go out to the landfill sites and examine actual samples taken from the deposited waste, and make sure that the sites I manage do not get overloaded.

▶ **What inspired you to enter the field of waste management?**
James: In August of 1965, I was a kid when riots broke out in the Watts neighborhood of Los Angeles, California. The damage and destruction caused by the riots really made an impression on me. I remember thinking that if people just had a nice place to live, such destruction would not be happening.

Since I really enjoyed building things at the time, I started to think about how great it would be to build a city. I remember thinking about how I could work with architects and other people to plan and build cities that would instill pride and inspiration in the people who lived there.

▶ **So how did those ideals lead to your current position?**
James: Well, I never forgot that goal. After a tour of duty in the U.S. Army, I went to school at Clark-Atlanta University to get a degree in urban planning. Then I went to Georgia Institute of Technology to pursue a master's degree in city planning with an emphasis on industry and the environment. After that, I got my current job, and my career began.

Now I feel that I can help build a name for landfills—a name of respect and quality.

I'm also gaining a lot of firsthand knowledge about what goes into the development of a city. You see, it's impossible to manage the waste of a city without knowing what types of businesses and housing developments exist in the city, how they are distributed, and how they function. In addition, it takes a lot of our time and energy to manage the waste produced by a city and to look for ways to *minimize* it in order to maintain a balance with the environment.

▶ **Can you give us an example of a specific city-planning situation you've been faced with?**

James: Sure! As you probably know, the Olympic games were held in Atlanta in 1996. In order to prepare for this huge event I had to consider many issues, such as: How many restroom facilities will be needed for the games? Where will they be needed? What will happen to the waste from those facilities each day? Who will be responsible for handling the waste materials? What kind of strains will be placed on our current system of waste management? I met with city planners and Olympic officials to discuss these questions, and together we developed an effective plan for handling these problems.

▶ **Have you encountered much controversy about whether landfilling is a safe method for disposing of waste?**

James: Oh, yes! Many people, including government officials, politicians, business people, community organizers, and individuals, are concerned about the safety of landfills for individuals and for the environment as a whole.

James helps reduce the fears and concerns of individuals by giving them tours of the landfills he manages.

▶ **What do you do to reassure those who disapprove of landfilling?**

James: I show them our facilities and demonstrate our elaborate system of safety checks and balances. By doing that, I can reassure people that our waste facilities are safe for local residents and the environment as a whole. You'd be surprised how many individual residents, school teachers, students, and politicians support our efforts. I've even gotten letters of approval from citizens and politicians who oppose the whole concept of landfilling waste. We've also had a few citizens bake cookies for us! And I'll never forget one letter I got from a third-grade student who had recently toured our facilities. The student wrote, "Thank you. I want to be an environmentalist when I grow up."

▶ **What personal qualities do you consider most important for a person in your career?**

James: Technical aptitude, broad-based education, common sense, open-mindedness, and the ability to define options and consider better ways of doing things. In addition, the person must have an appreciation for the environment. Finally, the person must show a passion and dedication for his or her work. That passion should not be fueled by a desire for instant rewards, but instead driven by the knowledge that what he or she is doing is making a real, long-term difference in the world.

James's work helps keep the city of Atlanta beautiful.

MORE ON THIS CAREER

For more information on this career, contact one of the following organizations.
Environmental Protection Agency, 401 M Street SW, Washington, D.C. 20460
Air and Waste Management Association, Gateway Building 1, 3rd Floor, Pittsburgh, PA 15222

377

FISH AND WILDLIFE TROOPER

Someone's been killing deer out of season in an Oregon forest. Diane Stout, trooper and law enforcement officer for the Oregon State Police, Fish and Wildlife Division, wants to catch the offender. So she sets up a decoy—an artificial deer—and hides in some nearby bushes. After waiting in silence for some time, she hears something. A large man with a 30.06-caliber rifle appears in the distance and slowly raises his gun toward the decoy. Diane watches silently. Suddenly, though, he becomes nervous. He jerks down the gun and takes off in a full sprint. Diane leaps out of the bushes and pursues. But as she nears the offender, he turns and aims his rifle at her. Suddenly Diane's life is in danger . . .

Diane Stout stakes out a poacher in this Oregon forest

I may find some offenders, but they're almost always quick to comply. But every once in a while I'll run into an angry person who will challenge me.

▶ **Is this sort of thrilling adventure something you encounter every day?**

Diane: No, but I'm never really sure what's going to happen on any given day. Some days are really exciting. Other days I'll spend all my time patrolling and not have a single problem. I may find some offenders, but they're almost always quick to comply. But every once in a while I'll run into an angry person who will challenge me.

We have kind of a unique situation here in Oregon in that the Oregon State Police has a Fish and Wildlife law enforcement division. So I'm a state trooper who has the authority to enforce all Oregon state laws. However, my primary job responsibility is to enforce fish and wildlife and environmental protection laws. As a state trooper, I am also required to provide assistance in any kind of accident. This is a lot of responsibility—I have to be well-schooled in first aid, firearms, and emergency medicine, as well as many laws and regulations.

▶ **So what does your daily work involve?**

Diane: Well, I begin each day by determining where to direct my time. I consider what hunting seasons are in progress and what problems we are likely to have from people who are hunting out of season or who are hunting incorrectly. I also consider any new or seasonal fishing regulations that are in effect, and any problems we may have with regard to those. In addition, I communicate with wildlife biologists who monitor game populations and habitat conditions. They let me know if they've seen any problems or have any concerns that I could check out. Also, we sometimes get complaints from residents about people who are poaching, dumping hazardous substances, or harming the environment in some other way. So, because my priorities are always different, each day (or night, if I do a night patrol) is unique.

▶ **What is the connection between your job and the environment?**
Diane: The areas I patrol are full of valuable natural resources—trees, lakes, rivers, wildlife. People use these resources in a variety of ways. Whether the main interest is fishing or camping or hunting or boating or whatever, I want those resources available for people to enjoy for a long time. So my job is to help keep the areas safe and clean, and the ecosystems healthy.

▶ **Does seeing the "bad side" of people all the time ever get to you?**
Diane: Yes, of course. People litter and dump hazardous wastes and abuse all sorts of hunting and fishing regulations. Sometimes their offenses are shocking, and depressing! But by informing people of the laws and enforcing the laws, I think that I'm actually doing something to improve the situation. So I feel really, really good about what I do for a living. Besides, there are a lot of terrific people out there too, so it's not just the bad ones that I run into.

▶ **What are the most frustrating aspects of your job?**
Diane: Limited funding. There are only four officers patrolling two counties. I have Polk County, Oregon, which includes a 60 mi. radius. It's a big area, and I often wish I could be in several places at once. We definitely need more enforcement, but the funds just aren't available.

This is especially true in situations that require investigation. For example, when I

Part of Diane's job involves informing people of new fishing and hunting regulations.

find barrels of chemicals dumped along a rural river, it's seldom obvious who left them there. So I have to conduct an investigation that may involve court orders and search warrants and trials. Undertaking an investigation of this sort takes a lot of time. Knowing that you don't have the time to really do it right is frustrating.

▶ **What is your educational background and experience?**
Diane: I have three years of college in industrial drafting, one year of training as a medical assistant, and five years of police reserve experience.

▶ **Do you work with other people?**
Diane: No, not on a regular basis. If there's a case to investigate or prosecute, I may work with a lawyer or another officer. But you do have to like people to be effective in this job because so much time is spent talking to people about what they're doing!

MORE ON THIS CAREER

If you are interested in becoming a law enforcement officer in environmental protection, contact the United States Department of the Interior, **U.S. Fish and Wildlife Service,** Department of Labor, Washington, D.C. 20240; the United States Department of the Interior, **National Park Service,** Department of Labor, Washington, D.C. 20240; or the **National Park Rangers Association,** P.O. Box 108, Larned, KS 67550.

ENVIRONMENTAL LAWYER

Jana L. Walker used to be a nurse, but now she's showing her concern for individuals and their safety in a different way. She owns her own law practice that focuses on environmental protection and Native American issues.

Jana is a member of the Cherokee nation. She supports the "Great Law" of the Six Nations Iroquois Confederacy: "In our every deliberation, we must consider the impact of our decisions on the next seven generations." According to Jana, the Great Law is particularly relevant to environmental issues. This is because, she says, it reflects the need to establish laws to protect our natural resources for future generations *now*, before lands and waters are permanently damaged and species are driven to extinction.

Jana L. Walker, shown here next to the Río Grande in New Mexico, is working to improve the quality of river water running through tribal lands.

▶ **What inspired you to change from nursing to law?**

Jana: Well, I'd always been interested in law, but I guess I never thought I'd be able to do it. But after seven years of nursing, I was really ready for a more independent career. So I made getting through law school my goal. Now I know that it's never too late to get additional education or to fulfill a personal goal.

After law school, I worked at a couple of different law firms—one large and one small. Then I decided that what I really wanted to do was practice law on my own. So I started a solo law practice to focus on Indian and environmental law issues. These issues are very important to me as an inhabitant of the planet, as an attorney, and as an Indian.

▶ **What is the relationship between environmental law and the Indian nations?**

Jana: Well, tribal lands have suffered from many environmental problems. You see, although the first federal environmental laws were enacted several decades ago, those laws did not address Indian tribes and reservations. And the tribes lacked the money to start these programs on their own. As a result, there are now over 53 million acres of tribal lands that have had little or no environmental protection for many years. So the environmental movement that took off in other parts of the country during the 1970s is only now reaching many Indian lands.

▶ **What kinds of environmental problems do you encounter?**

Jana: The problems range from leaking underground storage tanks to acid rain to radioactive contamination to water pollution to illegal, or "wildcat," dumping of trash.

▶ **Those are tough problems. What can you do about them?**

Jana: I help tribes set up regulatory programs to protect the wildlife, land, air, and water resources of the reservations. I also review environmental bills that could affect Indian lands to determine whether they would have a positive or negative impact. Then I lobby for those bills that would help tribal programs. It's an awful lot of reading and writing—definitely not what a television lawyer does!

The environmental movement that took off in other parts of the country during the 1970s is only now reaching many Indian lands.

The work Jana does in her New Mexico office/home is improving the quality of life for many tribal people.

▶ **What are the most frustrating aspects of your work?**

Jana: It's frustrating to see a tribe begin to move forward with environmental regulation and then have its efforts challenged by a neighboring community. For example, I know of a case in which the tribe wanted to establish water quality standards for a large river that ran through its reservation. The river is listed as one of the 10 most endangered rivers in America because of severe pollution. The Environmental Protection Agency approved of the tribal standards. Then officials for a large city upriver learned that the new standards would limit their use of the river for municipal waste discharge. So the city planners disputed the EPA's approval of the new standards. As a result, the improvements in water quality are again delayed for the tribal people as well as for other communities downstream from this city. This is frustrating! Persistence and the ability to cooperate with government authorities are necessary tools in such a situation.

Jana hopes that actions taken because of her work and the work of others will increase awareness about, and help solve, serious environmental problems such as water pollution.

▶ **What personal qualities do you think are most important in your field?**

Jana: Determination and self-motivation are musts. It's a long haul getting a law degree. Then, once you're a lawyer, the law is constantly changing. That means you must be willing to continue to learn and to study these changes. Creativity is also essential because many times a law may not directly address your client's problem or need. As a result, you often have to weave together several legal theories to address a particular situation.

▶ **What message would you like to send to high school students today?**

Jana: I'd like to emphasize that protecting the Earth is everybody's job. But before we can tackle the work, we must become aware of the environment and how we fit into this world. And often that's not something you can learn from a book. It's only after we become truly conscious of nature and the environment that we can begin to see how our actions affect it and what steps must be taken to protect the Earth. So my advice is, go out and enjoy the natural world, and develop a real appreciation for it!

MORE ON THIS CAREER

If you're interested in learning more about a lawyer's work, check with your high school guidance counselor. You may be able to get a part-time or summer job in a law office. Or contact the **American Bar Association,** Law Student Division, 750 North Lake Shore Drive, Chicago, IL 60611, (312) 988-5000 for more information.

ENVIRONMENTAL EDUCATOR

As a child who watched *The Undersea World of Jacques Cousteau* on public television every chance she got, Niki Espy dreamed of one day studying aquatic mammals for a living. She went to college with the intent of continuing on to graduate school to do behavioral studies in marine biology. But while pursuing a bachelor's degree in biology, she got a job interning as a naturalist.

Seven years later, Niki is still a park naturalist and an environmental educator. She works at the Wehr Nature Center, which is a Milwaukee county park in Franklin, Wisconsin. Niki enjoys it so much that her dream of becoming a marine biologist is—perhaps temporarily, perhaps permanently—on hold. According to Niki, "What hooked me is that I can teach, do research, learn, work with kids and animals, be outdoors a lot, and talk. These are all of my favorite things!"

▶ **Think about it!** Every culture, whether it's Native American, Asian, Middle Eastern, African American, or European, has a history of trying to explain the natural world.

▶ **What does your daily work involve?**

Niki: It varies so much—I'll just tell you about some of the stuff I do. First of all, the Wehr Nature Center is a beautiful 220-acre facility with prairie, oak savanna, woodland, and wetland ecosystems—including a terrific lake. What I do is educate people about these resources. I conduct hikes and give nature talks to students from local schools; I tell preschoolers stories and lead them through activities; and I give workshops for teachers and community leaders.

Each day I talk to people who visit the nature center. I show them the animals that we keep here. Sometimes I'll have a conversation with a visitor to explain, for example, "why that snake isn't nasty!" I also help take care of the animals, which means doing yucky stuff like cleaning out cages, and doing interesting stuff like helping animals that are injured or sick.

I also plan public events such as Earth Day activities and assist with Halloween nature walks. And I have several ongoing projects that I work on when I have time, such as adding to and maintaining the center's insect collection and establishing a library of multicultural resources for the center.

Here Niki Espy (second from left) tells a group of students about "Foxy" the fox snake. She hopes her work will help eliminate misconceptions and increase respect for wildlife.

How does your work relate to environmental issues?

Niki: Many of our programs have the general goal of helping visitors become more appreciative of natural resources. And some programs are related to a specific environmental topic, such as recycling. On Earth Day, for instance, I had a group of toddlers make some recycled paper, create an Earth Day greeting card out of it, and then send it to President Clinton. We just got a letter back from him—it's pretty cool!

I also helped develop a biodiversity studies program. It involves taking older students out to examine one of the natural ecosystems here. The students measure the physical and biological characteristics of the ecosystem and look for problems such as pollution. We then go back to the center, tabulate the information, and think about plans for improving any problem situations.

You mentioned a multicultural library. What are your goals in terms of multicultural education?

Niki: I guess the way I see it is that the environment links together all cultures. Think about it! Every culture, whether it's Native American, Asian, Middle Eastern, African American, European, or whatever, has a history of trying to explain the natural world. Their stories, poems, and traditions show a variety of viewpoints that stem from different circumstances. I think I can help people appreciate the variety of cultures in our diverse society today by sharing those stories.

Do you think that all cultural groups share a concern for environmental issues?

Niki: Yes, I think everyone cares. But I also think that environmental issues often take a back seat to more pressing social issues such as crime, unemployment, soaring school dropout rates, and drug abuse. So the attitude may be, "Yeah, this environmentalism stuff is kinda neat, but who can worry about that right now?"

As an environmental educator, what can you do about this attitude?

Niki: What I try to do is sneak in there and teach people something about our natural world without their knowing that they're being taught. I try to spark their interest. That way maybe I can change their perspective and open their eyes a little bit.

What is your most memorable work experience?

Niki: One experience I can think of actually happened before I started working here, but it really affected me. It was when I went with a class to look for eagles. We'd gotten up at 5:30 A.M. and headed out to a nearby river. By the time we got there we were really excited about seeing the eagles. An hour later, when we still hadn't seen any, we were beginning to wonder why we'd gotten up so early. We started piling back into the van to return to the school when someone suddenly yelled "Here they come!" To see a bald eagle—that was just, like, WOW! We were closer than half a mile from the eagles. They're so big and so grand. Even as they were flying in you could just see their huge, white feathers. It was *humbling.* You need to have that kind of thing to humble you.

I've also seen the birth of triplet fawns in the wild. Whooo, that was neat. Sometimes you can go weeks without having any remarkable experiences because you may be chained to your desk doing paperwork or something, and then there are other times when it's just constant awe. It's great!

MORE ON THIS CAREER

For more information about a career as an environmental educator or as a naturalist, contact the **Environmental Careers Organization,** 179 South Street, Boston, MA 02111, or contact your state's **Department of Natural Resources.**

CLIMATE RESEARCHER

One summer when Dr. Richard Somerville was just a child, he built a weather station in his backyard. His creation grew out of a fascination for the great power of weather—a phenomenon that affects everyone every day. So with instruments made out of coffee cans, balloons, and rubber bands, Richard began keeping track of daily weather conditions and questioning how the world's weather systems worked. As time went on, he began to question more than just the weather—he looked at clouds, oceans, and the world of living things as well. These pursuits led Richard to the prestigious Scripps Institution of Oceanography. Today he is a professor of meteorology and the director of the climate research division of the Scripps Institution, which is part of the University of California at San Diego.

▶ **What exactly is meteorology?**
Richard: Simply put, it is the science of the atmosphere—especially the study of weather and weather forecasting.

▶ **What most appeals to you about your job?**
Richard: Probably the most exciting aspect of any scientist's work involves those few, rare "Eureka!" moments when you realize that you've discovered something that no one else on Earth knows about. That's quite a feeling. It's also rewarding to know that you're adding to the knowledge of others, transferring important pieces of information to important people who can use that information to improve this world.

▶ **What does your research involve?**
Richard: Well, I do research on the greenhouse effect, on climate changes in general, and on the effects of long-range climate changes. I also study El Niño events and Indian monsoons. I see how these events and phenomena affect people—such as people involved in agriculture. The climate *really* affects the way people live!

I'm also researching whether the activities of humans are affecting the atmosphere. For

▶ **There are two general classes of technology that are most important to my work: satellites and computers.**

This computer simulation of increasing global temperatures allows Richard to study the possible repercussions of a changing climate on our planet.

example, each year, the world's growing population uses more and more energy by burning coal, oil, natural gas, and wood. When all of these substances are burned, they add carbon dioxide to the atmosphere. So I study the atmosphere to see how much the added carbon dioxide is intensifying the greenhouse effect. Then I try to determine how those changes will affect humans. You see, the more we know about the atmosphere, the better we can predict what will happen next.

▶ **How is your research data used?**

Richard: Many of my findings can affect public policy. For instance, How should the energy of the world be generated? I can help policymakers explore this question by providing them with data about the effects of fuels such as coal, oil, and gas on the atmosphere. Then I can recommend that they establish policies to reduce human reliance on those fuel sources. I can also encourage the use of resources such as solar, wind, and hydroelectric power.

▶ **What tools do you use to obtain your data?**

Richard: There are two general classes of technology that are most important to my work: satellites and computers. Together these two items have virtually revolutionized this field by hugely expanding what we've been able to observe and understand. Satellites, for example, can provide us with a whole different perspective of our world. The photographs generated by a satellite allow us to look at global temperatures as well as specific weather and sea conditions. Data are also collected on clouds, soil, and vegetation. By analyzing these observations, we can monitor changing conditions and identify possible problem areas.

Computers help us make sense of the data. Computer equipment in the satellites helps to answer our questions and helps us to better visualize the data. Personal computers help us record and summarize our findings. Then we have "super computers," which can simulate the motions of the atmosphere and the ocean, and thereby help us to answer questions and make predictions.

We also have access to ships and airplanes that are loaded with highly specialized equip-ment. These research platforms can be sent to specific areas of the world to gather more information about a situation or condition.

▶ **What are the most frustrating aspects of your job?**

Richard: Other demands that limit the time I spend doing research. There's a large fraction of time and energy that must be spent making research possible—you have to find money, so you spend lots of time writing proposals and doing other administrative work.

▶ **What school subjects turned out to be the most important for your career?**

Richard: You might be surprised. Math and science classes are essential, but in retrospect I value my English courses the most. Scientists are writers—the final products of their research are shown in published papers.

▶ **What personal qualities do you think are most essential for a successful person in your field?**

Richard: There are an enormous variety of scientists—some are sloppy, some are organized, some like to work alone, some in teams. One thing all good scientists have in common, though, is dedication—they all want to do science above anything else. I think Thomas Edison's famous quotation, "Genius is 1 percent inspiration and 99 percent perspiration," is really on the mark. Not everyone can be born a genius, but anyone who is really dedicated can have a good career in science.

This scientist uses state-of-the-art equipment to gather information about changes in ocean temperatures over time.

MORE ON THIS CAREER

If you are interested in learning more about a career in meteorology, contact the **American Meteorological Society,** 45 Beacon Street, Boston, MA 02108.

Any job can be Environmental

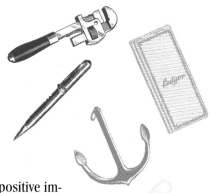

You don't have to be in an environmentally oriented field to make a positive impact on the environment. The following four people are excellent examples of how you can make a difference through your career even if it's not your job to do so.

Gun Denhart is the cofounder and chief executive officer of Hanna Andersson, in Portland, Oregon. Hanna Andersson is a company that specializes in selling baby clothing and children's clothing through a mail-order catalog service.

As a parent, Gun knows that children outgrow their clothing very quickly. So she instituted a program called "Hanna-downs." The program allows customers to send outgrown clothes that were originally purchased from Hanna Andersson

This clothing will be recycled thanks to an innovative program designed by Gun Denhart.

back to the company for recycling. Participating customers receive credit toward a purchase of new clothing that is equal to 20 percent of what they originally spent on the returned items. Hanna Andersson then donates the clothing to children in need. Over the years, Hanna Andersson's customers have sent back over 240,000 pieces of clothing, and Hanna Andersson has issued more than $1 million in credits. These clothes could have ended up in a landfill but have instead clothed kids all over the world.

How many natural resources does it take to run a luxury hotel? *A lot,* according to **Lewis Ware.** As director of housekeeping for the Boston Park Plaza Hotel & Towers, in Boston, Massachusetts, Lewis has spent the last several years implementing an aggressive natural-resource conservation program for his department.

Lewis's program began several years ago when the hotel's owners asked the company's managers to integrate environmental action into their daily business operations. Lewis was quick to respond—he had conserved energy, water, and other resources at home for years and was thrilled to learn that he now had full support to implement such programs at work.

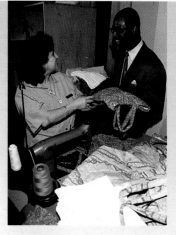

One of Lewis's innovative programs includes turning old table linens into chefs' aprons and taking worn bedspreads, pillows, and extra soap to homeless shelters.

Lewis has implemented many positive changes in the housekeeping department. Some of them include replacing harmful chemical cleaners with less harmful ones, replacing 2 million 1 oz. plastic shampoo and conditioner containers with elegant refillable ones, purchasing soap and shampoo products made from all-natural ingredients, and setting up a program to recycle in-room wastes such as bottles, cans, newspapers, and telephone books.

Thanks to the efforts of dedicated individuals like Lewis Ware, the Boston Park Plaza Hotel has earned much national recognition. This recognition includes the prestigious President's Environment and Conservation Challenge Gold Medal for 1992.

Jeff Hahn began his career as a legislative analyst for the Austin, Texas, office of Motorola Corporation. His job was to make sure that the laws passed in the state of Texas did not interfere with the company's ability to conduct business. Motorola is a company that manufactures electronic devices such as computer chips, cellular telephones, digital pagers, and two-way radios.

Jeff Hahn teaches local school children about their environment

Manufacturing computer chips requires the use of a number of hazardous chemicals that must be properly handled and disposed of after use. Jeff knew the public was concerned about the way companies manage the chemicals they use during manufacturing, so he began to look for ways to tell people how Motorola takes care of its waste. Soon he had taken this task one step further by telling people in the community how they could use the same methods to manage hazardous chemicals in their own homes.

Today, Jeff spends most of his time creating programs to educate Motorola employees and members of the community about how to improve the local environment. For example, Jeff wrote the *Discovery Pack*, a book filled with experiments and projects that teach kids how they can help protect the environment. The book has already been distributed to all Austin elementary schools, and plans are underway to deliver the *Discovery Pack* to other Motorola facilities around the nation and the world.

Jeff says he never thought that he'd be so heavily involved in promoting the environment, but his career has simply "taken off" into environmental issues, and he couldn't be happier about it!

Debbie Aguirre is the president of Tierra Pacifica Corporation, a construction and real-estate services company in Irvine, California. Debbie has been in the construction business for nearly 20 years. In that time, she's noticed that there are often excessive amounts of waste and many non-energy-efficient practices involved in construction projects. About 10 years ago Debbie decided that construction didn't have to be so wasteful, and she began thinking of ways to cut back on construction waste.

Today, Debbie's company is located in an energy-efficient facility—complete with a recycling and paper-reduction program. But perhaps even more significant is Debbie's corporate waste-management program. This program involves meeting with clients before starting construction to discuss how Tierra Pacifica can incorporate recycled products into the project, reduce construction waste, and make the construction process as energy efficient as possible.

Many of the materials used at this construction site are made from recycled materials, thanks to Debbie Aguirre's innovative thinking.

For example, Tierra Pacifica recently used several recycled materials to construct a new parking facility next to a local hospital. The materials included a type of asphalt base made with recycled ground glass; wheel stops and benches were made from recycled plastic.

According to Debbie, "Construction is a field not known for its environmental sensitivity. We would like to become a model for other construction companies so that they might take a more active stance in improving their relationship with the environment."

EcoSkills

What do bat houses, toilets, and shopping bags have in common? Well, not much unless you are developing skills for improving your relationship with the environment. This EcoSkills section contains plans, tips, and information for doing such things as building a home for bats, planting a tree, making a water-saving device for a toilet, and changing your shopping habits. All of the projects are inexpensive and fun to do, and either help reduce your impact on the environment or help improve your natural surroundings. In addition, several of the projects can actually save your household money. So roll up your sleeves and develop your EcoSkills!

Contents

388

ECOSKILLS

BOOSTING YOUR HOME'S
ENERGY EFFICIENCY

Many people don't realize the impact that energy production has on the environment.

No matter what kind of energy plant serves your area, the production of that energy carries with it certain environmental risks. For example, when we burn coal to create electricity, many pollutants are released into the air. These pollutants may cause environmental problems such as global warming and acid rain. The more energy each of us uses, the more we contribute to these problems. So it makes environmental sense to conserve energy. Conservation is also a good way to save money—just a few energy-saving measures can substantially lower an energy bill.

Could the energy efficiency of your home be improved? Perform the following energy audit to find out.

The Wind Test

One day when it's windy outside, fasten a sheet of tissue paper onto a hanger with a piece of tape, as shown below. Next, hold the hanger in front of a window at the point where the window meets the wall. Hold the hanger still. If the paper moves, you've found a draft. Note the location of the draft in your EcoLog. Check all around the window, making comments about the drafts you find.

Then examine all of the other windows, doors, electrical outlets, plumbing pipes, and baseboards that are on the outer walls of your home. Note every place where the tissue moves.

These drafts of air that you've discovered can add 20 to 35 percent to your heating and cooling bills. Fortunately, you can seal these air leaks with weatherstripping and caulk. Weatherstripping is for moving parts, such as doors and window frames. Caulk is for sealing cracks along joints and edges. These materials are relatively inexpensive, can be found at any hardware store, and can save 7 to 20 percent on your heating and cooling bills.

This simple device could help you improve the energy efficiency of your home.

For More Information

Your local electric company can probably send you a packet of energy- and cost-saving ideas. In addition, your city may sponsor thorough in-house energy audits as well as rebates and loans for improving the energy efficiency of your home. Contact your city's electric utilities conservation department for more information.

Eliminating Pests
NATURALLY

Ahuge cockroach is crawling across your floor. How will you get rid of it? Don't reach for an expensive store-bought chemical that could possibly contaminate the local water supply or even harm someone in your household. Instead, try a natural remedy!

Cockroaches Make a roach trap by putting honey in the bottom of a jar and setting it upright where the pests are most likely to visit. The sweet smell of the honey will lure roaches into the jar, but the stickiness of the substance will make it impossible for them to escape. You could also line the cracks where you think roaches are entering your home with bay leaves. The smell of bay leaves repels roaches. Prevent roaches from entering your home by keeping all food covered and stored and by cleaning dirty dishes. Seal cracks in walls, baseboards, and ducts with caulk so that roaches and other pests can't get in.

Ants Sealing cracks with caulk will also help keep ants out of your home. In the meantime, squeeze fresh lemon or lime juice into the holes or cracks. Then leave the peels where you've seen ants. Scatter mint around your shelves and cabinets, or pour a line of cream of tartar, red chili pepper, salt, paprika, dried peppermint, or talcum powder where ants enter your home. These substances either repel or kill the pests. Another effective remedy for ridding your home of ants or cockroaches is to sprinkle a mixture of equal parts of boric acid and confectioners' sugar in dry areas where ants and cockroaches are found. The pests will eat the sugar and then die from the effects of the boric acid. **Caution:** *If ingested, boric acid is acutely toxic to pets and small children. Use boric acid only in areas that are out of reach of kids and pets.*

Ticks and Fleas

If your pet has a problem with ticks or fleas, try feeding the animal brewer's yeast or vitamin B. Also wash your pet regularly with soap and water, then dry the animal and spray an herbal mixture of rosemary and water onto its coat. (You can make the mixture by steeping $\frac{1}{2}$ cup of fresh or dried rosemary in one quart of boiling water. Let the liquid cool, pour it into a pump bottle, and then spray it onto your animal's coat.)

You can control the ticks and fleas in your yard by sprinkling the grass with diatomaceous earth, which is available at many nurseries. Diatomaceous earth consists of tiny glasslike skeletons of diatoms (a type of single-celled algae). These organisms scratch the outer layer of an insect's body as it crawls along the ground. Bacteria then enter the insect's body through the open wounds, and the insect dies of disease. **Caution:** *Diatomaceous earth can be harmful to your lungs if inhaled. Wear a protective mask when spreading the substance.*

You can help reduce the number of ticks and fleas that bother your pet by bathing it frequently and spraying an herbal mixture on its coat.

For More Information

Your city's environmental and conservation services department (if you have one) may have some other remedies for pests and some recipes for nontoxic household cleaners. Also check your local bookstore or library for books on natural pesticides, organic gardening, and chemical-free homes.

On your next few shopping trips, think about the products you choose. If you're like most Americans, you'll probably be amazed at how many wasteful shopping habits you have.

Environmental Shopping

Try to count how many products you've used today. It's probably not as easy as you think. In the first few minutes of your day, you may have used a dozen products.

All of those products and their packaging are made from valuable resources. More often than not, once those resources are used, they're tossed in a trash can and eventually hauled to the local landfill.

You can cut back on the amount of waste you send to the landfill and conserve resources in the process. On your next few shopping trips, think about the products you choose. If you're like most Americans, you'll probably be amazed at how many wasteful shopping habits you have. But after a while you'll begin to know instinctively which products are best for you and the environment.

Your Personal Shopping Guide

Read the following information, and think of a way to reproduce it so that you (and other members of your household) have it handy when you set out on a shopping trip. For example, you may want to copy the questions and answers on the side of a brown paper bag. That way you'll have a shopper's guide, and you'll need one less sack at the checkout stand. Another option is to write your guidelines on the back of an old grocery receipt and then adhere the receipt to the refrigerator with a magnet so that it will be handy for the other shoppers in your household. The options are limitless, so be creative, and try to incorporate recycled items into your design.

Review Figure 12-18, shown on page 315. Is there anything from the list you could add to your personal shopping guide?

Do I really need this product? Can I use something I already have?	Borrow or rent products you don't use often.
Is this a "throwaway" item that is designed to be used once or twice and then thrown away?	Avoid using disposable products whenever possible. Nondisposable alternatives may be more expensive initially, but in the long run they often save you money.
Does this product have more packaging than it really needs?	Look for alternatives with less packaging or wrapping. Purchase products in bulk or in a larger size so that in the long run you use less packaging (and save money!). Buy fresh vegetables and fruit instead of frozen or canned products.
Was this product's container or packaging made with recycled materials?	Choose products that have recycled paper, aluminum, glass, plastic, or other recycled materials in their packaging.
Is this product's container or packaging made from cardboard, aluminum, glass, or another material that I can easily recycle?	Find out which materials you can conveniently recycle, and then buy those sorts of containers. Also, think of ways to reuse old containers rather than throwing them out.
Does this product have bleaches, dyes, or fragrances added to it? Does it contain phosphates? Is it made from a petroleum-based synthetic fabric, such as polyester?	Phosphates and many other chemicals can pollute water sources. Look for natural, organic, and phosphate-free alternatives. When purchasing clothing, choose cotton or wool over synthetic fabrics.
Does the company that makes this product have a good environmental record?	You may have to do a little research to answer this one. Try the references listed below.
Although this product has a "green" label, is it really good for me and the environment?	Don't be deceived by advertising and product labeling; carefully examine the contents of a product before you purchase it.
Do I really need a shopping bag to carry home the items I'm purchasing? If so, will I be more likely to recycle or reuse a plastic shopping bag or a paper one?	If you purchase just one or two items, tell the grocer that you don't need a bag to carry the products. For more items, bring old paper or plastic sacks with you when you go to the store, or use a canvas bag, which will last through many trips.
How much energy do I spend getting to the store?	If possible, ride your bike or walk to the store. If not, condense several short trips for one or two items into one longer trip for a bigger supply of items.

For More Information

Green Products by Design: Choices for a Cleaner Environment, by Gregory Eyring. Upland, PA: Diane Publications, 1998.

Mother Nature's Shopping List: A Buying Guide for Environmentally Concerned Consumers, by Michael D. Shook. New York: Carol Publishing Group, 1995.

By making your own compost heap, you can reduce the amount of waste you send to the local landfill and create an excellent natural fertilizer for your garden.

MAKING YOUR OWN COMPOST HEAP

Why on Earth would you want to pile a bunch of garbage in your yard and let it rot? Crazy as the idea may sound, it's actually a very good one—copied straight from nature itself.

Compost is the natural product of the Earth's organic decaying process. When a dead organism decomposes, nutrients are returned to the soil. A compost heap is a collection of organic materials such as leaves, grass, and fruit peelings that will decompose over time to create rich, fertile soil. By making your own compost heap, you can reduce the amount of waste you send to the local landfill and create an excellent natural fertilizer for your garden.

There are many opinions on how to construct the best compost heap—it can be as basic or as fancy as you like. Either way, composting is easy, and it's almost impossible to foul up the process.

A compost heap can be placed just about anywhere in the yard. Either a sunny or a shady spot will be fine. You will want to keep it out of the way of normal activity, however.

Many people choose a spot on a concrete slab or a grassy area and then simply pile their materials there. (See the photo below.) This method is easy and effective.

This is an easy and effective way to make your own compost heap.

Anatomy of a Compost Heap

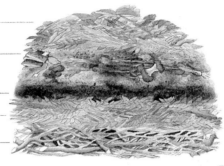

Leaves and grass clippings

Garden and kitchen wastes

Soil from your garden

Leaves and grass clippings

Small tree branches and twigs

A compost heap contains a mishmash of many different organic materials. Most of your heap will probably consist of grass clippings and leaves. You can also add raw vegetables, other uncooked food scraps, coffee grounds, tea bags, cotton, dust, discarded plants, and weeds. Avoid adding pet manure, cooked foods, and meat of any kind. If you add raw food wastes, cover them with leaves to keep away flies and to prevent an unpleasant odor.

Your heap will begin to decompose through the action of microorganisms. It's a good idea to shovel a couple of scoops of soil from your yard into the heap. The microorganisms in the soil will immediately begin decomposing the items in the heap.

Turn the heap at least once a month to keep it well aerated and active. Once the organic matter has broken down to the point that no single item is recognizable, it's ready to work into your garden's soil. The entire process can take anywhere from two months to one year, depending on the kinds of materials being decomposed and how often the heap is turned. Composting is more of an art than a science, so be prepared to experiment!

Compost Container

If you choose to contain your compost pile, you will be able to add more materials to a smaller area. You can buy a ready-made container from a hardware store, or you can build one yourself.

If you decide to build one, you may wish to use metal stakes and chicken wire to create a container like the one shown at right. Keep in mind, however, that as long as the container allows air to get in and out, the type of container you choose is limited only by your imagination!

You can build this container for your compost heap with a few materials from your local hardware store.

Metal stakes

Chicken wire

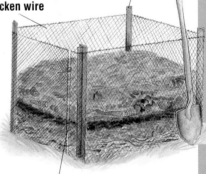

Loose wire can be twisted around two sections of chicken wire to create a "door" for easy turning.

For More Information

Consult your library for a manual on composting. You might find one of these helpful.

Let it Rot! The Home Gardener's Guide to Composting, 3d ed., by Stu Campbell. Pownal, VT: Storey Books, 1998.

Rodale Book of Composting, edited by Grace Gershuny and Deborah L. Martin. Emmaus, PA: Rodale Press, 1992.

To attract wildlife to your home, you simply need to provide native plants and the sorts of water sources and shelters naturally available to the wildlife in your area.

Creating a Wildlife Garden

anicured lawns and nonnative vegetation are not part of a natural ecosystem. Although these have been standard in urban and suburban neighborhoods for years, they usually require pesticides, fertilizers, water, and attention just to survive. In addition, they often exclude wildlife by removing some of their natural sources of food, water, and shelter.

To attract wildlife to your home, you simply need to provide native plants and the sorts of water sources and shelters naturally available to the wildlife in your area.

Plants

Plants are probably the most crucial element of your wildlife garden. Whether you have a lot of space for planting a wildflower meadow, a balcony on which you can create a container garden full of native plants, or a few windows to which you can attach boxes full of bright and cheery wildflowers, you will need a variety of native plants. Check with a local nursery, library, or bookstore for recommendations.

Water

People often overlook the need all animals have for water. Although some animals obtain enough water from the foods they eat, most require additional water for drinking and bathing.

Water sources are easy to provide. Many people purchase hanging or standing birdbaths from a nursery or hardware store. Others create ponds. You can make a simple pond by setting an old trash-can lid upside down in a corner of your yard and filling it with water. Surround your water source with plants, rocks, and other items so that the wildlife can find cover if necessary. In addition, make sure your pond or birdbath is at least partially shallow so that no animal is in danger of drowning, and keep the water clean.

Food and Shelter

Many different kinds of birdhouses and feeders are available at nature stores, hardware shops, and nurseries. Most of these can be hung on a balcony, and some can even be adhered to a window. Or, you could make your own birdhouse or feeder. A milk jug with a large hole cut in its side that is filled with seed and hung from a tree or balcony is an excellent way to feed many birds. If you would like to attract bats to your yard, see pages 400–403 for directions on how to make (or purchase) a bat house.

Woodpiles, rock piles, and brush piles are valuable sources of shelter for wildlife such as lizards and toads that might not frequent your backyard habitat otherwise. The most successful pile is one that incorporates different-sized spaces among the various components. You can make your pile attractive by planting vines in and around it.

Caution: *A shelter like the one described above may also attract poisonous snakes. Find out if any live in your area; if so, you may want to refrain from making a shelter pile.*

For More Information

Consult your library or bookstore for books on gardening with plants native to your area, gardening for the wildlife in your area, and Xeriscape techniques. You might find these books helpful.

Noah's Garden: Restoring the Ecology of Our Own Back Yards, by Sara Bonnett Stein. Boston: Houghton Mifflin, 1995.

Your Backyard Wildlife Garden: How to Attract and Identify Wildlife in Your Yard, by Marcus Schneck. New York: St. Martin's Press, 1992.

Planting a Tree

In many towns and cities across America today, more trees are dying or being cut down than are being planted. If you live in an urban environment, you can help reverse this disturbing trend by planting a tree.

No matter where you live, you'll undoubtedly find a tree a welcome addition to your neighborhood. If you don't have a yard or can't plant a tree in your yard, consider getting a small tree to put in a pot on your patio or balcony. Or you could participate in a community tree-planting project. Check with a library, nursery, or environmental organization to find out if there are any tree-planting projects in your area.

Finding the Right Tree

There are countless varieties of trees that you can choose from. The following guidelines should help you find the tree that best suits your needs.

Go Native Native trees usually don't require fertilizers, pesticides, or excessive watering. So choose a native tree, and save yourself considerable time, money, and effort.

Long-Living or Quick-Growing? Most people want a tree that will grow quickly to its full height. Unfortunately, many fast-growing trees have a long list of serious problems. As a result, they often do not live as long as slower-growing varieties. So choose a medium- to slow-growing tree, and look forward to watching it mature over the years. (Many slow-growing trees can live more than 100 years!)

Follow the Sun Think about the effect the tree will have on its surroundings. For example, a tree planted within 4.5 m (15 ft.) of your home's south or west side can shade the house in the summer. If the tree is deciduous (sheds its leaves in the fall), sunlight can filter through the branches in the winter and help keep your home warm.

Watch Those Roots and Branches Keep in mind that roots can seriously damage sidewalks, driveways, and sewage systems and that branches can damage shingles, windows, and house siding. Therefore, keep trees that will have large root systems or branches an appropriate distance from anything they might damage.

Cost Trees sold in plastic 1–5 gal. containers range from $3 on sale to $50 or more for rare or nonnative species.

Seeking Advice The nursery is an obvious place to get advice about trees you could plant, but nearby college agricultural departments, university extension offices, U.S. Forest Service offices, and city government offices can also help you. Sometimes they even have trees for sale, often at their cost.

Planting Your Tree

The following directions will help you give your tree a good start.

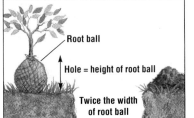

Root ball

Hole = height of root ball

Twice the width of root ball

1. Dig a square hole *exactly* the same depth as the root ball and approximately twice as wide. Use a ruler or measuring tape to make sure the hole is the right depth. The sides of the hole do not have to be smooth. In fact, it is better if they are rough and jagged, as shown in the diagram at left.

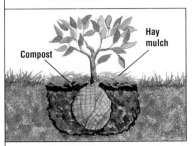

2. Now put the tree in the hole, and refill the hole with the soil you took out. You may want to mix the soil with some organic material such as bark mulch or finished compost (*well-decomposed* organic matter). Do not use pure manure, sand, bark, or peat moss. Compact the soil slightly but not too firmly. Water the tree slowly and deeply to help the soil settle into the hole.

Compost

Hay mulch

3. It's a good idea to cover the area around your newly planted tree with about 1 in. of compost and 3 in. of mulch (shredded hardwood bark, wood chips, or hay). The compost will serve as a natural fertilizer that gives the tree necessary nutrients, and the mulch will help the soil retain moisture.

Caring for Your Tree

The first couple of years of the tree's life are especially important. Don't just plant the tree and forget about it! Water the tree thoroughly when the top 3–4 in. of soil dry out or if the tree's leaves start to wilt.

For More Information

Global ReLeaf Forests: American Forests, P.O. Box 2000, Washington, D.C. 20013; (800) 368-5748

Tree People: 12601 Mulholland Drive, Beverly Hills, CA 90210-1332; (818) 753-4600 (Ask about their Campus Forester program and their book titled *The Simple Act of Planting a Tree.*)

Give a bat a home and keep annoying insects, such as mosquitoes, at bay.

Building a
Bat House

I f mosquitoes bother you, you should love bats. A single little brown bat is capable of eating 600 mosquitoes in just one hour. Other bats pollinate flowers and disperse the seeds of the fruit they eat, helping many plants to reproduce. Bats are a vital part of nearly every ecosystem on Earth.

Despite the importance of bats, people have feared and persecuted them for centuries, incorrectly believing them to be vicious creatures that attack humans. This fear is due to misunderstanding. Bats are actually useful creatures that, like most wild animals, generally avoid contact with humans. The chance of catching a disease from a bat is actually very small. If you simply avoid handling bats, you have nothing to fear.

Unfortunately, many bat species in the world today are threatened with extinction. Nearly 40 percent of those living in the United States are on the endangered list or are official candidates for it. You can do your part to help these unique creatures by building a bat house.

Bat houses come in many shapes and sizes. This activity provides plans for building the popular (white) house shown at right. For other options, see "For More Information" on page 403.

Getting Started

To build a bat house for 30 or more bats, collect the following materials. Because you will be working with sharp tools, exercise extreme caution.

Materials

- one 8' long piece of 1" × 8" untreated lumber (for the front and back pieces)*
- one 5' long piece of 2" × 2" untreated lumber (for the ceiling and sides)*
- one 5' long piece of 1" × 4" untreated lumber (for the roof and the posting board for mounting the bat house)*
- one piece of $15\frac{1}{2}$" × 21" fiberglass window screening (Do not use metal screening.)
- nails (approximately sixteen 8d galvanized nails and thirty 6d galvanized nails)
- safety goggles
- staple gun and staples, or approximately 16 upholstery tacks
- metal utility knife
- hammer
- saw
- measuring tape
- silicone caulk (may or may not be necessary)
- small can of exterior latex paint or varnish (light colored or clear if you live in a warm southern climate and dark if you live in a colder northern climate)
- ladder (to mount the bat house)

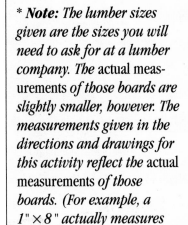

Note: The lumber sizes given are the sizes you will need to ask for at a lumber company. The actual measurements of those boards are slightly smaller, however. The measurements given in the directions and drawings for this activity reflect the actual measurements of those boards. (For example, a 1" × 8" actually measures $\frac{3}{4}$" × $7\frac{3}{4}$".)

1. Cut the 5' long piece of 1" × 4" lumber into two pieces, one piece $16\frac{1}{2}$" long (roof) and the other 3' long (posting board).
   Caution: *Exercise extreme caution while sawing.*

2. Cut the 1" × 8" × 8' board into six pieces, each measuring $15\frac{3}{4}$" in length. Next, cut one of these pieces lengthwise to make a strip measuring 1" wide; then cut the strip to $12\frac{3}{4}$" long. Be as accurate as possible when sawing.

3. Using 6d nails, nail three of the pieces you cut in step 2 (note: all three should be identical in size) to the posting board, as shown in Diagram A. Fit the three boards together as tightly as possible.

4. Using the staple gun or upholstery tacks, tightly secure the fiberglass screening to the three boards you assembled in step 3. (Use the side without the posting board.)

5. Cut the 2" × 2" × 5' piece into two pieces measuring $21\frac{3}{4}$" long (sides) and one piece measuring $12\frac{3}{4}$" long (ceiling).

6. Construct the internal frame by nailing the sides, ceiling, and entrance restriction (this is the $12\frac{3}{4}$" piece you cut off of one of the six identical boards in step 1) together with 8d nails, as shown in Diagram B.

7. Nail the back pieces to the internal frame, using 6d nails.

8. Using 6d nails, secure the front three pieces to the internal frame, allowing a gap of $\frac{1}{2}$" for ventilation between the bottom and middle pieces. (Note: the bottom piece is smaller than the other two.) See Diagram B.

9. Nail the roof to the top of the structure, allowing the excess to extend over the front of the bat house. See Diagram C.

10. Be sure the house is as draft-free as possible. If there are gaps between the pieces in the top two-thirds of the house, seal those spaces with silicone caulk. Gaps in the lower third of the house will allow ventilation for the bats.

11. Paint or varnish the exterior of the bat house.

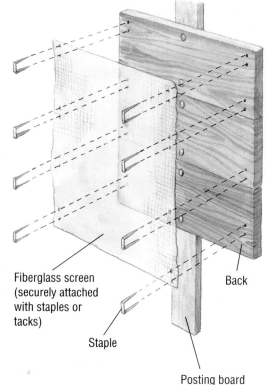

Fiberglass screen (securely attached with staples or tacks)

Staple

Back

Posting board

Diagram A

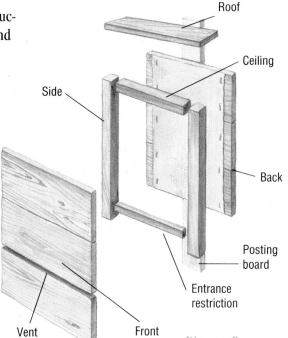

Roof

Ceiling

Side

Back

Posting board

Entrance restriction

Vent

Front

Diagram B

ECOSKILLS

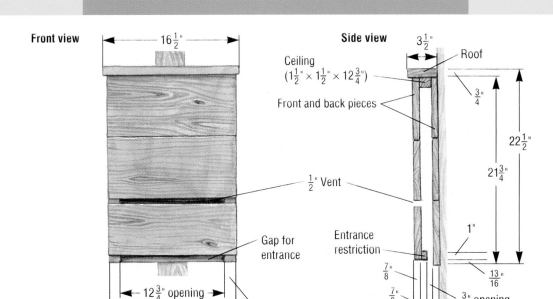

Front view

16½"

Diagram C

½" Vent

Gap for entrance

12¾" opening

15¾"

1½"

Side view

3½"

Roof

Ceiling
(1½" × 1½" × 12¾")

Front and back pieces

Entrance restriction

¾"

22½"

21¾"

1"

13/16"

⅞"

⅞"

¾" opening

⅞"

3"

Mounting Your Bat House

Mount your bat house at least 12 ft. high (ideally, 15–20 ft. or more) on a sturdy pole or on the side of a building away from lights. You can also put the house in a tree as long as the tree's leaves do not shade the bat house too heavily in the summer. If possible, the bat house should be within a mile or so of a water source such as a lake, river, or creek. The amount of sunlight the bat house receives will influence whether bats will inhabit it. All bat houses should receive at least 4 hours of sunlight per day.

If you live in the southern United States, the bat house will need protection from the sun's heat. Position the house so that it receives sunlight in the morning but not in the afternoon. Paint the house white or light brown to reflect the sun's rays.

If you live in the northern part of the country, paint the bat house black or dark brown to retain the sun's heat. Position the house so that it will receive 4–6 hours of sunlight if it is black or 6–12 hours of sunlight if it is painted dark brown. If you live in the central United States, you can paint the house any color, but make sure it receives at least 4 hours of sunlight.

Check your bat house regularly for signs of habitation. If the house is occupied, you can look at the bats with a flashlight, but only for brief periods. If bats don't immediately take up residence, don't get discouraged. It might take a while for them to find your house, especially in the winter (when many species hibernate). Be prepared to experiment with different colors of paint and different locations.

For More Information

For more information about how to attract bats to your house or how to build a more elaborate bat house, or to purchase a ready-made bat house, contact:
Bat Conservation International
P.O. Box 162603
Austin, Texas 78716
(512) 327-9721

FLUSHING LESS WATER

A typical American uses over 100 gal. of water before he or she even leaves for work or school in the morning, and much of that water is wasted.

Many Americans are beginning to change their wasteful practices, however. One simple and inexpensive way you can waste less water is by making a water-displacement device for your toilet's tank. This device takes up space in the tank so that less water is required to fill the tank with every flush. It only takes about 10 minutes to make, and with it you can save 1–2 gal. of water every time you flush. This may not sound like much, but it adds up quickly. Most toilets use 5–7 gal. of water with every flush. If a toilet is flushed an average of eight times per day, it uses around 52 gal. of water per day, or 18,980 gal. per year. If you can save $1\frac{1}{2}$ gal. of water with every flush, you'll save 4,380 gal. of water each year. If just 250 other people take similar measures, over 1 million gal. of water could be saved each year.

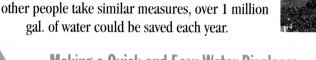

Making a Quick and Easy Water Displacer

1. Remove the label from a plastic container. (Milk jugs, juice bottles, and dishwashing soap bottles work well. Be prepared to experiment with different-sized containers.) Drop a few rocks into the container to weigh it down, fill the container with water, and put the lid back on.

2. Place the container in the toilet tank, as shown at left.

3. Be certain that the container doesn't interfere with the flushing mechanism inside the tank.

4. Experiment with different containers. Your goal is to use the largest container that the tank will hold while still maintaining an effective flush.

One Final Important Note

The more water you save, the less you pay for. No matter which water-saving device you install, your water bill should be noticeably lower.

For More EcoSkills Projects . . .

The following books offer more suggestions for how you can work toward a better environment.

How to Make the World a Better Place: 116 Ways You Can Make a Difference, by Jeffery Holender and Linda Catling. New York: W.W. Norton & Company, Inc., 1995.

The Next Step: 50 More Things You Can Do to Save the Earth, by Earthworks. Kansas City, MO: Andrews & McMeel, 1991.

You Can Make a Difference: Be Environmentally Responsible, by Judith Getis. New York: WCB/McGraw-Hill, 1998.

Green Earth Resource Guide: A Comprehensive Guide About Environmentally-Friendly Services and Products, by Cheryl Gorder. Tempe, AZ: Blue Bird Publications, 1991.

Where We Live: A Citizen's Guide to Conducting a Community Environmental Inventory, by Donald F. Harker and Elizabeth Ungar Natter. Washington, D.C.: Island Press, 1994.

Beyond Recycling: A Re-User's Guide: 336 Practical Tips: Save Money and Protect the Environment, by Kathy Stein. Santa Fe, NM: Clear Light, 1997.

It's So Natural: An A–Z of Environmentally Friendly Hints, Tips & Remedies for Home, Health & Garden, by Alan B. Hayes. New York: HarperCollins, 1997.

The Healthy House: Creating a Safe, Healthy and Environmentally Friendly Home, by Sydney Baggs. New York: HarperCollins, 1997.

Eco-Renovation: The Ecological Home Improvement Guide, by Edward Harland. White River Junction, VT: Chelsea Green, 1994.

The Wild Lawn Handbook, by Stevie Daniels. New York: Macmillan General Reference, 1995.

Good Bugs For Your Garden, by Allison Mia Starcher. Chapel Hill, NC: Algonquin Books, 1995.

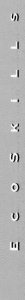

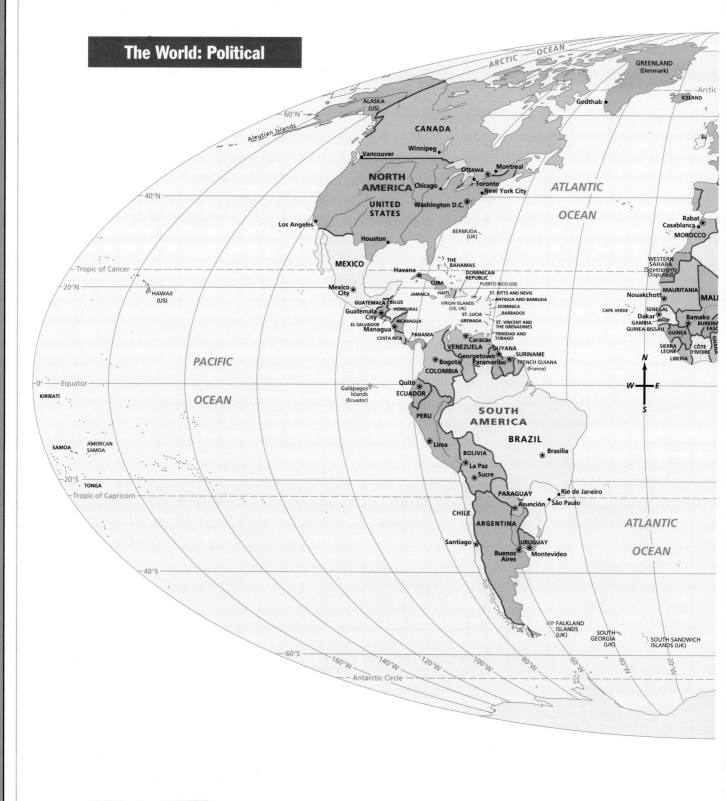

The World: Political

ARCTIC OCEAN

GREENLAND
(Denmark)

Arctic

ICELAND

ALASKA
(US)

60°N

Aleutian Islands

CANADA

NORTH
AMERICA

Vancouver • • Winnipeg

Ottawa ⊛ • Montreal
Chicago • Toronto
• New York City

40°N

UNITED
STATES

Washington D.C. ⊛

ATLANTIC

OCEAN

Los Angeles •

Houston •

BERMUDA
(UK)

Rabat ⊛
Casablanca •
MOROCCO

MEXICO

Havana ⊛

THE
BAHAMAS

WESTERN
SAHARA
(Sovereignty
Disputed)

Tropic of Cancer

20°N

HAWAII
(US)

CUBA

DOMINICAN
REPUBLIC

PUERTO RICO (US)

Nouakchott ⊛
MAURITANIA

MALI

Mexico
City ⊛

JAMAICA

HAITI

ST. KITTS AND NEVIS

CAPE VERDE

Dakar ⊛ SENEGAL
GAMBIA
GUINEA-BISSAU

Bamako
⊛ BURKINA
FASO

GUATEMALA BELIZE
Guatemala
City ⊛ HONDURAS
EL SALVADOR
Managua

VIRGIN ISLANDS
(US, UK)
ANTIGUA AND BARBUDA
DOMINICA

GUINEA

ST. LUCIA
BARBADOS

SIERRA
LEONE

CÔTE
D'IVOIRE
GHANA

GRENADA

ST. VINCENT AND
THE GRENADINES

NICARAGUA

PANAMA

TRINIDAD AND
TOBAGO

LIBERIA

COSTA RICA

Caracas ⊛
VENEZUELA

GUYANA

Georgetown ⊛ SURINAME
⊛ Bogotá Paramaribo ⊛
COLOMBIA FRENCH GUIANA
(France)

N

Galápagos
Islands
(Ecuador)

Quito ⊛
ECUADOR

W ⊕ E

PACIFIC

0° Equator

KIRIBATI

PERU

SOUTH
AMERICA

S

OCEAN

SAMOA
AMERICAN
SAMOA

BRAZIL

• Lima

BOLIVIA

⊛ Brasília

TONGA

20°S

Tropic of Capricorn

La Paz ⊛
⊛ Sucre

PARAGUAY

Rio de Janeiro •

Asunción ⊛ • São Paulo

CHILE

ARGENTINA

ATLANTIC

Santiago ⊛

Buenos
Aires ⊛ URUGUAY
• Montevideo

OCEAN

40°S

FALKLAND
ISLANDS
(UK)

SOUTH
GEORGIA
(UK)

SOUTH SANDWICH
ISLANDS (UK)

60°S

160°W 140°W 120°W 100°W 80°W 60°W 40°W 20°W

Antarctic Circle

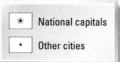

⊛ National capitals

• Other cities

SCALE: at Equator

0   500   1,000   1,500   2,000 Miles

0   1,000   1,500 Kilometers

Projection: Mollweide

ENVIRONMENTAL ATLAS

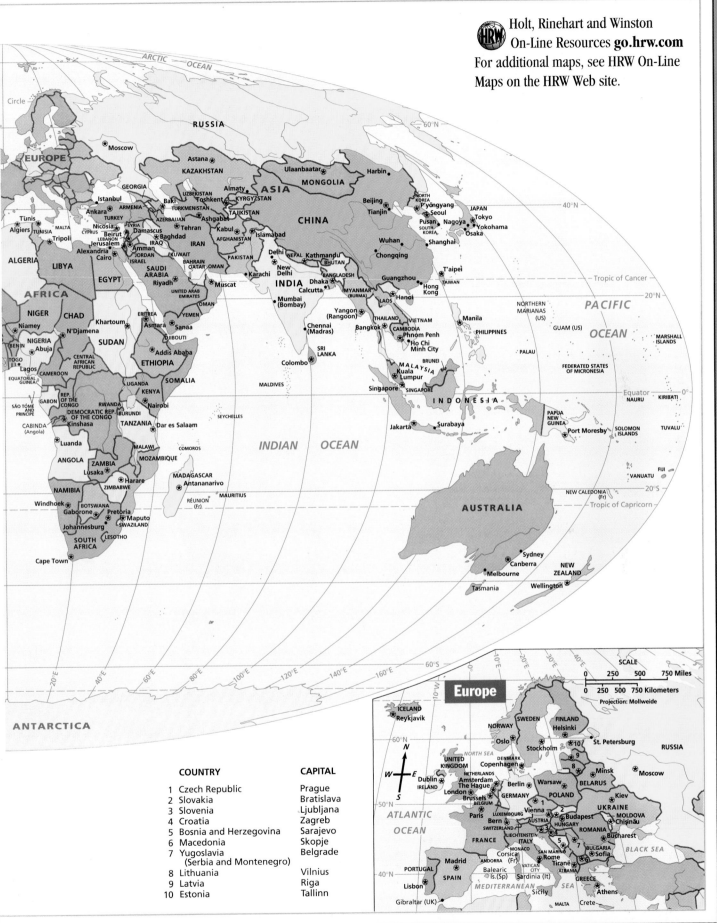

Holt, Rinehart and Winston
On-Line Resources **go.hrw.com**
For additional maps, see HRW On-Line
Maps on the HRW Web site.

ARCTIC OCEAN

Circle

EUROPE

RUSSIA

Moscow

KAZAKHSTAN

Astana

Ulaanbaatar

MONGOLIA

Harbin

ASIA

GEORGIA

Istanbul

UZBEKISTAN

Almaty

Beijing

NORTH KOREA

JAPAN

Toshkent

KYRGYZSTAN

P'yongyang

Seoul

Tokyo

ARMENIA

Ankara

Baki

TURKEY

AZERBAIJAN

TAJIKISTAN

Tianjin

Nagoya

Yokohama

TURKMENISTAN

Ashgabat

CHINA

SOUTH KOREA

Pusan

Osaka

Nicosia

Tünis

Algiers

MALTA

CYPRUS

SYRIA

Damascus

Tehran

Kabul

Islamabad

Wuhan

Shanghai

TUNISIA

Beirut

LEBANON

IRAQ

Baghdad

AFGHANISTAN

Chongqing

Tripoli

Jerusalem

Amman

JORDAN

ISRAEL

KUWAIT

IRAN

PAKISTAN

Delhi

NEPAL

Kathmandu

BHUTAN

Alexandria

Cairo

BAHRAIN

QATAR

OMAN

New Delhi

Guangzhou

T'aipei

Tropic of Cancer

ALGERIA

LIBYA

EGYPT

SAUDI ARABIA

Riyadh

UNITED ARAB EMIRATES

Karachi

INDIA

Calcutta

Dhaka

BANGLADESH

Hong Kong

TAIWAN

Muscat

OMAN

Mumbai (Bombay)

MYANMAR (BURMA)

Hanoi

PACIFIC OCEAN

AFRICA

NIGER

CHAD

Khartoum

ERITREA

YEMEN

Sanaa

Chennai (Madras)

Yangon (Rangoon)

LAOS

VIETNAM

Manila

NORTHERN MARIANAS (US)

GUAM (US)

MARSHALL ISLANDS

Niamey

N'Djamena

Asmara

THAILAND

Bangkok

CAMBODIA

Phnom Penh

PHILIPPINES

PALAU

BENIN

NIGERIA

Abuja

SUDAN

DJIBOUTI

SRI LANKA

Ho Chi Minh City

FEDERATED STATES OF MICRONESIA

TOGO

Lagos

CENTRAL AFRICAN REPUBLIC

Addis Ababa

Colombo

BRUNEI

EQUATORIAL GUINEA

CAMEROON

ETHIOPIA

SOMALIA

MALDIVES

MALAYSIA

Kuala Lumpur

Equator

NAURU

KIRIBATI

SÃO TOMÉ AND PRÍNCIPE

GABON

REP. OF THE CONGO

UGANDA

KENYA

Nairobi

Singapore

SINGAPORE

INDONESIA

CABINDA (Angola)

DEMOCRATIC REP. OF THE CONGO

RWANDA

BURUNDI

TANZANIA

Dar es Salaam

SEYCHELLES

Jakarta

Surabaya

PAPUA NEW GUINEA

Port Moresby

SOLOMON ISLANDS

TUVALU

Kinshasa

INDIAN OCEAN

Luanda

MALAWI

COMOROS

ANGOLA

ZAMBIA

MOZAMBIQUE

FIJI

Lusaka

MADAGASCAR

Antananarivo

VANUATU

NAMIBIA

Harare

ZIMBABWE

RÉUNION (Fr.)

MAURITIUS

NEW CALEDONIA (Fr)

Tropic of Capricorn

Windhoek

BOTSWANA

Gaborone

Pretoria

SWAZILAND

Maputo

AUSTRALIA

Johannesburg

LESOTHO

SOUTH AFRICA

Cape Town

Sydney

Canberra

NEW ZEALAND

Melbourne

Tasmania

Wellington

ANTARCTICA

20°E 40°E 60°E 80°E 100°E 120°E 140°E 160°E 60°S

60°N 40°N 20°N 0° 20°S

ENVIRONMENTAL ATLAS

COUNTRY	CAPITAL
1 Czech Republic	Prague
2 Slovakia	Bratislava
3 Slovenia	Ljubljana
4 Croatia	Zagreb
5 Bosnia and Herzegovina	Sarajevo
6 Macedonia	Skopje
7 Yugoslavia (Serbia and Montenegro)	Belgrade
8 Lithuania	Vilnius
9 Latvia	Riga
10 Estonia	Tallinn

Europe

SCALE

0 250 500 750 Miles

0 250 500 750 Kilometers

Projection: Mollweide

ICELAND

Reykjavik

NORWAY

SWEDEN

FINLAND

Helsinki

Oslo

Stockholm

10

St. Petersburg

RUSSIA

NORTH SEA

DENMARK

Copenhagen

9

8

Minsk

Moscow

UNITED KINGDOM

NETHERLANDS

Amsterdam

The Hague

Berlin

Warsaw

BELARUS

Dublin

IRELAND

London

Brussels

BELGIUM

GERMANY

POLAND

Kiev

UKRAINE

ATLANTIC OCEAN

LUXEMBOURG

Paris

Bern

SWITZERLAND

Vienna

1

AUSTRIA

2

Budapest

HUNGARY

MOLDOVA

Chişinău

FRANCE

LIECHTENSTEIN

3

4

5

7

ROMANIA

Bucharest

MONACO

SAN MARINO

Rome

ITALY

6

BULGARIA

Sofia

BLACK SEA

Corsica (Fr)

VATICAN CITY

Tiranë

ALBANIA

PORTUGAL

Madrid

ANDORRA

Sardinia (It)

GREECE

SPAIN

Balearic Is.(Sp)

Athens

Lisbon

Gibraltar (UK)

MEDITERRANEAN SEA

Sicily

MALTA

Crete

N W E S

80°N 70°N 60°N 50°N 40°N

10°W 0° 10°E 20°E 30°E 40°E

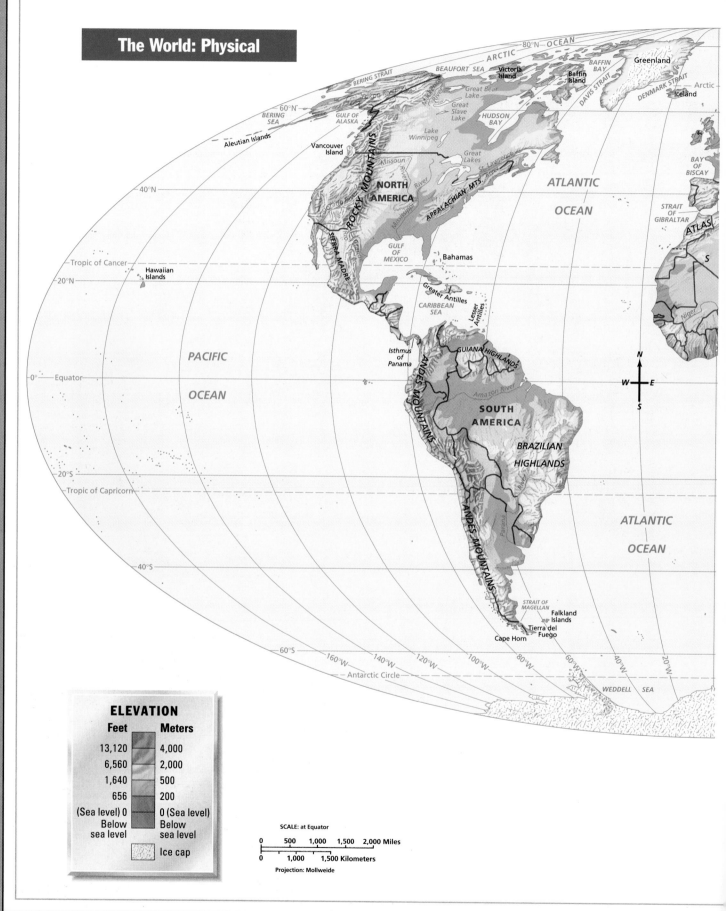

The World: Physical

ARCTIC OCEAN

80°N

BEAUFORT SEA

Victoria Island

BAFFIN BAY

Greenland

BERING STRAIT

Yukon River

Mackenzie River

Great Bear Lake

Great Slave Lake

HUDSON BAY

DAVIS STRAIT

Baffin Island

DENMARK STRAIT

Iceland

Arctic

60°N

BERING SEA

GULF OF ALASKA

ROCKY MOUNTAINS

Lake Winnipeg

Great Lakes

St. Lawrence River

BAY OF BISCAY

Aleutian Islands

Vancouver Island

Missouri River

NORTH AMERICA

APPALACHIAN MTS.

ATLANTIC

STRAIT OF GIBRALTAR

40°N

Colorado River

Mississippi River

OCEAN

ATLAS

SIERRA MADRE

GULF OF MEXICO

Bahamas

S

Tropic of Cancer

Hawaiian Islands

20°N

Greater Antilles

CARIBBEAN SEA

Lesser Antilles

Niger

PACIFIC

Isthmus of Panama

ANDES MOUNTAINS

GUIANA HIGHLANDS

N

0° Equator

Amazon River

SOUTH AMERICA

W E

OCEAN

BRAZILIAN HIGHLANDS

S

20°S

Tropic of Capricorn

Paraná

ATLANTIC

40°S

ANDES MOUNTAINS

OCEAN

STRAIT OF MAGELLAN

Falkland Islands

Tierra del Fuego

Cape Horn

60°S

160°W 140°W 120°W 100°W 80°W 60°W 40°W 20°W

Antarctic Circle

WEDDELL SEA

ELEVATION

Feet	Meters
13,120	4,000
6,560	2,000
1,640	500
656	200
(Sea level) 0	0 (Sea level)
Below sea level	Below sea level
	Ice cap

SCALE: at Equator

0   500   1,000   1,500   2,000 Miles

0   1,000   1,500 Kilometers

Projection: Mollweide

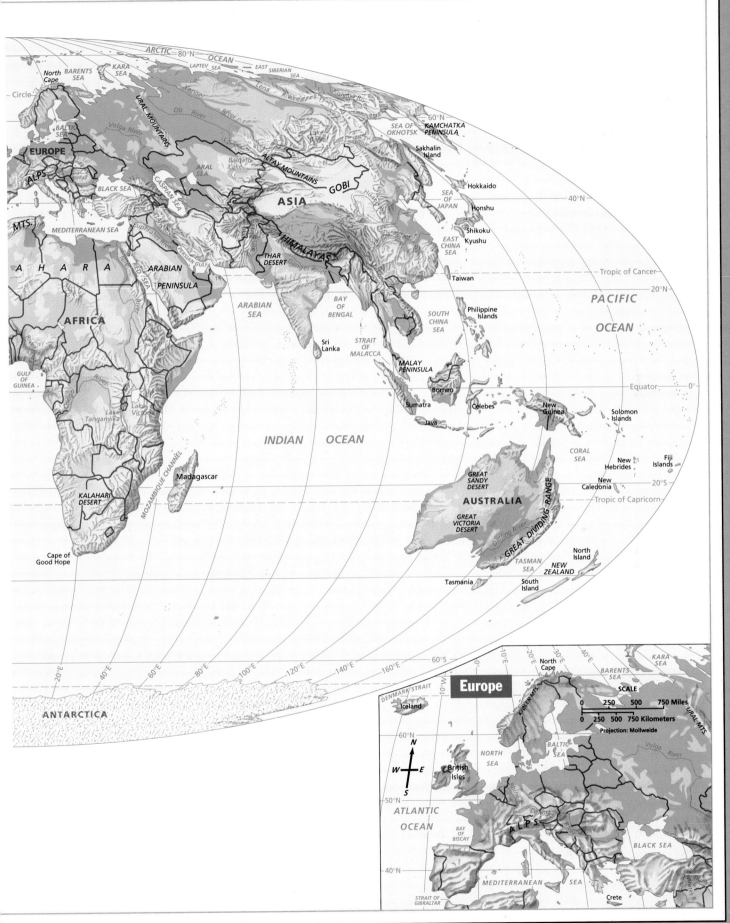

ARCTIC 80°N OCEAN
LAPTEV SEA EAST SIBERIAN SEA
North Cape
BARENTS SEA
KARA SEA
Circle
Yenisey River
Lena River
Kolyma River
60°N
SEA OF OKHOTSK
KAMCHATKA PENINSULA
BALTIC SEA
URAL MOUNTAINS
Ob River
Volga River
Sakhalin Island
EUROPE
Lake Baikal
Balqash Lake
ALTAY MOUNTAINS
Hokkaido
ALPS
ARAL SEA
ASIA
GOBI
Honshu
40°N
SEA OF JAPAN
BLACK SEA
CASPIAN SEA
Huang He
Shikoku
Kyushu
MTS.
MEDITERRANEAN SEA
Euphrates River
PERSIAN GULF
HIMALAYAS
EAST CHINA SEA
A H A R A
ARABIAN PENINSULA
RED SEA
THAR DESERT
Ganges River
Taiwan
Tropic of Cancer
20°N
PACIFIC
ARABIAN SEA
BAY OF BENGAL
South China Sea
Philippine Islands
OCEAN
AFRICA
Niger River
GULF OF GUINEA
Congo River
Sri Lanka
STRAIT OF MALACCA
MALAY PENINSULA
SOUTH CHINA SEA
Lake Tanganyika
Lake Victoria
Sumatra
Borneo
Celebes
New Guinea
Solomon Islands
Equator 0°
INDIAN OCEAN
Java
MOZAMBIQUE CHANNEL
Madagascar
CORAL SEA
New Hebrides
Fiji Islands
20°S
KALAHARI DESERT
GREAT SANDY DESERT
New Caledonia
Tropic of Capricorn
Darling River
AUSTRALIA
GREAT VICTORIA DESERT
GREAT DIVIDING RANGE
North Island
Cape of Good Hope
TASMAN SEA
NEW ZEALAND
20°E 40°E 60°E 80°E 100°E 120°E 140°E 160°E 60°S
Tasmania
South Island
ANTARCTICA

Europe

10°W 0° 10°E 20°E 30°E 40°E
KARA SEA
North Cape
BARENTS SEA
DENMARK STRAIT
KJOLEN MTS.
SCALE
0 250 500 750 Miles
0 250 500 750 Kilometers
Projection: Mollweide
URAL MTS.
Iceland
BALTIC SEA
Volga River
60°N
N
W E
S
NORTH SEA
British Isles
50°N
ATLANTIC OCEAN
ALPS
Danube
BLACK SEA
BAY OF BISCAY
40°N
MEDITERRANEAN SEA
STRAIT OF GIBRALTAR
Crete

The World's Climate Regions

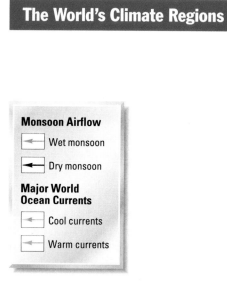

Monsoon Airflow

← Wet monsoon

◄— Dry monsoon

Major World Ocean Currents

← Cool currents

← Warm currents

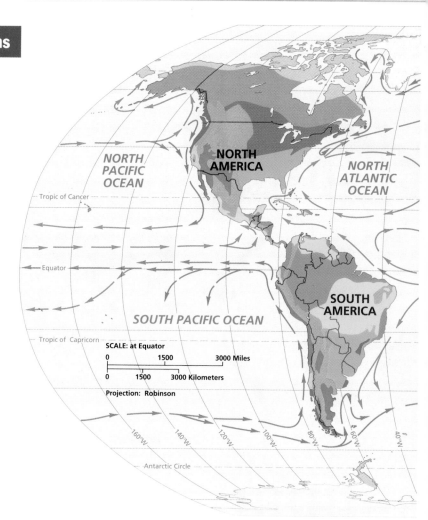

	Climate	Geographic Distribution	Major Weather Patterns	Vegetation
Low Latitudes	**HUMID TROPICAL**	along Equator; particularly equatorial South America, Zaire Basin in Africa, Southeast Asia	warm and rainy year-round, with rain totaling anywhere from 65 to more than 450 in. (165–1,143 cm) annually; typical temperatures are 90°–95°F (32°–35°C) during the day and 65°–70°F (18°–21°C) at night	tropical rain forest
	TROPICAL SAVANNA	between humid tropics and deserts; tropical regions of Africa, South and Central America, southern and Southeast Asia, Australia	warm all year; distinct rainy and dry seasons; precipitation during the summer of at least 20 in. (51 cm) and in some locations exceeding 150 in. (380 cm); summer temperatures average 90°F (32°C) during the day and 70°F (21°C) at night; typical winter temperatures are 75°–80°F (24°–27°C) during the day and 55°–60°F (13°–16°C) at night	tropical grassland with scattered trees
Dry/Semiarid	**DESERT**	centered along 30° latitude; some middle-latitude deserts in interior of large continents and along western coasts; particularly Saharan Africa, southwest Asia, central and western Australia, southwestern North America	arid; precipitation of less than 10 in. (25 cm) annually; sunny and hot in the tropics and sunny with great temperature ranges in middle latitudes; typical summer temperatures for lower-latitude deserts are 110°–115°F (43°–46°C) during the day and 60°–65°F (16°–18°C) at night, while winter temperatures average 80°F (27°C) during the day and 45°F (7°C) at night; in middle latitudes, the hottest month averages 70°F (24°C)	sparse drought-resistant plants; many barren, rocky, or sandy areas
	STEPPE	generally bordering deserts and interiors of large continents; particularly northern and southern Africa, interior western North America, central and interior Asia and Australia, southern South America	semiarid; about 10–20 in. (25–51 cm) of precipitation annually; hot summers and cooler winters with wide temperature ranges similar to desert temperatures	grassland; few trees
Middle Latitudes	**MEDITERRANEAN**	west coasts in middle latitudes; particularly southern Europe, part of southwest Asia, north-western Africa, California, southwestern Australia, central Chile, southwestern South Africa	dry, sunny, warm summers and mild, wetter winters; precipitation averages 15–20 in. (38–51 cm) annually; typical temperatures are 75°–80°F (24°–27°C) on summer days; the average winter temperature is 50°F (10°C)	scrub woodland and grassland
	HUMID SUBTROPICAL	east coasts in middle latitudes; particularly southeastern United States, eastern Asia, central southern Europe, southeastern parts of South America, South Africa, and Australia	hot, humid summers and mild, humid winters; precipitation year-round; coastal areas are in the paths of hurricanes and typhoons; precipitation averages 40 in. (102 cm) annually; typical temperatures are 75°–90°F (24°–32°C) in summer and 45°–50°F (7°–10°C) in winter	mixed forest

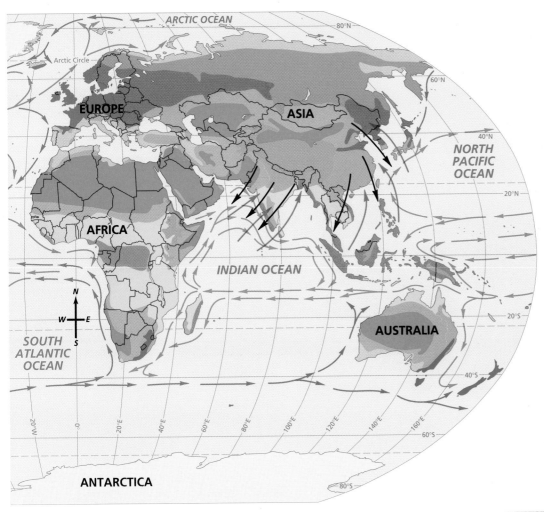

ARCTIC OCEAN

Arctic Circle

EUROPE

ASIA

NORTH PACIFIC OCEAN

AFRICA

INDIAN OCEAN

N
W — E
S

SOUTH ATLANTIC OCEAN

AUSTRALIA

ANTARCTICA

80°N

60°N

40°N

20°N

20°S

40°S

60°S

80°S

	Climate	Geographic Distribution	Major Weather Patterns	Vegetation
Middle Latitudes	**MARINE WEST COAST**	west coasts in upper-middle latitudes; particularly northwestern Europe and North America, southwestern South America, central southern South Africa, southeastern Australia, New Zealand	cloudy, mild summers and cool, rainy winters; strong ocean influence; precipitation averages 20–60 in. (51–152 cm) annually, with some coastal mountains receiving more than 200 in. (508 cm); average temperature in hottest month usually is between 60°F and 70°F (16°–21°C); average temperature in coolest month usually is above 32°F (0°C)	temperate evergreen forest
	HUMID CONTINENTAL	east coasts and interiors of upper-middle-latitude continents; particularly northeastern North America, northern and eastern Europe, northeastern Asia	four distinct seasons; long, cold winters and short, warm summers; precipitation amounts vary, usually 20–50 in. or more (51–127 cm) annually; average summer temperature is 75°F (24°C); average winter temperature is below freezing	mixed forest
High Latitudes	**SUBARCTIC**	higher latitudes of interior and east coasts of continents; particularly northern parts of North America, Europe, and Asia	extremes of temperature; long, cold winters and short, warm summers; low precipitation amounts all year; precipitation averages 5–15 in. (13–38 cm) in summer; temperatures in warmest month average 60°F (16°C), but can warm to 90°F (32°C); winter temperatures average below 0°F (–18°C)	northern evergreen forest
	TUNDRA	high-latitude coasts; particularly far northern parts of North America, Europe, and Asia, Antarctic Peninsula, subantarctic islands	cold all year; very long, cold winters and very short, cool summers; low precipitation amounts; precipitation average is 5–15 in. (13–38 cm) annually; warmest month averages 40°F (4°C); coolest month averages a little below 0°F (–18°C)	moss, lichens, low shrubs; permafrost bogs in summer
	ICE CAP	polar regions; particularly Antarctica, Greenland, Arctic Basin islands	freezing cold; snow and ice year-round; precipitation averages less than 10 in. (25 cm) annually; average temperatures in warmest month are not higher than freezing	no vegetation
	HIGHLAND	high mountain regions, particularly western parts of North and South America, eastern parts of Asia and Africa, southern and central Europe and Asia	greatly varied temperatures and precipitation amounts over short distances as elevation changes	forest to tundra vegetation, depending on elevation

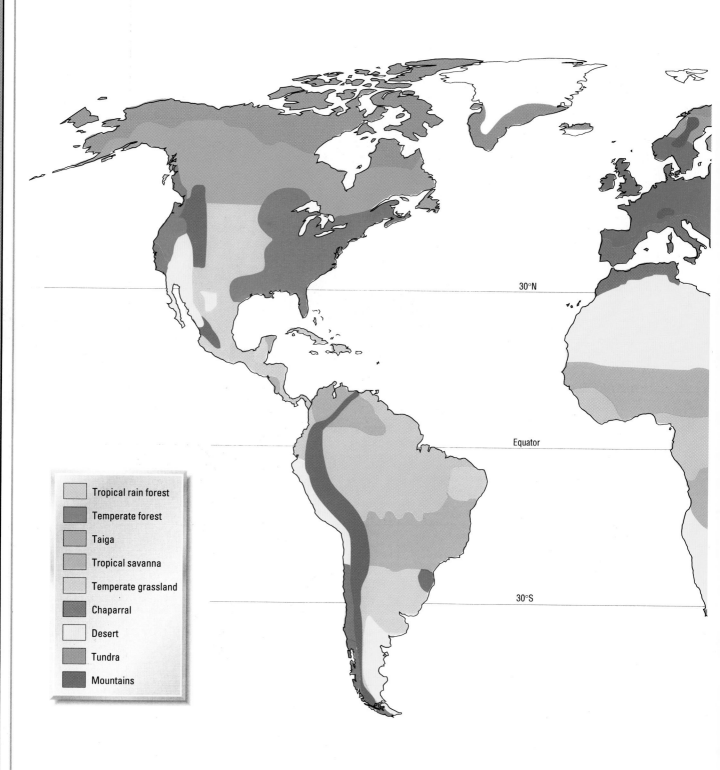

The World's Biomes

- Tropical rain forest
- Temperate forest
- Taiga
- Tropical savanna
- Temperate grassland
- Chaparral
- Desert
- Tundra
- Mountains

30°N

Equator

30°S

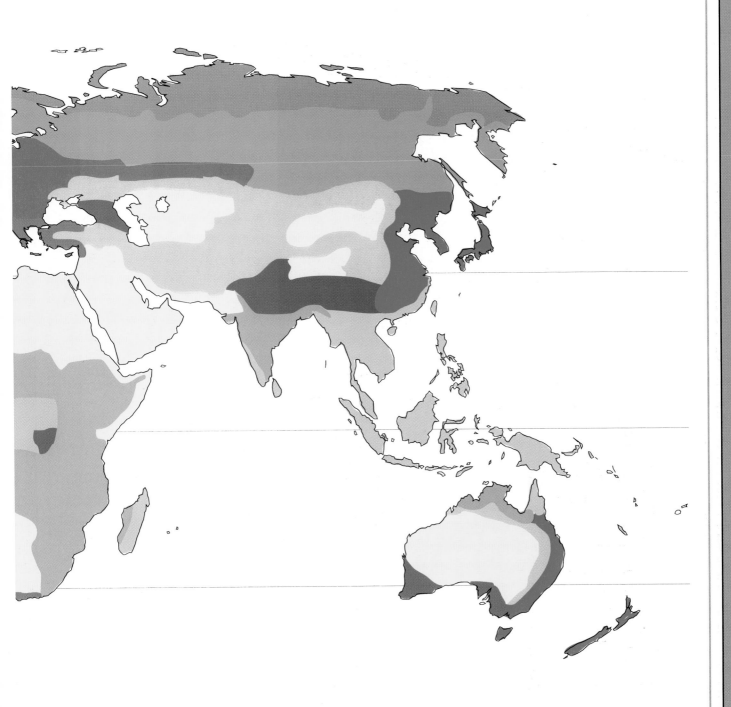

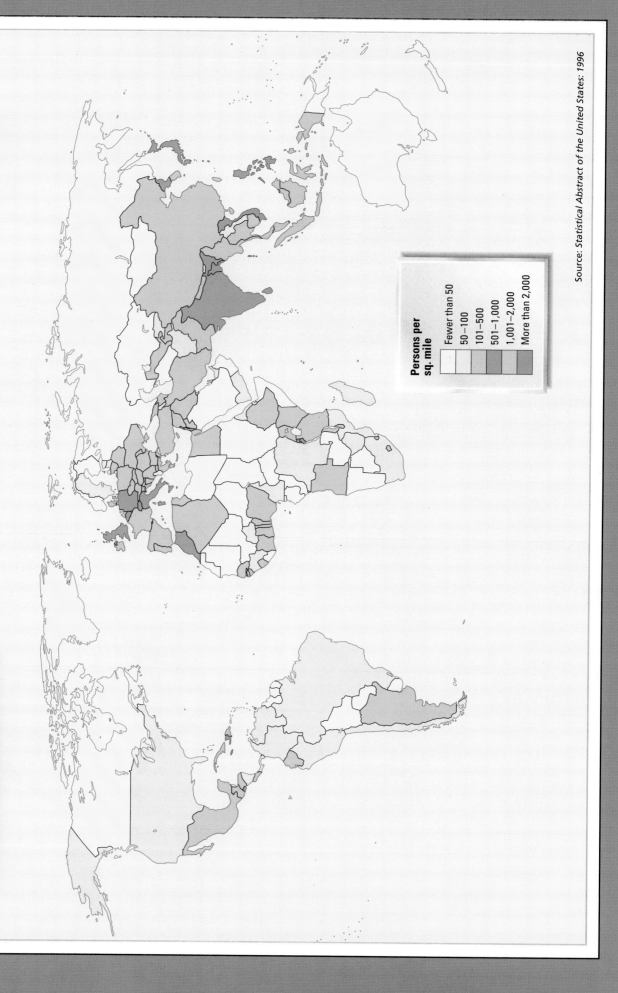

World Population Density

Persons per sq. mile

Fewer than 50
50–100
101–500
501–1,000
1,001–2,000
More than 2,000

Source: Statistical Abstract of the United States: 1996

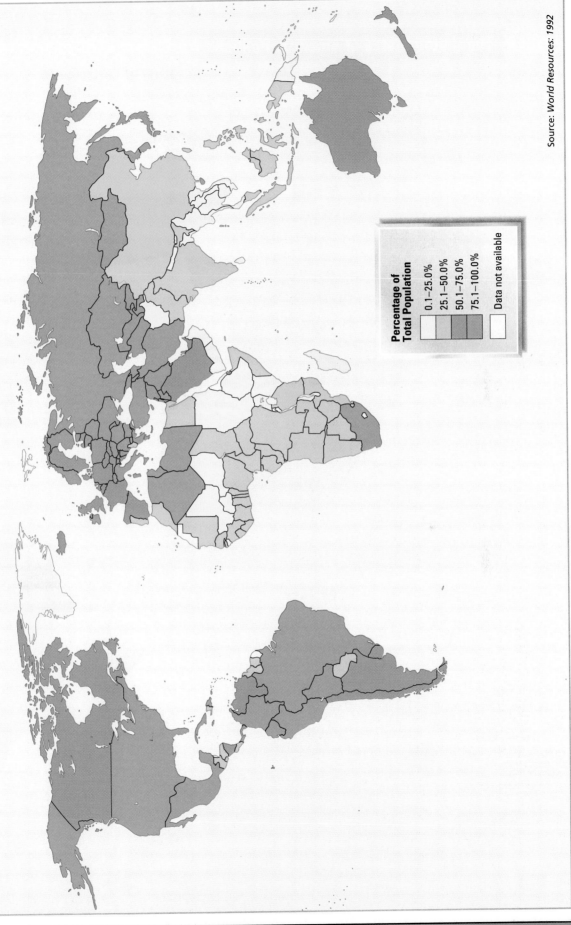

World Urban Population

Percentage of Total Population

- 0.1–25.0%
- 25.1–50.0%
- 50.1–75.0%
- 75.1–100.0%
- Data not available

Source: *World Resources: 1992*

ENVIRONMENTAL ATLAS

The United States of America: Political

130°W 125°W 120°W 115°W 110°W 105°W 100°W

45°N
40°N
35°N
30°N
25°N

STRAIT OF JUAN DE FUCA

PACIFIC OCEAN

PUGET SOUND

WASHINGTON
Seattle
Olympia ★ Tacoma
Spokane •
Portland •
Salem ★
Eugene •
OREGON

Franklin D. Roosevelt Lake
Pend Oreille

IDAHO
Boise ★
Pocatello •

Flathead Lake

MONTANA
Helena ★
Billings •
Fort Peck Lake
Yellowstone Lake

NORTH DAKOTA
Bismarck ★
Fargo •
Lake Sakakawea

Lake Oahe

SOUTH DAKOTA
Pierre ★
Sioux Falls •

WYOMING
Casper •
Cheyenne ★

NEBRASKA
Omaha •
Lincoln •

Cape Mendocino
Goose Lake
Shasta Lake
Pyramid Lake

NEVADA
Reno •
Carson City ★
Lake Tahoe

Great Salt Lake
Salt Lake City ★
Utah Lake Provo •

UTAH

Lakewood • Aurora
Denver •
COLORADO
Colorado Springs •

Kansas City
Topeka ★
KANSAS
Wichita •

Concord
Berkeley
Oakland
San Francisco
Hayward
Sunnyvale
Fremont
San Jose
Sacramento •
Stockton •
Modesto •

SAN FRANCISCO BAY
MONTEREY BAY

Fresno •
CALIFORNIA
Bakersfield •

Oxnard
Glendale Pasadena
Pomona
Los Angeles
Inglewood
Channel/Torrance
Islands
Long Beach
Santa Ana
Garden Grove
Huntington Beach
San Diego
San Bernardino
Ontario
Riverside
Fullerton
Anaheim

Salton Sea

Las Vegas •

Lake Powell
Lake Mead

ARIZONA
Glendale
Phoenix ★ Scottsdale
Mesa •
Tucson •

Santa Fe ★
Albuquerque •
NEW MEXICO

El Paso •

Amarillo •
Lubbock •
Abilene •
Odessa •

Keystone Lake
Tulsa •
OKLAHOMA
Oklahoma City ★
Eufaula Lake

Lake Texoma

Irving • Garland
Fort Worth • Dallas
Arlington
TEXAS
Waco •
Austin ★
Houston
Pasadena
San Antonio •
Laredo •
Amistad Reservoir
Corpus Christi •
Padre Island

MEXICO

To understand the relative locations of Alaska and Hawaii as well as the vast distances separating them from the rest of the United States, see the map on page 406.

Kauai
Niihau Oahu
Honolulu ★ Molokai
HAWAII Lanai Maui
Kahoolawe
PACIFIC OCEAN
Hawaii

22°N
19°N
160°W 155°W

SCALE
0   75   150 Miles
0   75   150 Kilometers

N
W   E
S

ARCTIC OCEAN
Arctic Circle
RUSSIA
BERING STRAIT
Nome •
St. Lawrence Island
St. Matthew Island
Nunivak Island

Yukon River
Fairbanks •
ALASKA
Anchorage •
CANADA

BERING SEA
SCALE
0   250   500 Miles
0   250   500 Kilometers
Projection: Albers Equal Area

Attu Island
Aleutian Islands

PACIFIC OCEAN

Kodiak Island
GULF OF ALASKA
Juneau ★
Alexander Archipelago

55°N
50°N
60°N
65°N
60°N
55°N
170°E 180 170°W 160°W 150°W 140°W 130°W

N
W   E
S

GULF OF CALIFORNIA

CANADA

MINNESOTA
Duluth

Lake Superior
Lake Huron
Lake Michigan
Lake Ontario
Lake Erie

MAINE
Augusta

Montpelier
VT.
N.H.
Concord

MASS.
Boston
Worcester
Providence
R.I.
Cape Cod

Springfield
Hartford
CONN.
Waterbury
Bridgeport
Stamford
New Haven
Long Island Sound
Long Island

WISCONSIN
Madison
Milwaukee

MICHIGAN
Grand Rapids
Flint
Lansing
Sterling Heights
Warren
Livonia
Detroit
Jackson
Ann Arbor

NEW YORK
Buffalo
Rochester
Syracuse
Albany

Paterson
Newark
Elizabeth
Yonkers
New York City
Jersey City
Trenton
N.J.

IOWA
Cedar Rapids
Davenport
Des Moines

Rockford
Chicago
Gary
South Bend
Fort Wayne
Peoria

Toledo
Cleveland
Youngstown
Akron

PENNSYLVANIA
Allentown
Pittsburgh
Harrisburg
Philadelphia

DELAWARE
Dover
DELAWARE BAY

Springfield
INDIANA
Indianapolis
Dayton
Cincinnati

OHIO
Columbus

Baltimore
MD.
Annapolis
Washington, D.C.
Arlington
Alexandria

ILLINOIS

WEST VIRGINIA
Charleston

VIRGINIA
Richmond
CHESAPEAKE BAY

Independence
Kansas City
Lake of the Ozarks
St. Louis
Jefferson City

Louisville
Evansville
Frankfort
Lexington

KENTUCKY

Hampton
Norfolk
Newport News
Portsmouth
Virginia Beach
Chesapeake
Roanoke

MISSOURI
Springfield

Lake Barkley
Kentucky Lake

Nashville
Knoxville
TENNESSEE
Chattanooga

Greensboro
Durham
Raleigh
Winston-Salem

NORTH CAROLINA
Charlotte

Cape Hatteras

Fayetteville

Memphis

ARKANSAS
Little Rock

Huntsville

SOUTH CAROLINA
Columbia

Atlanta
GEORGIA
Macon
Columbus

MISSISSIPPI
Jackson
Meridian

ALABAMA
Birmingham
Montgomery

Savannah
Sea Islands

Shreveport

Mobile

Tallahassee
Jacksonville

LOUISIANA
Baton Rouge
Beaumont
New Orleans
Chandeleur Islands

Toledo Bend Reservoir

FLORIDA
Orlando
Cape Canaveral
Tampa
St. Petersburg
Lake Okeechobee

Fort Lauderdale
Hialeah
Miami

GULF OF MEXICO

Cape Sable
Florida Keys
STRAITS OF FLORIDA

THE BAHAMAS

CUBA

ATLANTIC OCEAN

N
W   E
S

SCALE
0   250   500 Miles
0   250   500 Kilometers
Projection: Albers Equal Area

Legend:
⊛ National capital
★ State capitals
• Other cities

Robinson Projection

45° N
40° N
35° N
30° N
25° N

90° W
85° W
80° W
75° W
70° W
65° W
60° W
50° N

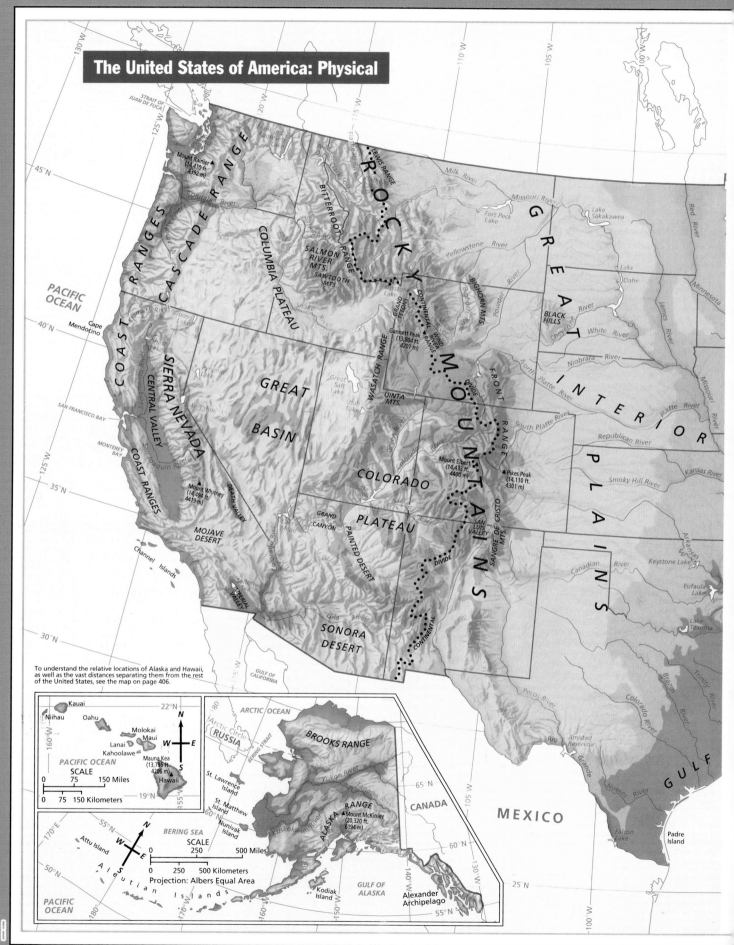

The United States of America: Physical

ENVIRONMENTAL ATLAS

PACIFIC OCEAN

STRAIT OF JUAN DE FUCA

COAST RANGES

CASCADE RANGE

Mount Rainier (14,410 ft. 4392 m)

Columbia River

COLUMBIA PLATEAU

BITTERROOT RANGE

LEWIS RANGE

R O C K Y

SALMON RIVER MTS.

SAWTOOTH MTS.

Snake River

GRAND TETONS

CONTINENTAL DIVIDE

WIND RIVER RANGE

Gannett Peak (13,804 ft. 4207 m)

Cape Mendocino

SIERRA NEVADA

CENTRAL VALLEY

GREAT BASIN

Pyramid Lake

Lake Tahoe

Great Salt Lake

Utah Lake

WASATCH RANGE

UINTA MTS.

M O U N T A I N S

FRONT RANGE

San Francisco Bay

COAST RANGES

MONTEREY BAY

Mount Whitney (14,494 ft. 4419 m)

DEATH VALLEY

COLORADO

Green River

Colorado River

PLATEAU

Mount Elbert (14,433 ft. 4400 m)

Pikes Peak (14,110 ft. 4301 m)

MOJAVE DESERT

Channel Islands

Salton Sea

IMPERIAL VALLEY

GRAND CANYON

PAINTED DESERT

SAN LUIS VALLEY

SANGRE DE CRISTO MTS.

DIVIDE

SONORA DESERT

Gila River

CONTINENTAL

Milk River

Missouri River

Fort Peck Lake

Yellowstone River

BIGHORN MTS.

Bighorn River

Powder River

G R E A T

Lake Sakakawea

Red River

BLACK HILLS

Lake Oahe

Cheyenne River

White River

I N T E R I O R

Niobrara River

North Platte River

South Platte River

Republican River

Smoky Hill River

P L A I N S

Platte River

Missouri River

James River

Minnesota

Kansas River

Canadian River

Keystone Lake

Eufaula Lake

Lake Texoma

Arkansas River

Pecos River

Rio Grande

Amistad Reservoir

Colorado River

Brazos River

Trinity River

Nueces River

Falcon Lake

Padre Island

MEXICO

GULF

GULF OF CALIFORNIA

To understand the relative locations of Alaska and Hawaii, as well as the vast distances separating them from the rest of the United States, see the map on page 406.

Kauai

Niihau

Oahu

Molokai

Maui

Lanai

Kahoolawe

Mauna Kea (13,796 ft. 4206 m)

Hawaii

PACIFIC OCEAN

SCALE

0   75   150 Miles

0   75   150 Kilometers

22°N

19°N

ARCTIC OCEAN

Arctic Circle

RUSSIA

BERING STRAIT

BROOKS RANGE

St. Lawrence Island

St. Matthew Island

Nunivak Island

Yukon River

Kuskokwim River

Tanana River

ALASKA RANGE

Mount McKinley (20,320 ft. 6194 m)

CANADA

Kodiak Island

GULF OF ALASKA

Alexander Archipelago

BERING SEA

Attu Island

Aleutian Islands

PACIFIC OCEAN

SCALE

0   250   500 Miles

0   250   500 Kilometers

Projection: Albers Equal Area

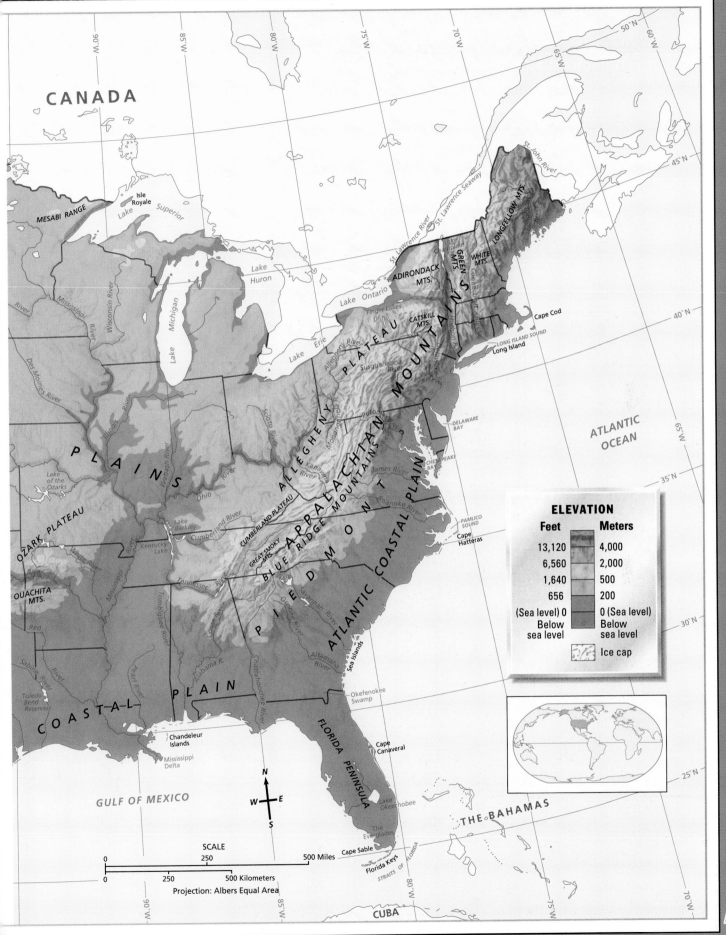

CANADA

MESABI RANGE

Isle Royale

Lake Superior

Lake Huron

Lake Michigan

Lake Ontario

Lake Erie

St. Lawrence River

St. Lawrence Seaway

LONGFELLOW MTS.

St. John River

WHITE MTS.

GREEN MTS.

ADIRONDACK MTS.

Finger Lakes

CATSKILL MTS.

Cape Cod

LONG ISLAND SOUND

Long Island

ALLEGHENY PLATEAU

APPALACHIAN MOUNTAINS

Susquehanna River

Allegheny River

DELAWARE BAY

Des Moines River

Wisconsin River

Mississippi River

River

P L A I N S

Illinois River

Wabash River

Scioto River

Ohio

Kanawha River

Monongahela R.

Potomac R.

James River

CHESAPEAKE BAY

Lake of the Ozarks

OZARK PLATEAU

Lake Barkley

CUMBERLAND PLATEAU

Cumberland River

Kentucky Lake

GREAT SMOKY MTS.

BLUE RIDGE MOUNTAINS

Roanoke River

PAMLICO SOUND

Cape Hatteras

White River

River

OUACHITA MTS.

Red

Mississippi River

Tennessee River

Tombigbee River

P I E D M O N T

A T L A N T I C   C O A S T A L   P L A I N

Savannah River

Oconee River

Altamaha River

Sea Islands

Sabine River

Toledo Bend Reservoir

Pearl River

Alabama R.

Chattahoochee River

C O A S T A L   P L A I N

Chandeleur Islands

Mississippi Delta

Okefenokee Swamp

FLORIDA PENINSULA

Cape Canaveral

Lake Okeechobee

The Everglades

Cape Sable

Florida Keys

STRAITS OF FLORIDA

GULF OF MEXICO

N
W   E
S

THE BAHAMAS

CUBA

ATLANTIC OCEAN

ELEVATION

Feet	Meters
13,120	4,000
6,560	2,000
1,640	500
656	200
(Sea level) 0	0 (Sea level)
Below sea level	Below sea level

Ice cap

SCALE

0   250   500 Miles

0   250   500 Kilometers

Projection: Albers Equal Area

RUSSIA

BERING SEA

Bering Strait

Arctic Circle

ARCTIC OCEAN

BEAUFORT SEA

GULF OF ALASKA

AMUNDSEN GULF

GREENLAND (Den.)

ICELAND

Baffin Bay

Davis Strait

Hudson Strait

LABRADOR SEA

Hudson Bay

GULF OF ST. LAWRENCE

PACIFIC OCEAN

HAWAII

SCALE
0   100   200 Miles
0   100   200 Kilometers

Projection: Albers Equal Area

To understand the relative location of Hawaii as well as the vast distance separating it from the rest of the United States, see the map on page 406.

Tropic of Cancer

PACIFIC OCEAN

SCALE
0   500   1000 Miles
0   500   1000 Kilometers

Projection: Azimuthal Equal Area

MEXICO

GULF OF MEXICO

BAHAMAS

CUBA

ATLANTIC OCEAN

BERMUDA (U.K.)

Tropic of Cancer

N
W   E
S

Humid tropical	Marine west coast	
Tropical savanna	Humid continental	
Desert	Subarctic	
Steppe	Tundra	
Mediterranean	Ice cap	
Humid subtropical	Highland	

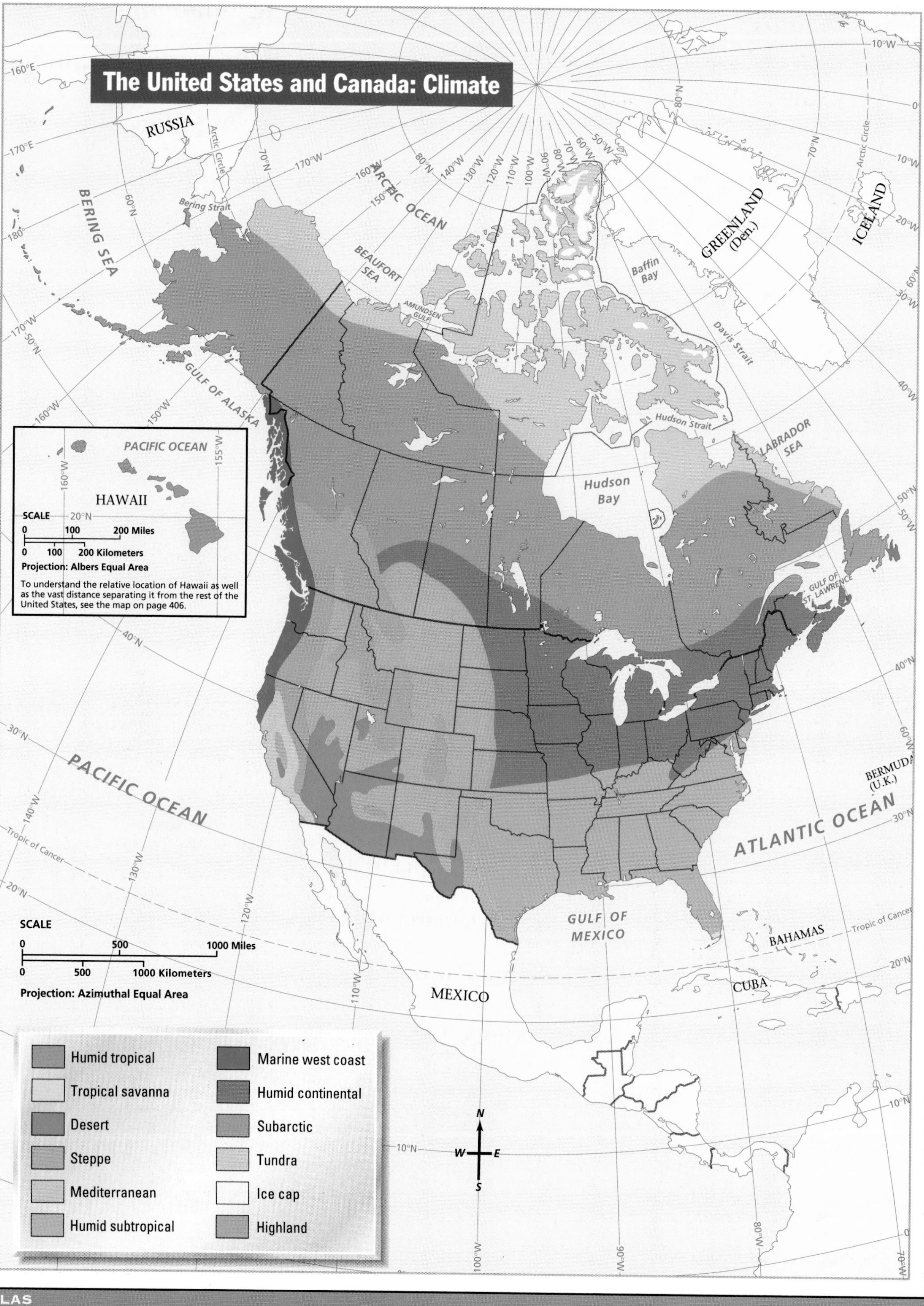

The United States and Canada: Population

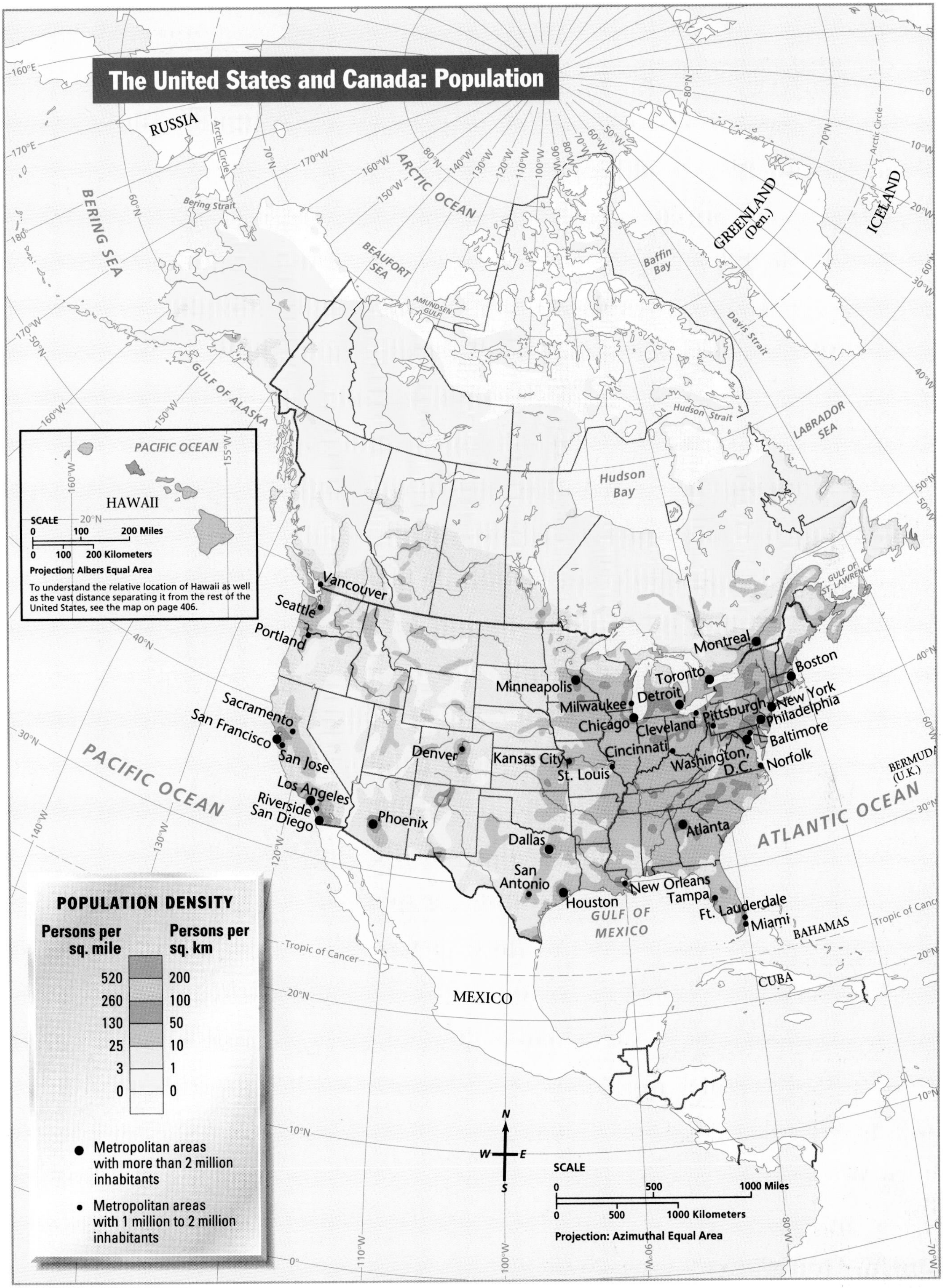

HAWAII

SCALE
0 — 100 — 200 Miles
0 — 100 — 200 Kilometers
Projection: Albers Equal Area

To understand the relative location of Hawaii as well as the vast distance separating it from the rest of the United States, see the map on page 406.

see the map on page 406.

Vancouver
Seattle
Portland
Sacramento
San Francisco
San Jose
Los Angeles
Riverside
San Diego
Phoenix

Denver

Minneapolis
Milwaukee
Chicago
Kansas City
St. Louis
Dallas
San Antonio
Houston
New Orleans

Montreal
Toronto
Detroit
Cleveland
Cincinnati
Pittsburgh
Washington, D.C.
Boston
New York
Philadelphia
Baltimore
Norfolk

Atlanta
Tampa
Ft. Lauderdale
Miami

POPULATION DENSITY

Persons per sq. mile	Persons per sq. km
520	200
260	100
130	50
25	10
3	1
0	0

● Metropolitan areas with more than 2 million inhabitants

• Metropolitan areas with 1 million to 2 million inhabitants

Tropic of Cancer

SCALE
0 — 500 — 1000 Miles
0 — 500 — 1000 Kilometers

Projection: Azimuthal Equal Area

N
W E
S

The United States and Canada: Economy

RUSSIA

BERING SEA

Bering Strait

Arctic Circle

ARCTIC OCEAN

BEAUFORT SEA

AMUNDSEN GULF

Anchorage

GULF OF ALASKA

Baffin Bay

GREENLAND (Den.)

ICELAND

Hudson Strait

Davis Strait

LABRADOR SEA

Hudson Bay

GULF OF ST. LAWRENCE

PACIFIC OCEAN

Honolulu

HAWAII

SCALE
0   100   200 Miles
0   100   200 Kilometers

Projection: Albers Equal Area

To understand the relative location of Hawaii as well as the vast distance separating it from the rest of the United States, see the map on page 406.

Vancouver

Edmonton
Calgary

Seattle

Portland

Regina

WHEAT BELT

Winnipeg

Spokane

Minneapolis-St. Paul

DAIRY BELT

Quebec

Montreal

Rochester

Boston

Halifax

PACIFIC OCEAN

San Francisco-Oakland

San Jose

Salt Lake City

Denver

CORN BELT

Milwaukee

Detroit

Chicago

Cleveland

Buffalo

Toronto

Pittsburgh

New York-Newark-Nassau

Philadelphia

Baltimore

Washington, D.C.

Norfolk-Newport Beach

BERMUDA (U.K.)

Los Angeles-Long Beach

Anaheim-Santa Ana

San Diego

Phoenix

WHEAT BELT

Kansas City

St. Louis

Indianapolis

Columbus

Cincinnati

Louisville

Nashville

Charlotte

Raleigh-Durham

Greensboro-Winston-Salem

Greenville

Atlanta

Birmingham

ATLANTIC OCEAN

Dallas-Ft. Worth

Austin

San Antonio

Houston

New Orleans

Tampa-St. Petersburg

Miami

BAHAMAS

GULF OF MEXICO

MEXICO

Straits of Florida

CUBA

HAITI

DOMINICAN REPUBLIC

JAMAICA

PUERTO RICO (U.S.)

Tropic of Cancer

Legend

⛉	Livestock raising
	Commercial farming
•	Manufacturing and trade
	Commercial fishing
	Forests
🐄	Dairying
	Limited economic activity
⚒	Coal
🔥	Natural gas
⚓	Oil
✳	Major nuclear power plant
	Hydroelectric power
Au	Gold
Ag	Silver
U	Uranium
▲	Other minerals
⬆	Timber

N
W   E
S

SCALE
0   500   1000 Miles
0   500   1000 Kilometers

Projection: Azimuthal Equal Area

ECONOMICS AND THE ENVIRONMENT

If people, businesses, and nations realize that certain actions are bad for the environment, why do they keep doing them? At least part of the answer can be explained by economics.

Economics is the study of how people choose to use limited resources, such as wood or silver, to satisfy their needs and desires.

People express their preferences for resources by assigning them value. *Value* is the amount of money people are willing to pay for something. If many people are willing to pay $20 for a 1999 NBA Championship T-shirt, the value of that shirt is $20. Value is not always the same as price, however. A black-market dealer might sell the T-shirt for $10. Since the shirt's price does not reflect its value, an economist would say the shirt is *undervalued.*

The economy usually functions best when the prices of products and services reflect their values. Fortunately, we value many products enough to pay prices that include the producers' costs as well as some amount of profit. Unfortunately, environmental costs are often not included in the prices we pay.

For example, before 1978, spray deodorants contained chemicals that destroyed atmospheric ozone. But the cost of this destruction, in terms of damage from increased UV light, was not included in the price of the deodorants. Products are often undervalued if you consider the cost their use or production has on the environment.

Think about the many environmental costs that are not included in the prices we pay. For packaged products, consider the land used for landfills. For pesticides, consider the contamination of groundwater supplies. And for gasoline, consider the carbon dioxide added to the air. Economists call costs that are not included in an item's prices *externalities* because these costs are "external to" the price.

Why are environmental costs usually not included in the prices we pay? Environmental costs often affect resources that people share—what economists call *common property resources.* We have little incentive to stop overusing common property resources for two reasons. First, we personally benefit from using these resources but share the damage with everyone else who uses them. Second, since no one person or business owns common property resources, no one can fairly charge for their use.

Consider a lake as an example of a common property resource. Suppose people use the lake and shore for boating, fishing, picnicking, and swimming. The environmental cost of using the lake is that it may become overcrowded and dirty, and plant and animal species may be harmed. But would these costs, many of which are often difficult to observe, stop you from using the lake? If people using the lake were charged a price that included these hidden costs, fewer people would use the lake, and the lake environment would be better cared for.

A branch of economics called *environmental economics* aims to get citizens, businesses, and governments to consider the full environmental costs of their economic decisions. Environmental economists argue that just as you should get what you pay for, you should pay for what you get.

423

THE METRIC SYSTEM IS USED FOR MAKING MEASUREMENTS IN SCIENCE.
THE OFFICIAL NAME OF THIS SYSTEM IS THE SYSTÈME INTERNATIONAL
D'UNITÉS, OR INTERNATIONAL SYSTEM OF MEASUREMENTS (SI).

SI Conversions

SI Units	From SI to English	From English to SI
Length		
kilometer (km) = 1,000 m	1 km = 0.62 mile	1 mile = 1.609 km
meter (m) = 100 cm	1 m = 3.28 feet	1 foot = 0.305 m
centimeter (cm) = 0.01 m	1 cm = 0.394 inch	1 inch = 2.54 cm
millimeter (mm) = 0.001 m	1 mm = 0.039 inch	
micrometer (μm) = 0.000 001 m		
nanometer (nm) = 0.000 000 001 m		
Area		
square kilometer (km^2) =100 hectares	1 km^2 = 0.3861 square mile	1 square mile = 2.590 km^2
hectare (ha) = 10,000 m^2	1 ha = 2.471 acres	1 acre = 0.4047 ha
square meter (m^2) = 10,000 cm^2	1 m^2 = 10.765 square feet	1 square foot = 0.0929 m^2
square centimeter (cm^2) = 100 mm^2	1 cm^2 = 0.155 square inch	1 square inch = 6.4516 cm^2
Volume		
liter (L) = 1,000 mL = 1 dm^3	1 L = 1.06 fluid quarts	1 fluid quart = 0.946 L
milliliter (mL) = 0.001 L = 1 cm^3	1 mL = 0.034 fluid ounce	1 fluid ounce = 29.57 mL
microliter (μL) = 0.000 001 L		
Mass		
kilogram (kg) = 1,000 g	1 kg = 2.205 pounds	1 pound = 0.4536 kg
gram (g) = 1,000 mg	1 g = 0.0353 ounce	1 ounce = 28.35 g
milligram (mg) = 0.001 g		
microgram (μg) = 0.000 001 g		
Temperature		

°F 0 20 40 60 80 100 120 140 160 180 200 220

°C −20 −10 0 10 20 30 40 50 60 70 80 90 100

Freezing point of water

Room temperature

Normal human body temperature

The top of the thermometer is marked off in degrees Fahrenheit (°F). To read the corresponding temperature in degrees Celsius (°C), look at the bottom side of the thermometer. For example, 50°F is the same temperature as 10°C. You may also use the formulas at the right for conversions.

Conversion of Fahrenheit to Celsius:
$$°C = \frac{5}{9}(°F - 32)$$

Conversion of Celsius to Fahrenheit:
$$°F = (\frac{9}{5}°C) + 32$$

GENERAL GUIDELINES FOR LABORATORY SAFETY

In the laboratory, you can engage in hands-on explorations, test your scientific ideas, and build practical laboratory skills. However, the laboratory can be a safe place or dangerous place, depending on your knowledge of and adherence to safe laboratory practices. Read and follow the basic safety guidelines described below.

BEFORE YOU BEGIN AN INVESTIGATION...

◆ Be prepared. Study assigned Investigations before class. Resolve any questions about procedures before starting work.

◆ Keep your work area uncluttered. Store books, backpacks, jackets, or other items you do not need out of the way.

◆ Arrange the materials you are using for an Investigation in an orderly fashion on your work surface. Keep laboratory materials away from the edge of the work surface.

◆ Tie back long hair and remove dangling jewelry. Roll up sleeves and secure loose clothing.

◆ Do not wear contact lenses while performing an experiment that involves chemicals. If you must wear them by a doctor's order, inform your teacher before beginning such an experiment.

◆ Avoid wearing sandals or open-toed shoes in the laboratory because they will not protect your feet if any chemical, glassware, or other object is dropped on them.

◆ Know the location of the nearest phone. Find out where emergency telephone numbers, such as the number for the nearest poison control center, can be found.

◆ Find out where laboratory safety equipment (such as eyewash stations and fire extinguishers) is stored, and know how to operate this equipment.

◆ Know the fire evacuation routes established by your school.

◆ Before you begin the experiment, review the supplies you will be using and the safety issues you should be concerned about. Be on the alert for the safety symbols shown at right. The symbols indicate particular safety concerns.

WHILE YOU ARE WORKING...

◆ Approach all laboratory work with a mature and serious attitude. Most accidents are caused by carelessness or horseplay. Decrease your risk by concentrating on your work and staying alert.

◆ Never perform an experiment not authorized by your teacher.

◆ Never work alone in the laboratory.

◆ Wear safety goggles and a lab apron when you are working with chemicals, hot liquids, lab burners, hot plates, or apparatus that could break or shatter.

◆ Wear protective gloves when working with toxic or irritating chemicals or preserved specimens and when handling plants, animals, or other items as directed by your teacher.

◆ Never look directly at the sun through any optical device or use direct sunlight to illuminate a microscope. The focused light can seriously damage your eyes.

 Wear lab apron

 Wear safety goggles

 Wear gloves

 Sharp/pointed object

 Electrical hazard

 Dangerous chemical/poison

 Flame/heat

 Glassware

 Plants

 Live animals

 Biohazard

- When heating substances in a test tube, always point the test tube *away* from yourself and others.
- Keep your hands away from the sharp or pointed ends of scalpels, scissors, and other sharp instruments.
- Observe all of the safety symbols that accompany the procedural steps of Investigations. Employ specific safety practices that are called for.
- Never put anything in your mouth, and never touch or taste substances in the laboratory unless your teacher instructs you to do so.
- If your teacher instructs you to smell a chemical in the laboratory, follow the correct procedure. The correct method is to gently fan your hand over the substance, waving its vapors toward your nose. Do not put your nose directly over the substance.
- Never eat, drink, chew gum, or apply cosmetics in the laboratory. Do not store food or beverages in the lab area.
- Report any accident, chemical spill, or unsafe incident to your teacher immediately.
- Check labels on containers of chemicals to be certain you are using the right material.
- When diluting an acid or base with water, always add the acid or base to water. Do NOT add water to the acid or base.
- Dispose of chemicals according to your teacher's instructions.
- Never return unused chemicals to the containers you obtained them from. Do not put any object into a bottle containing a laboratory chemical.

FINISHING UP

- Dispose of materials and wash used glassware and instruments according to your teacher's instructions.
- Clean tables and sinks.
- Put away all equipment and supplies.
- Make sure all water faucets, gas jets, burners, and electrical appliances are turned off.
- Return all laboratory materials and equipment to their proper places.
- Wash your hands thoroughly with soap after completing an Investigation.

EMERGENCY PROCEDURES

Don't panic. In a common laboratory emergency follow these instructions.

In the event of a fire, alert the teacher and leave the laboratory immediately.

If your clothes catch fire, STOP, DROP, and ROLL! The quickest way to smother a fire is to stop immediately, drop to the floor, and roll.

If your lab partner's clothes or hair catches fire, grab the nearest fire blanket and use it to extinguish the flames. Inform your teacher.

If a chemical gets into your eyes or on your face, wash immediately with plenty of water for at least 15 minutes. Flush under each eyelid, and have a classmate notify the teacher.

If a chemical spills on your skin or clothing, wash it off immediately with plenty of water, and notify your teacher.

If a chemical spills on the floor, do not clean it up yourself. Keep your classmates away from the area, and alert your teacher immediately.

If you receive a cut, even if it is just a small one, notify your teacher.

SAFETY WITH ANIMALS IN THE LABORATORY

Observing and experimenting with animals can vastly enrich your understanding of environmental science. Yet you must use extreme caution to assure your own safety as well as the safety and comfort of animals you work with. General rules are as follows.

- Do not touch any animal unless your teacher specifically gives you permission.
- Do not tease or disturb any animal unnecessarily.
- Do not bring any animal into the laboratory without your teacher's permission.
- Wear gloves or other appropriate protective gear when working with animals.
- Wash your hands after touching any animal.
- Inform your teacher immediately if you are scratched, bitten, stung, or otherwise harmed by an animal.
- Always follow your teacher's instructions regarding the care of laboratory animals. Ask questions if you do not clearly understand what you are supposed to do.
- Keep each laboratory animal in a suitable, escape-proof container in a location where the animal will not be frequently disturbed. Animal containers should provide adequate ventilation, warmth, and light.
- Keep the container clean. Clean cages of small birds and mammals daily.
- Provide water at all times.
- Feed animals regularly, according to their individual needs.
- If you are responsible for the care or feeding of animals, arrange for necessary care on weekends, holidays, and during vacations.
- No study that involves inflicting pain on a vertebrate animal should ever be conducted.
- Vertebrate animals must not be exposed to excessive noise, exhausting exercise, overcrowding, or other distressing stimuli.
- When an animal must be removed from the laboratory, your teacher will provide a suitable method.

SAFETY WITH PLANTS IN THE LABORATORY

Plants, as living organisms, deserve care and safe keeping. Some guidelines for their proper care are given below. On the other hand, many plants or plant parts present a safety hazard to you. Some plants or plant parts are poisonous to the point of fatality, depending on the weight of the person and the amount of plant material ingested. A common-sense approach is to take the following precautions with *all* plants.

- Never place any part of any plant in your mouth unless instructed to do so by your teacher. Seeds obtained from commercial growers can be particularly dangerous because such seeds may be coated with hormones, fungicides, or insecticides.

427

◆ Do not rub sap or juice of fruits on your skin or into an open wound.

◆ Never inhale or expose your skin or eyes to the smoke of any burning plant or plant parts.

◆ Do not bring unknown wild or cultivated plants into the laboratory.

◆ Do not eat, drink, or apply cosmetics after handling plants without first scrubbing your hands.

◆ Provide adequate light and water and appropriate soil and temperature for plants growing in the laboratory.

◆ If you are responsible for plants, make necessary arrangements for their care on weekends, holidays, and during vacations.

SAFE AND SUCCESSFUL FIELDWORK

Environmental scientists conduct much of their research in the field. For environmental scientists—and environmental science students like you—there are three important issues to consider when working in the field. One issue is your personal safety. Another issue is the successful completion of the scientific work you set out to do. The third consideration is protection of the environment you have come to study. The following guidelines will help you achieve these three goals.

◆ Dress in a manner that will keep you comfortable, warm, and dry. Wear long pants rather than shorts or a skirt. Wear sturdy shoes with closed toes. Do not wear sandals or heels. Wear waterproof shoes if you will be working in wetlands.

◆ Bring rain gear if there is any possibility of rain.

◆ Bring sunglasses, sunscreen, and insect repellent as needed.

◆ Do not go alone beyond where you can be seen or heard; travel with a partner at all times.

◆ Do not approach wild mammals, snakes, snapping turtles, or other animals that may sting, bite, scratch, or otherwise cause injury.

◆ Do not touch any animal in the wild without specific permission from your teacher.

◆ Find out whether there are likely to be poisonous plants or dangerous animals where you will be going. Learn how to identify any hazardous species.

◆ Do not pick wildflowers or touch plants or plant parts unless your teacher gives you permission. Do not eat wild plants.

◆ Report any hazard or injury to your teacher immediately.

◆ Be sure you understand the purpose of your field trip and any assignments you have been given. Bring all needed school supplies, and keep them organized in a binder, backpack, or other container.

◆ Be aware of the impact you are having on the environments you visit. Just walking over fragile areas can harm them, so stay on trails unless your teacher gives you permission to do otherwise.

◆ Sketching, photographing, and writing field notes are generally more appropriate than collecting specimens for observation. Collecting from a field site may be permitted in certain cases, but always obtain your teacher's permission first.

◆ Do not leave garbage behind at the field site. Strive to leave natural areas just as you found them.

CHEMISTRY REVIEW

ATOMS AND ELEMENTS

Every object in the universe is made up of particles of some kind of matter. Matter is anything that takes up space and has mass. All matter is made up of elements. An element is a substance that cannot be separated into simpler components by ordinary chemical means. This is because each element consists of only one kind of atom. An atom is the smallest unit of an element that has all of the properties of that element.

ATOMIC STRUCTURE

Atoms are made up of small particles called subatomic particles. The three major types of subatomic particles are **electrons, protons,** and **neutrons.** Electrons have a negative electrical charge, protons have a positive charge, and neutrons have no electrical charge. The protons and neutrons are packed close to one another to form the **nucleus.** The protons give the nucleus a positive charge. The electrons of an atom move in a region around the nucleus known as an **electron cloud.** The negatively charged electrons are attracted to the positively charged nucleus. An atom may have several energy levels in which electrons are located.

ATOMIC NUMBER

To help in the identification of elements, scientists have assigned an **atomic number** to each kind of atom. The atomic number is equal to the number of protons in the atom. Atoms with the same number of protons are all the same kind of element. In an uncharged, or electrically neutral, atom there are an equal number of protons and electrons. Therefore, the atomic number also equals the number of electrons in an uncharged atom. The number of neutrons, however, can vary for a given element. Atoms of the same element that have different numbers of neutrons are called **isotopes.**

PERIODIC TABLE OF THE ELEMENTS

A periodic table of the elements is shown on the next page. In a periodic table, the elements are arranged in order of increasing atomic number. Each element in the table is found in a separate box. As you go from left to right, each element has one more electron and one more proton than the element to its left. Each horizontal row of the table is called a **period.** Changes in chemical properties across a period correspond to changes in the elements' electron arrangements. Each vertical column of the table, known as a **group,** lists elements with similar properties. The elements in a group have similar chemical properties because they have the same number of electrons in their outer energy level. For example, the elements helium, neon, argon, krypton, xenon, and radon all have similar properties and are known as the noble gases.

MOLECULES AND COMPOUNDS

When the atoms of two or more elements are joined chemically, the resulting substance is called a **compound.** A compound is a new substance with properties different from those of the elements that compose it. For example, water (H_2O) is a compound formed when atoms of hydrogen (H) and oxygen (O) combine. The smallest complete unit of a compound that has all of the properties of that compound is called a **molecule.**

A chemical formula indicates what elements a compound contains. It also indicates the relative number of atoms of each element present. The chemical formula for water is H_2O, which indicates that each water molecule consists of

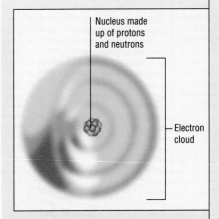

Nucleus made up of protons and neutrons

Electron cloud

The nucleus of the atom contains the protons and neutrons. The protons give the nucleus a positive charge. The negatively charged electrons are in the electron cloud surrounding the nucleus.

1																		18
1 **H** Hydrogen	2												13	14	15	16	17	**2** **He** Helium
3 **Li** Lithium	**4** **Be** Beryllium												**5** **B** Boron	**6** **C** Carbon	**7** **N** Nitrogen	**8** **O** Oxygen	**9** **F** Fluorine	**10** **Ne** Neon
11 **Na** Sodium	**12** **Mg** Magnesium	3	4	5	6	7	8	9	10	11	12		**13** **Al** Aluminum	**14** **Si** Silicon	**15** **P** Phosphorus	**16** **S** Sulfur	**17** **Cl** Chlorine	**18** **Ar** Argon
19 **K** Potassium	**20** **Ca** Calcium	**21** **Sc** Scandium	**22** **Ti** Titanium	**23** **V** Vanadium	**24** **Cr** Chromium	**25** **Mn** Manganese	**26** **Fe** Iron	**27** **Co** Cobalt	**28** **Ni** Nickel	**29** **Cu** Copper	**30** **Zn** Zinc		**31** **Ga** Gallium	**32** **Ge** Germanium	**33** **As** Arsenic	**34** **Se** Selenium	**35** **Br** Bromine	**36** **Kr** Krypton
37 **Rb** Rubidium	**38** **Sr** Strontium	**39** **Y** Yttrium	**40** **Zr** Zirconium	**41** **Nb** Niobium	**42** **Mo** Molybdenum	**43** **Tc** Technetium	**44** **Ru** Ruthenium	**45** **Rh** Rhodium	**46** **Pd** Palladium	**47** **Ag** Silver	**48** **Cd** Cadmium		**49** **In** Indium	**50** **Sn** Tin	**51** **Sb** Antimony	**52** **Te** Tellurium	**53** **I** Iodine	**54** **Xe** Xenon
55 **Cs** Cesium	**56** **Ba** Barium	**57** **La** Lanthanum	**72** **Hf** Hafnium	**73** **Ta** Tantalum	**74** **W** Tungsten	**75** **Re** Rhenium	**76** **Os** Osmium	**77** **Ir** Iridium	**78** **Pt** Platinum	**79** **Au** Gold	**80** **Hg** Mercury		**81** **Tl** Thallium	**82** **Pb** Lead	**83** **Bi** Bismuth	**84** **Po** Polonium	**85** **At** Astatine	**86** **Rn** Radon
87 **Fr** Francium	**88** **Ra** Radium	**89** **Ac** Actinium	**104** **Rf** Rutherfordium	**105** **Db** Dubnium	**106** **Sg** Seaborgium	**107** **Bh** Bohrium	**108** **Hs** Hassium	**109** **Mt** Meitnerium	**110** •	**111** •								

Atomic Number — 11 / Symbol — **Na** / Name — Sodium

• Elements synthesized but not officially named

58 **Ce** Cerium	**59** **Pr** Praseodymium	**60** **Nd** Neodymium	**61** **Pm** Promethium	**62** **Sm** Samarium	**63** **Eu** Europium	**64** **Gd** Gadolinium	**65** **Tb** Terbium	**66** **Dy** Dysprosium	**67** **Ho** Holmium	**68** **Er** Erbium	**69** **Tm** Thulium	**70** **Yb** Ytterbium	**71** **Lu** Lutetium
90 **Th** Thorium	**91** **Pa** Protactinium	**92** **U** Uranium	**93** **Np** Neptunium	**94** **Pu** Plutonium	**95** **Am** Americium	**96** **Cm** Curium	**97** **Bk** Berkelium	**98** **Cf** Californium	**99** **Es** Einsteinium	**100** **Fm** Fermium	**101** **Md** Mendelevium	**102** **No** Nobelium	**103** **Lr** Lawrencium

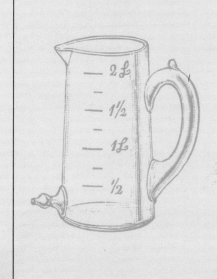

two atoms of hydrogen and one atom of oxygen. The subscript number is used after the symbol for an element to indicate how many atoms of that element are in a single molecule of the compound.

CHEMICAL EQUATIONS

A chemical reaction occurs when a chemical change takes place. (In a chemical change, new substances with new properties are formed.) A chemical equation is a useful way of describing a chemical reaction by means of chemical formulas. The equation indicates what substances react and what the products are. For example, when carbon and oxygen combine, they can form carbon dioxide. The equation for this reaction is as follows: $C + O_2 \rightarrow CO_2$

ACIDS, BASES, AND pH

An ion is an atom or group of atoms that has an electrical charge because it has lost or gained one or more electrons. When an acid, such as hydrochloric acid (HCl), is mixed with water, it separates into ions. An **acid** is a compound that produces hydrogen ions (H^+) in water. The hydrogen ions then combine with a water molecule to form a hydronium ion (H_3O^+). A solution that contains hydronium ions is an acidic solution. A **base,** on the other hand, is a substance that produces hydroxide ions (OH^-) in water.

To determine whether a solution is acidic or basic, scientists use pH. **pH** is a measure of how many hydronium ions are in solution. The pH scale ranges from 0 to 14. The middle point, pH = 7, is neutral, neither acidic nor basic. Acids have a pH of less than 7; bases have a pH of more than 7. The lower the number, the stronger the acid. The higher the number, the stronger the base. A pH scale is shown in Figure 6-18, on page 162.

GLOSSARY

A

abiotic factors (ay by AWT ik) nonliving parts of an ecosystem (35)

acid precipitation (pree sip uh TAY shun) highly acidic rain, sleet, or snow that results from the release of oxides of sulfur and nitrogen into the air from burning fossil fuels (161)

acid shock sudden influx of acidic water caused by melting acidic snows that rush into lakes and streams, killing large numbers of fish and amphibians and affecting the offspring of others (162)

adaptation (ad up TAY shun) an inherited trait that increases an organism's chance of survival and reproduction in a certain environment (46)

aesthetic (es THET ik) relating to something that is beautiful or pleasing (20)

Agenda 21 a program adopted at Earth Summit that is a blueprint for protecting the environment and promoting sustainable development (356)

age-structure histogram illustration that depicts in comparative ways the age and sex of a population (341)

agricultural revolution change from a hunting and gathering society to an agricultural society that began about 10,000 years ago (337)

air pollution (puh LOO shun) condition in which the air contains substances harmful to living things (151)

algal bloom (AL gul) excessive algae growth that forms large, floating mats (137)

amaranth (AM uh ranth) plant that can survive with little water, producing a grainlike fruit rich in protein (239)

applied science study and activity that uses information provided by pure science to solve problems; examples are engineering and medicine (13)

aquaculture (AK wuh kul chur) cultivation of fish for human use or consumption (238)

aquifer (AK wuh fur) an underground rock formation that contains water (126)

arable land (AR uh bul) fertile land that can be plowed to grow crops (231)

artificial eutrophication (yoo trawf i KAY shun) eutrophication that occurs because of the introduction of inorganic plant nutrients into a body of water through sewage and fertilizer runoff (137)

asbestos (as BES tus) mineral that separates into long, threadlike fibers; frequently used for insulation (160)

atmosphere (AT mus fir) the thin layer of gases that surrounds the Earth (173)

atomic explosion (uh TOM ik) uncontrolled release of nuclear energy (284)

autotroph (AW toh trawf) self-feeding organism that obtains its nutrients by synthesis from the environment, such as green plants (56)

B

bar graph a graph in which parallel bars are used to compare data (18)

bedrock solid rock that lies below the layers of soil (232)

benthic zone (BEN thik) bottom of a body of water; inhabited by decomposers, insect larvae, and clams (100)

biodegradable material (by oh di GRAY duh bul) a material that can be broken down by living things into simpler chemicals (305)

biodiversity (by oh duh VUR suh tee) term used to indicate the number and diversity of species on Earth (254)

Biodiversity Treaty (by oh duh VUR suh tee) agreement resulting from the Earth Summit that encourages wealthier countries to give money to poorer countries for the protection of potentially valuable species (266)

biological magnification (by uh LAWJ i kul mag ni fi KAY shun) accumulation of increasingly large amounts of a toxin within the tissues of organisms at each successive trophic level (136)

biological pest control (by uh LAJ i kul) pest control using living organisms or naturally produced chemicals (243)

biomass (BY oh mas) organic matter in plants or plant products (293)

biomes (BY ohms) regions that have distinctive climates and organisms and that contain many separate but similar ecosystems (79)

biosphere (BY oh sfir) the layer around the Earth in which life occurs naturally, extending from about 8 km above the Earth to the deepest part of the ocean, which is about 8 km deep (9)

biotic factors (by AWT ik) living parts of an ecosystem (35)

biotic potential (by AWT ik poh TEN shul) rate at which a population would grow if every new individual survived to adulthood and reproduced at maximum capacity; the characteristic maximum growth rate for a population (333)

bronchial asthma (BRAWN kee ul AZ muh) chronic disorder of the bronchial tubes characterized by wheezing and difficulty in breathing (157)

C

canopy (KAN uh pee) in a forest, the covering of tall trees whose intertwining branches absorb a great amount of sunlight and shade the area beneath (82)

captive-breeding program breeding endangered or threatened species in zoos and wild animal parks (267)

carbohydrate (kar boh HY drayt) organic compound, such as starch or sugar, made of carbon, hydrogen, and oxygen in which the ratio of hydrogen to oxygen is 2:1 (228)

carbon cycle process in an ecosystem in which producers take in carbon dioxide from the atmosphere during photosynthesis and consumers, having eaten producers, release carbon into the atmosphere as carbon dioxide (63)

carnivore (KAR nuh vohr) consumer that eats only other consumers (57)

carrying capacity the maximum number of individuals an environment can support for a long period of time (335)

catalytic converter (kat uh LIT ik) device attached to the exhaust system of automobiles to clean exhaust gases before they leave the car (153)

cellular respiration (SEL yoo lur res puh RAY shun) process of breaking down food to yield energy (57)

CFCs (chlorofluorocarbons) (klohr oh FLOOR uh kar bunz) human-made chemical compounds that are restricted in use because they destroy ozone (186)

chaparral (shap ur RAL) coastal biome with a Mediterranean climate and low-lying vegetation (94)

chronic bronchitis (KRAWN ik brawn KYT is) recurring inflammation of the mucous lining of the bronchial tubes (157)

Clean Air Act act passed by U.S. Congress that gave the EPA authority to regulate automobile emissions (153)

Clean Water Act act passed by U.S. Congress to restore and maintain the chemical, physical, and biological integrity of the nation's waters (138)

clear-cutting method of harvesting trees in which all of the trees are removed from a land area, as opposed to selective cutting (205)

climate (KLY mut) the average weather in an area over a long period of time (176)

climatogram (kly MAT oh gram) graph that shows monthly variations in temperature and precipitation (116)

climax community (KLY maks) final, stable community that forms when land is left undisturbed (67)

coevolution (koh ev uh LOO shun) two or more species evolving in response to each other (46)

commensalism (kuh MEN sul iz um) relationship between two species in which one species benefits and the other is neither harmed nor helped (42)

community (kuh MYOO nuh tee) a group of interacting populations of different species (37)

competition (kawm puh TISH un) the relationship between species that attempt to use the same limited resource (40)

compost (KAWM pohst) mixture of decomposing vegetable refuse, manure, and plants that is used as fertilizer and soil conditioner (312)

consumer (kun SOOM ur) organism that gets its energy by eating other organisms; heterotroph (56)

consumption crisis situation in which natural resources are being used up, wasted, or polluted faster than they can be renewed, replaced, or cleaned up (11)

contour plowing (KAWN toor) plowing across the slope of a hill to prevent soil from being washed away (236)

control constant factor used in an experiment to test a hypothesis (16)

Convention on International Trade in Endangered Species (CITES) offshoot of the IUCN that is responsible for limiting the sale of ivory and the killing of elephants (265)

coral reef limestone islands in the sea built by coral animals (107)

D

data (DAYT uh) observed or gathered information from which conclusions can be drawn (17)

DDT powerful insecticide; its use is limited by law because of its potential to damage the environment (58)

decomposer (dee kuhm POHZ ur) consumer that gets its food by breaking down dead organisms, causing them to rot (57)

deep-well injection method of hazardous-waste disposal in which wastes are pumped deep into the ground, below the level of the groundwater (320)

deforestation (dee fohr est AY shun) clearing trees from an area without replacing them (205)

demographer (di MAWG ruh fur) one who is involved

with the statistical science dealing with the distribution, density, and vital statistics of human populations (338)

demographic transition (dem uh GRAF ik tran ZISH un) theory that states that the economic and social progress of the industrial revolution affects a population in three stages (338)

desalinization (dee sal uh nuh ZAY shun) process in which salt is removed from salt water, as from the oceans, rendering the water fit for drinking and cooking (128)

desert biome that receives less than 10 in. of precipitation a year (95)

desertification (di zurt uh fi KAY shun) deterioration of land to the point that it becomes desertlike (235)

developed countries highly industrialized countries with high incomes and high standards of living (11)

developing countries less industrialized countries in which the average income and standard of living are low (11)

distillation (dis tuh LAY shun) process of heating a liquid and cooling and condensing the resultant vapor to separate substances and produce a more-refined liquid (128)

drought (DROUT) period when rainfall is less than average, causing crop failure (229)

drought-resistance (DROUT) characteristic of a plant that allows it to survive in areas of light or sporadic rainfall (96)

E

Earth Summit conference dealing with the environment and development sponsored by the United Nations in 1992 (355)

ecology (ee KAWL uh jee) the study of how living things interact with each other and with their nonliving environments (14)

ecosystem (EK oh sis tum) all living organisms in a certain area as well as their physical environment (34)

ecosystem approach (EK oh sis tum) conservation method that concentrates on protecting an entire ecosystem (268)

electric generator device that converts mechanical energy into electric energy (280)

electricity flow of electrons, the tiny particles that whirl around the nucleus of an atom (280)

emigration (em i GRAY shun) act of organisms leaving one area to locate in another (331)

emphysema (em fuh SEE muh) swelling of the lung tissue due to the permanent loss of elasticity or destruction of the alveoli (157)

endangered species (SPEE sheez) a species whose numbers have fallen so low that it is likely to become extinct in the near future (261)

Endangered Species Act (SPEE sheez) 1973 act of U.S. Congress designed to protect any plant or animal species in danger of extinction (261)

energy (EN ur jee) the quantity that describes the capacity to do work (55)

energy conservation (EN ur jee kawn sur VAY shun) use of energy efficiently without necessarily reducing effectiveness (287)

energy pyramid (EN ur jee PIR uh mid) diagram in the form of a pyramid that shows how energy is lost from one trophic level to the next (61)

environment (en VY run munt) the surroundings of an organism that affect its life and development (4)

environmental impact statement (en vy run MEN tul IM pakt) an assessment of the effect that a proposed project or law will have on the environment (361)

environmental refugees (en vy run MEN tul ref yoo JEEZ) people driven from their homes by severe environmental damage (345)

environmental resistance (en vy run MEN tul ree ZI stuns) the combined effect of all the factors that limit population growth

environmental science (en vy run MEN tul) study of how humans interact with the environment (4)

erosion (ee ROH zhun) the wearing away of topsoil by wind or water (234)

estivating (ES tuh vayt ing) practice of lying dormant underground during the summer (96)

estuary (ES tyoo er ee) aquatic ecosystem in which fresh water from rivers mixes with salt water from the ocean, forming a nutrient trap (105)

eutrophication (yoo trawf ih KAY shun) process that increases the amounts of nutrients, especially nitrogen and phosphorus, in a marine or aquatic ecosystem (101)

evolution (ev uh LOO shun) change in the genetic characteristics of a population from one generation to the next (44)

exosphere (EKS oh sfir) outermost portion of the Earth's atmosphere (175)

exotic species (eg ZOT ik SPEE sheez) species that is not native to a particular region (258)

experiment activity designed to test a hypothesis under controlled conditions (16)

extinction (ek STINK shun) the irreversible disappearance of a population or a species (46)

F

family planning practice of people who take measures to ensure that they will have the size of family they want (346)

famine (FAM in) widespread food shortage (229)

Federal Mining Act act of U.S. Congress to regulate the filing and settling of land claims in the West (216)

fertile soil (FURT ul) soil that can support the rapid growth of healthy plants (232)

fire-maintained communities communities where natural fires caused by lightning make secondary succession possible (68)

food chain the sequence in which energy is transferred from one organism to the next as each organism eats and is then eaten by another (59)

food web diagram showing the feeding relationships between organisms in an ecosystem (60)

fossil fuel (FAWS ul) organic substance such as coal, oil, and natural gas that is used as an energy source and is formed from the remains of organisms that lived millions of years ago (281)

fresh water water that contains little salt (122)

G

gasohol (GAS uh hol) blend of gasoline and alcohol for motor fuel (294)

genetic disorder (juh NET ik) a condition caused by abnormal genes that negatively affects an organism's form or function; may be caused by inbreeding (263)

genetic engineering (juh NET ik) scientific activity that develops desirable characteristics in an organism by altering its genes or inserting new genes in the organism's cells (250)

geothermal energy (jee oh THUR mul) energy that is drawn from heat within the Earth and used to drive electric generators (292)

germ plasm (PLAZ um) genetic material contained within the reproductive cells of organisms (268)

global warming predicted increase in Earth's temperature due to an increase in greenhouse gases in the atmosphere (184)

greenhouse effect warming effect on the air caused by heat rising from the surface of the Earth and being trapped by gases in the troposphere (180)

greenhouse gases the gases in the atmosphere that trap and radiate heat (181)

green revolution the introduction of new farming techniques and new varieties of crops, especially grains, in Asia and Latin America (229)

groundwater water that seeps down through the soil and is stored underground (126)

H

habitat (HAB i tat) place where an organism lives (38)

hazardous wastes (HAZ uhr dus) wastes that are toxic or highly corrosive or that explode easily (316)

heavy metals dense metals, such as lead and mercury, that can be toxic to organisms (321)

herbivore (HUR buh vohr) consumer that eats only producers (57)

heterotroph (HET ur oh trawf) consumer organism that gets its energy from eating other organisms (56)

high-level radioactive waste extremely hazardous radioactive waste from nuclear plants (328)

host (HOHST) organism from which a parasite takes its nourishment (41)

hunter-gatherers people who obtain their food by hunting, fishing, and gathering wild plant foods (336)

hydrocarbon (hy droh KAR bun) compound, such as methane, that is composed of hydrogen and carbon and vaporizes at normal temperatures (156)

hydroelectricity (hy droh ee lek TRIS i tee) electricity produced by converting the energy of moving water (292)

hypothesis (hy PAWTH uh sis) a testable explanation for a specific problem or question, based on what has already been learned (15)

I

immigration (im uh GRAY shun) act of organisms moving into one area from another (331)

incinerator (in SIN ur ayt ur) plant used for burning solid waste material (309)

infectious disease (in FEK shus) disease that can be transmitted to another member of the species (263)

infrastructure (in fruh STRUK chur) the necessary structures, including roads, buildings, bridges, and sewers, that a society builds for public use (199)

International Union for the Conservation of Nature and Natural Resources (IUCN) a collaboration of almost 200 governments and over 300 conservation organizations to protect species and habitats (264)

International Whaling Commission (IWC) an international agency whose purpose is to limit whaling practices for the preservation of various species (356)

irrigation (ir uh GAY shun) process of supplying water to an area by artificial means, such as ditches and sprinklers (125)

J

J-curve curved line showing exponential growth (333)

K

keystone species species of great importance to an ecosystem because its loss might cause the complete collapse of the ecosystem (258)

krill small, shrimplike crustaceans; the main food of whales (59, 60)

L

landfill waste-disposal facility where wastes are put in the ground and covered each day with a layer of dirt, plastic, or both (306)

land-use planning determining the location of homes, businesses, and protected areas before an area is developed (201)

latitude (LAT uh tood) distance measured in degrees north and south of the equator, which is 0° latitude (177)

Law of the Sea Treaty United Nations treaty that states that the laws of a coastal nation extend to 22 km (12 nautical mi.) from its coastline (142)

leachate (LEECH ayt) water that contains toxic chemicals dissolved from wastes in a landfill (307)

lichen (LY kun) composed of a particular fungus and a particular alga growing in a symbiotic relationship and forming a dual organism (69)

limiting resources those resources that limit the growth of a certain population (335)

line graph graph in which data points are plotted and connected with lines to show relationships (18)

lipid (LIP id) organic compound that contains fats and other substances that living organisms use to get energy (228)

littoral zone (LIT uh rul) the shallow-water area near the shores of lakes and ponds where sunlight reaches the bottom (100)

Love Canal location of burial of tons of hazardous chemicals from industrial waste (316, 318–319)

low-input farming farming that does not use a lot of energy, pesticides, fertilizer, and water (238)

M

malaria (muh LER ee uh) infectious disease carried by mosquitoes (242)

malnutrition (mal noo TRISH un) poor health condition caused by not consuming enough necessary nutrients (228)

marsh land covered with water; contains nonwoody plants (102)

mass extinction extinction of many species during a relatively short period of time (253)

mass transit transportation facilities to move large numbers of people at a time (202)

melaleuca tree (mel uh LOOK uh) tree imported from Australia to Florida that is threatening the existence of native plants (258)

mesosphere (MES oh sfir) atmospheric zone above the stratosphere (175)

methane (METH ayn) colorless, odorless, flammable gas present in natural gas and formed by the decomposition of plant matter (307)

mineral solid substance found in nature that consists of a single element or compound (210)

mineral resources minerals that have economic value and are useful to humans in some way (210)

multiple-use management term used to indicate variety of ways that land can be used to best serve the majority of people (214)

municipal solid waste (myoo NIS uh pul) trash produced by households and businesses (306)

mutualism (MYOO choo ul iz um) a relationship between two species in which both benefit (41)

N

native species as opposed to exotic species, native species is one original to a particular region (258)

natural resource any natural substance that humans use, such as sunlight, soil, water, plants, and animals (5)

natural selection term used to describe the unequal survival and reproduction of organisms that results from the presence or absence of particular inherited traits (43)

niche (NICH) an organism's way of life (38)

nitrogen cycle (NY truh jun) process by which atmospheric nitrogen is converted into compounds for use by plants and animals, eventually returned by decay (64)

nitrogen-fixing bacteria (NY truh jun, bak TIR ee uh) bacteria that convert nitrogen gas from the atmosphere into a form that plants can use (64)

nonpoint pollution (puh LOO shun) pollution that comes from many sources rather than from a single specific site; an example is pollution that reaches a body of water from streets and storm sewers (133)

nonrenewable resources resources that can be used up faster than they can be replenished naturally, such as coal, oil, and natural gas (6, 282)

non-urban land rural land, such as forest, grassland, and farmland, that is not densely populated and that does not have a large infrastructure (204)

no-till farming procedure in which the seeds of the next crop are planted in slits cut into the soil through the remains of the previous crop (237)

nuclear energy (NOO klee ur) energy that exists within the nucleus of an atom (283)

nuclear fission (NOO klee ur FIZ shun) process in which subatomic bonds that bind the components of the atomic nucleus are broken apart, releasing huge amounts of energy (283)

nuclear fusion (NOO klee ur FYOO shun) the process in which lightweight atomic nuclei combine to form a heavier nucleus, releasing huge amounts of energy; basically the opposite of nuclear fission (286)

O

observation use of our senses to report the characteristics of properties and phenomena (14)

omnivore (AWM ni vohr) consumer that eats both plants and animals (57)

open-pit mining method of mining in which large holes are dug in the ground to remove materials such as ore, sand, gravel, and building stone (210)

open space areas purposely left undeveloped for the enjoyment of urban residents (203)

Operation GreenThumb (OGT) program sponsored by New York City's Department of General Services enabling nonprofit organizations to create community vegetable and flower gardens (224)

ore rock that contains minerals (210)

organic farming (ohr GAN ik) method of growing plants without synthetic pesticides or fertilizers (238)

organism (OHR guh niz um) an individual living thing (37)

overgrazing damage to a grassland caused by too many animals eating in a limited area; often so harmful that the grass cannot recover (208)

overpopulation condition in which an area cannot support its human population with its available resources, or in which the population, because of growth, suffers problems that affect its general welfare (342)

ozone (OH zohn) form of oxygen with molecules made of three oxygen atoms (186)

P

pampas (PAWM puz) large, treeless plains of Argentina and other parts of South America (92)

parasite (PAR uh syt) organism that lives in or on another organism and feeds on it without immediately killing it (41)

parasitism (PAR uh syt iz um) the relationship between a parasite and its host (41)

particulate (par TIK yoo lit) very small, separate particles, as in soot and ash (152)

passive solar heating (PAS iv SOH lur) system in which sunlight is used to heat buildings directly without pumps or fans (288)

pathogens (PATH uh juns) disease-causing organisms, such as bacteria, viruses, and parasites (136, 244)

perennial grass (pur EN ee ul) tall grass plants that live several years (as opposed to annual grasses) and that have a tendency to shade the ground, limiting growth of smaller plants (68)

permafrost (PUR muh frawst) permanently frozen soil a few inches below the active soil in tundra biomes (97)

pest any organism that is not wanted or that exists in large enough numbers to cause damage (240)

pesticides (PES tuh sydz) substances that kill pests (241)

pheromone (FER uh mohn) chemical substance secreted externally by certain animals that conveys information to and produces certain responses in other animals of the same species (244)

pH number measure of the acidity or basicity of a substance (162)

photodegradable plastic (foht oh dee GRAY duh bul) plastic that will decompose into smaller pieces under certain kinds of radiant energy, especially ultraviolet light (314)

photosynthesis (foht oh SIN thuh sis) biological synthesis of chemical compounds in the presence of light; produces organic substances such as sugar (55)

pioneers (py uh NIRS) first organisms to colonize any newly available area and start the process of succession (67)

poaching illegal hunting (257)

point pollution (puh LOO shun) pollution discharged from a single source, such as from a factory or wastewater treatment plant (132)

pollution (puh LOO shun) the contamination of the air, water, or soil (8)

population (pawp yoo LAY shun) a group of individuals of the same species living in a particular place (37)

population crisis (pawp yoo LAY shun) situation in which the number of people grows so quickly that a region cannot support them (11)

prairie (PRER ee) large area of level or slightly rolling grasslands (92)

precipitation (pree sip uh TAY shun) rain, sleet, snow, or hail that has condensed from water vapor in the atmosphere and returns to the Earth's surface (63)

predation (pree DAY shun) the act of killing and eating another organism (39)

predator (PRED uh tur) organism that kills and eats another organism (39)

prediction (pree DIK shun) statement about what one expects will happen (15)

pressure vessel steel casing containing cooling fluid that surrounds the reactor in a nuclear power plant (284)

prey (PRAY) organism that is killed and eaten by a predator (39)

primary pollutant (PRY mer ee puh LOOT nt) pollutant put directly into the air by human activity, such as soot from smoke (152)

primary succession (PRY mer ee suk SESH un) succession that occurs in areas where no ecosystem has existed previously (69)

producer (proh DOOS ur) organism that makes its own food; autotroph (56)

protein (PROH teen) group of organic compounds used for food by living organisms and contained in meats and dairy products (228)

pure science study and activity that seek answers to questions about how the world works; examples are biology and physics (13)

R

radon gas (RAY dawn) gas produced naturally in the Earth by the decay of uranium (160)

rangeland grassland used for grazing animals (208)

reactor (ree AK tur) main element of nuclear power plant from which a steady, manageable amount of energy is released (284)

recharge zone area of land on the Earth's surface from which groundwater originates (127)

reclamation (REK luh may shun) the process of restoring land to the condition it was in before mining operations began (212)

recycling (ree SY kling) reusing discarded material (311)

reforestation (ree fohr is STAY shun) process of replacing trees that have died or been cut down (206)

remora (REM ur uh) small fish that cling to larger fish and other bodies by means of a sucking disc (42)

renewable resources abundant natural resources that are continually produced, such as trees and sunlight (6, 282)

reservoir (REZ ur vwawr) artificial lake used to store water, control drainage, and provide recreation (125)

resistance (ri ZIS tuns) the ability of a pest population to tolerate a particular pesticide (243)

resource anything that is ready for use or that can be drawn on for use by an organism (40)

Resource Conservation and Recovery Act (RCRA) act of U.S. Congress that requires new landfills to be built with safeguards to reduce pollution problems (307)

resource depletion (dee PLEE shun) exhaustion of a natural resource, such as the extraction of oil from the Earth or the absence of nutrients from soil that has been overused (5)

reverse osmosis (aws MOH sis) desalinization process in which pressure is used to push water through a semipermeable membrane that will not permit salts to pass (128)

rhizoids (RY zoidz) rootlike structures of mosses and ferns that attach them to rocks and substratum (104)

rhizome (RY zohm) creeping stem that lies below the soil but that differs from a root in having leaves and shoots and producing roots from its undersurface (87)

S

salinization (sal uh ni ZAY shun) the accumulation of salts in the soil (238)

savanna (suh VAN uh) tropical grassland biome with a short rainy season (90)

science systematized knowledge derived from observation, study, and experimentation; also the activity of specialists to add to the body of this knowledge (14)

scientific methods methods scientists use to answer questions; includes observing, hypothesizing and predicting, experimenting, organizing and interpreting, and reporting (14)

S-curve curved line that shows a population reaching its carrying capacity and then falling below it (335)

secondary pollutant (SEK un der ee puh LOOT nt) pollutant that forms when a primary pollutant or a naturally occurring substance, such as water, comes into contact with other primary pollutants and a chemical reaction takes place (152)

secondary succession (SEK un der ee suk SESH un) pattern of change in an area where an ecosystem has previously existed (67)

selective cutting method of harvesting only middle-aged or mature trees individually or in small groups (206)

sick-building syndrome condition of buildings with particularly poor air quality; frequently caused by sealed windows and poor air circulation (158)

sludge (SLUJ) solid material left over after wastewater treatment (136)

smog air pollution over urban areas that reduces visibility; combination of the words *smoke* and *fog* (156)

solar cells (SOH lur) devices that convert the sun's energy directly into electricity (290)

solar energy (SOH lur) energy from the sun (288)

solar water heating (SOH lur) system that uses solar energy to heat water for household use (289)

solid waste any discarded material that is not a liquid or gas (304)

specialists organisms that are adapted to exploit a particular resource to avoid competition (82)

species (SPEE sheez) a group of organisms that are able to produce fertile offspring and that resemble each other in appearance, behavior, and internal structure (37)

steppe (STEP) large, grassy plains area with few trees in southeast Europe and Asia (92)

stratosphere (STRAT uh sfir) one of the five layers of the atmosphere, lying immediately above the troposphere and extending from 10 km to about 50 km above the Earth's surface (175)

strip mining method of mining in which huge machines clear away large strips of the Earth's surface, as in phosphate mining (210)

subsistence farmers (sub SIS tuns) farmers who grow only enough food to feed their families (229)

suburban sprawl (suh BUR bun) low-density development that spreads out around cities (200)

succession (suk SESH un) the regular pattern of changes over time in the types of species in a community (66)

Superfund Act act passed by the U.S. Congress to discourage illegal dumping of hazardous wastes and to pay for the cleanup of abandoned waste sites (317)

surface impoundment (SUR fis im POUND ment) a pond with a sealed bottom that serves as a disposal facility in which wastes settle to the bottom (320)

surface water fresh water found above ground in lakes, ponds, rivers, and streams (123)

sustainable world world in which human populations can continue to exist indefinitely with a high standard of living and health (12)

swamp land covered with water; contains woody plants or shrubs (103)

synthetic fertilizer (sin THET ik) fertilizer produced in factories and used in place of manure and plant wastes (232)

T

taiga (TY guh) biome dominated by conifers and characterized by harsh winters; occurs just below the Arctic Circle; also called northern coniferous forest (88)

temperate deciduous forest (dee SIJ oo us) forest in an area of extreme seasonal variation in which trees drop their leaves each fall (86)

temperate grassland biome occurring in semi-arid interiors of continents; examples are the prairies of North America, the steppes of Russia and Ukraine, and the pampas of South America (92)

temperate rain forest cool, humid biome where tree branches are draped with mosses, tree trunks are covered with lichens, and the forest floor is covered with ferns (84)

thermal inversion (THUR mul in VUR shun) atmospheric condition in which the air above is warmer than the air below, sometimes trapping pollutants near the Earth's surface (155)

thermal pollution (THUR mul puh LOO shun) addition of excessive amounts of heat to a body of water, such as in runoff from industrial cooling systems (137)

thermosphere (THUR moh sfir) atmospheric zone above the mesosphere (175)

threatened species (SPEE sheez) species likely to become endangered if protective measures are not taken immediately (261)

topsoil loose surface layer of soil (232)

trophic level (TROHF ik) a step in the transfer of energy through an ecosystem; the level of a food chain that an organism occupies (60)

tropical rain forest warm, wet biome that occurs in a belt around the Earth near the equator and that contains the greatest diversity of organisms on Earth (80)

tropical savanna (suh VAN uh) plain or grassland characterized by scattered trees (90)

troposphere (TROH poh sfir) one of the five layers of the atmosphere, extending from the Earth's surface to about 10 km above the surface (175)

tundra (TUN druh) biome without trees, where grasses and tough shrubs grow in the frozen soil; extends from the Arctic Circle to the North Pole (97)

typhus (TY fus) infectious disease carried by lice (242)

U

ultraviolet (UV) light (ul truh VY oh lit) harmful light from the sun (186)

understory shrubs and plants that grow beneath the main canopy of a forest (82)

urban area land area with dense population and with the housing and infrastructure necessary for citizens' well-being (198)

urban crisis (UR bun) condition in which more people live in a city than its infrastructure can support (199)

urbanization (ur bun ih ZAY shun) movement of people from rural areas to cities (199)

urban-renewal project program to rebuild a worn-down urban area by providing improved facilities (202)

V

value what a person considers important, as when making a decision (20)

variable (VER ee uh bul) changed or changing factor used to test a hypothesis in an experiment (16)

VOCs (volatile organic compounds) chemical compounds that form toxic fumes (155)

W

wastewater treatment plant structure that filters out contaminants from wastewater (134)

water cycle the continual process by which water circulates between the atmosphere and the Earth (62)

water pollution (puh LOO shun) introduction of foreign substances into water that degrade its quality, limit its use, and affect organisms living in it or drinking it (131)

watershed entire area of land that is drained by a river (123)

weather conditions in the atmosphere at a particular place and particular moment (176)

wetland area of land covered by water for at least part of the year (102)

wilderness designated natural area where the land and the ecosystems it supports are protected (215)

wind energy (EN ur jee) energy captured as wind turns a turbine and generates electricity; an indirect form of solar energy (291)

Y

yield (YEELD) amount of crops produced per unit area (229)

INDEX

Polk County (FL) courthouse, *160*
pollutant(s)
  air (table), *152*
  of estuaries, 106
  natural, 151
  in oceans, 112
  in rivers, 104
pollution, defined, 8
  freshwater, 131–139
  nonpoint, *133*, 138
  ocean, 140–142
  and pesticides, 242
  point, 132–133
  See also air pollution; water pollution
pond, 38
  lake and, ecosystems, 100–102
poor and wealthy nations, 359
population, defined, 37, *331*
population, human, 336–341
  and birth rate, 338–340
  crisis, 11
  in developed and developing countries, 11
  and economic growth, 353
  explosion, investigating, 350–351
  growth of, *11, 333, 337*–338
  limiting growth of, 352–353
  rate of growth of, 333–334
  world, 254–258
positive feedback process, 182
potato famine in Ireland, 260
power plant, *281*
  biomass, *293*
prairies, 92
precipitation, 63, 176
  See also acid precipitation
predation, 39–40
predators, 39–40, 244
prescription drugs, from plants, 259
prey, 39
Pribilof Islands (AK), *332*–333
primary pollutant, 152–*153*
primary succession, 69–*70*
producers, 56, 74–75
protected habitat plan (map), *22*
protein, 228, 236
Prudhoe Bay (AK) oil production complex, 118–119

public lands
  chart of, *215*
  "for the asking," 216–217
  managing, 214–215
  troubled, 216–217
Public Rangelands Improvement Act of 1978, 209
Puerto Vallarta (Mexico), wild corn of, 260
Puget Sound, 6
pure science, 13

R

radiation poisoning, 285
radioactive wastes, 285
radioactivity, 285–286
radon gas, 160
rain forest, 38
  in Costa Rica, 30–31
  habitat, *270*
  preserving, 83
  See also temperate rain forest; tropical rain forest
rain-shadow effect, *95*
RAMSAR, 358
ranch aquaculture, 236
ranching, 208–209
  and wolves, 76–77
range, maintaining the, 209
recharge zone, 127
reclamation, *212*
recycled products, *314*
recycling, *12, 311*–312
  activities (diagram), *311*
  paint, *321*
  researcher, 313
  water, 139
red medusa jellyfish, *110*
reforestation, 206–207
refugees, environmental, *345*
reindeer in Alaska, *332*–334
religious values, 353
remoras, *42*
renewable resources, 6–7, 122, 282
research wildlife biologist, *374*–375
reservoir, *125*
resistance to pesticides, 243
Resource Conservation and Recovery Act (RCRA), 307–308, 317
resource depletion, 5–6
resources
  competition for, 40, *334*–335
  nonrenewable, 6, 282
  renewable, 6–7, 122
respiration, cellular, 57–58, 174
Reynolds, Michael, 370–371

rice, harvesting, *227*
Rio de Janeiro (Brazil), *355*–*356*
river, 124
  ecosystems, 103–104
rock, breakdown of, *70*
Rocky Mountain Institute (RMI), *288*–289
Rocky Mountains, 93
rosy periwinkle, *259*
Ruhr Valley (Germany), 163
rural areas, *198*

S

safety
  classroom and laboratory, xvi
  and genetic engineering, 251
  and nuclear fusion, 285–286
  and nuclear wastes, 301
Sahel region (Africa), *235*–236
salamanders, *260*
salinization, 238–239
salt-tolerant crops, 238–239
Saudi Arabia, desalinization in, 128–129
savanna, 38, *90*–91
Schulz, Charles M., 330
science, described, 13–19
scientific article, 19
scientific method, 14–19
scientist, *14*–19
  ozone, 194–195
scrubbers, *155*
S-curve, *335*
sea levels and weather patterns, 184
sea otter, *141, 258*–259
seasons, cause of, 179
Seattle (WA), 6–7
secondary pollutant, 152–153
secondary succession, 67–68
selection. *See* natural selection
selective cutting of forests, *206*
Seneca, 153
Serrano, Angeles, 354
sewage. *See* wastewater
sewage disposal and mortality, 343
sharks, *42*
shopping, environmental, 392–393
sick-building syndrome, 158
Sierra Nevada (CA), 179
single variable, 16–17
sludge, *136*
smog, *156*
  See also air pollution

smoke, 156
snail darters, 264–265
Sofia Protocol, 164
soil
  fertile, 232, *233*
  formation of, 233
  organisms in (table), *233*
  worldwide erosion of (map), *234*
soil conservation, 236–238
soil erosion, 208, 234
solar cells, *290*–291
solar collectors, 289–290
solar design, investigating, 298–299
solar energy, 55, 288–291
  disadvantages of, 291
  and global circulation, 177
  and latitude, 177
  at RMI, 288–289
solar water heating, 289–291
solid waste, 303–309
  composition of, 306
  graph of, *306*
  municipal, 306
  See also waste
solid-waste treatment
  incinerators, *309*
  landfills, 5, 306–309
Solomon, Susan, 194–195
Somalia, *230*, 345
Somerville, Richard, *384*–385
Southern Hemisphere
  and global warming, 183
  and the sun, 179
South Pole, 177
Soviet Union, nuclear accidents in, *285*
soybeans, *64*
spadefoot toads, 96–97
species
  aesthetic reasons for preserving, 260
  defined, 37
  exotic, 258
  interactions of, 39–42
  keystone, 258
  known to exist (chart), *254*
  practical uses of, 259–260
  saving individual, 267–268
  See also endangered species; evolution
spotted owl, 276–277
spotted warbler
  hypothetical study of, 22–24
statement of forest principles, 358

steppes (Russia/
　　Ukraine), 92
Stout, Diane, *378–379*
stratosphere, 175, 186
strip-mining, 210
subsistence farming, 229
suburban sprawl, *200*
succession, 66–67
　　See also primary
　　　　succession; secondary
　　　　succession
sulfur dioxide, 9, 152, 154
sulfur pollution, 183
sulfuric acid, 161
sun, as the ultimate
　　source of energy, 55
sunlight
　　as energy resource, 282
　　and photosynthesis, 55
　　in sea, 109, 110
Superfund Act, *317*
surface impoundment, 320
surface water, 123–125
sustainable agriculture, 238
sustainable future
　　defined, 355
　　international cooperation
　　　　for, 355–359
　　and U.S. policies, 360–364
sustainable world, 12
swamps, 103
swim bladders, 110
synthetic materials, 305

T

taiga, *88–89*
taxol, 259
Tellico Dam (TN), 264
temperate deciduous
　　forests, *85–87*
temperate grasslands
　　characteristics of, *92–93*
　　threats to, *93*
temperate rain forests,
　　84–85
temperature, 176
territorial sea, 142
Texas Parks and Wildlife
　　Nongame Program, 53
thermal inversions, *155–156*
thermal pollution, 137–138
thermosphere, 175
Thoreau, Henry David, 252
threatened species, 261–262
Three Mile Island (PA), 286
topsoil, 232, 234
traits, 43, 44
Tread Lightly program, 218
tree, planting a, *398–399*
trees, and removal of
　　carbon dioxide, *185*
　　See also forests
trophic levels, 60–61

tropical rain forests, 9,
　　80–83, 183, *256*
　　biological diversity of,
　　　　80–81
　　See also rain forest
troposphere, 175, 176, 180
trout farm, *237*
tube worms, *56*
tundra, 97–99
turbine, 291
Turkey, dams in, 125
Two Forks Dam,
　　Platte River, *362*
typhoons, 184

U

ultraviolet (UV) light,
　　186–187
　　adverse effects of,
　　　　(table), *188*
ultraviolet radiation,
　　174, 186–*187*
understory vegetation, 53
United Nations, 342
United Nations Conference
　　on Environment and
　　Development, 266
United States
　　demographic
　　　　changes in, 338–339
　　environmental agencies
　　　　of (table), *361*
　　environmental
　　　　policies of, 360–364
　　land use in (graph), *198*
　　public land in, 213–218
U.S. Census Bureau, 198
U.S. Fish and Wildlife Ser-
　　vice, 4, 76, 261,
　　263, 270
U.S. Office of Technology
　　Assessment, 318
Upper Silesia (Poland), 158
uranium fuel pellets, *285*
uranium-235, 285
urban crisis, 199, 344
urbanization, 199–200
urban-rural connection, 198

V

values, *20*–24
　　cultural, 353
　　religious, 353
vinblastine, 259
viper fish, *110*
volatile organic compounds
　　(VOCs), 152, 155

W

Walker, Jana, 214, *380–381*
Ware, Lewis, *386*
waste(s)
　　as building materials,
　　　　370–371

hazardous, 316–322
　　and investigation of fast
　　　　food, 326–327
　　kinds of, 305
　　from mines, 211–212
　　nuclear, 285–286
　　in packaging, *310*
　　producing less, 310
　　radioactive, 285
　　solid, 303–309
　　solving problems of
　　　　(table), 315
　　where it goes, *306–309*
wastewater
　　treatment plants, 134, *135*
water
　　and human health, 121
　　and mortality rate,
　　　　343–344
　　flushing less, *404*
　　shortages, 128
　　towing, 129
　　See also fresh water;
　　　　groundwater; surface
　　　　water; water cycle;
　　　　water pollution
water conservation, 129–130
　　and plants vs. grasses, *130*
　　table of, *130*
water contaminants,
　　148–149
water cycle, *62–63,*
　　122, 123
water pollutants, 132
water pollution, 4, *131*
　　causes of, 131–132
　　cleaning up, 138–139
　　and ecosystems, 136–137
　　Elizabeth Philip on,
　　　　148–149
　　See also pollution,
　　　　freshwater; pollution,
　　　　ocean
water purification, 149
water resources, 121–130
water rights, 125
water table and storage of
　　nuclear wastes, 328
water-treatment plant, *124*
water usage
　　indoor (chart), *129*
　　in the United States
　　　　(graph), *121*
water vapor, 181
waterborne diseases, 343
watershed, *123*
wealthy and poor
　　nations, 359
weather, 176, 184
　　See also climate
weathering and soil forma-
　　tion (diagram), *234*
Weekly Bulletin, 362
Werner, Dagmar, 30–31

wetlands, 102–103, 268
　　location of, *102*
whales, 110, *260,* 356
whaling controversy,
　　356–357
whooping crane, 256–257
wilderness areas, 215–218
Wilderness Act of 1964, 215
wildlife biologist, research,
　　374–375
wildlife garden, creating a,
　　396–*397*
wind(s), 176
wind energy, 282, 291
windmill, 291
wolf recovery plan, 76–77
wood, worldwide
　　use of, 205
woodland ecosystems, 312
　　See also forest(s)
world
　　as a living system, 260
World Bank, 342
World Health
　　Organization, 33
World Wildlife Fund,
　　264–265

Y

Yamasaki, Mariko, *374–375*
yeast and water
　　purification, 149
Yellowstone National Park
　　(ID, WY), 76, *213*
　　fires in, 68–69
yield, crop, 229
Yucca Mountain (NV),
　　328–329

Z

zooplankton, 100, 106, 110

PHOTOGRAPHY CREDITS

Abbreviations used: (t) top, (c) center, (b) bottom, (l) left, (r) right, (bckgd) background

COVER PHOTO CREDITS

FRONT COVER: water testing, Tom Stewart/The Stock Market; erosion, Carr Clifton/Minden Pictures; Ganges delta, World Perspectives/Tony Stone Images; ferns, Pat O'Hara/Tony Stone Images; cheetah, Jeff Hunter/Image Bank; clouds, Robert Stahl/Tony Stone Images; windmills, Lester Lefkowitz/The Stock Market; lungs, Photo Researchers, Inc.; contour plowing, D. Wigget/Natural Selection; sunflower, Jim Brandenburg/Minden Pictures; highways, Jose Fuste Raga/The Stock Market

BACK COVER PHOTO

Pat O'Hara/Tony Stone Images

TITLE PAGE

Jim Brandenburg/Minden Pictures

TABLE OF CONTENTS

Page iv(tl), Surgio Purtell/FOCA; iv(bl), courtesy Cliff Lerner; v(tr), Laurance B. Aiuppy; v(br), Ernest H. Rogers/Sea Images; vi(tl), Frans Lanting/Minden Pictures; vi(cl), Sam Dudgeon/HRW photo; vi(bl), Audubon Society and General Electric vii(tr), Sam Dudgeon/HRW photo; vii(br), Victoria Smith/HRW photo; viii(tl), Dr. Jeffrey Kiehl/National Center for Atmospheric Research; viii(bl), Fernando Bueno/Image Bank; ix(tr), Sam Dudgeon/HRW Photo; ix(r), William E. Ferguson; ix(br), Ray Richardson/Animals Animals/Earth Scenes; x(tl), Sam Dudgeon/HRW photo; x(l), Cameramann International; xi(tr), Joe McDonald; xi(br), Jean-Leo Dugast/Panos Pictures; xii(tl), Solar Survival Architecture, Taos; xii(cl), Ron Sherman; xii(bl), Stephen Dalton/O.S.F./Animals Animals/Earth Scenes; xiii(tr), Michelle Bridwell/Frontera Fotos; xiii(cr), Richard T. Bryant; xiii(br), Art Wolfe, Inc.

TO THE STUDENT

Page xiv(tl), John Cancalosi/Peter Arnold, Inc.; xiv(c), Bob Wolf; xiv(bl), Sam Dudgeon/HRW photo; xiv(br), Karen Allen; xv(tl), The Zoological Society of San Diego; xv(r), Gerhard Gscheidle/Peter Arnold, Inc.

CHAPTER 1

Page 2(bckgd), Luiz C. Marigo/Peter Arnold, Inc.; 2(b), Harvey Lloyd/Peter Arnold, Inc.; 2(cl), Russell Dian/HRW photo; 2(c), Doug Cheeseman/Peter Arnold, Inc.; 2(cr), Jason Laure/Laure' Communications; 2-3(c), Y. Arthus-Bertrand/Peter Arnold, Inc.; 3(b), courtesy Cliff Lerner; 3(bl), Julie Robinson; 4(c), Peter Frank/Tony Stone Images; 5(tr), Art Wolfe/Tony Stone Images; 7(tr), Renee Lynn/Davis/Lynn Images; 7(bl), Visuals Unlimited; 7(cr), Wolfgang Kaehler; 8(t), Norbert Wu; 8(cl), Karen Allen; 9(tr), Ron Sherman/Tony Stone Images; 9(tl), Jacques Janhoux/Tony Stone Images; 9(bl), Francis and Donna Caldwell/Affordable Photo Stock; 10(br), Paula Lerner/Tony Stone Images; 10(tl), Elizabeth Harris/Tony Stone Images; 12(t), Renee Lynn/Davis/Lynn Images; 12(tl), Sam Dudgeon/HRW photo; 12(cr), Chromosohm Sohm/Tony Stone Images; 13(inset), Peter Yates/SABA Press Photos, Inc.; 13(bl), Paul S. Conklin; 13(br), Bruce Forster/Tony Stone Images; 14(cl), Brownie Harris/Tony Stone Images; 14(br), Terry Vine/Tony Stone Images; 14(bl), John Langford/HRW photo; 15(br), courtesy Cliff Lerner; 16(b), Anthony Toscano; 17(tr), Sam Dudgeon/HRW photo; 18(tr), Surgio Purtell/FOCA/HRW photo; 19(tl), Stock Editions/HRW photo; 21(t), Mickey Gibson/Animals Animals/Earth Scenes; 22(tl), Charles Mauzy/Tony Stone Images; 22(bl), Michelle Bridwell/Frontera Fotos; 23(tr); 29(br), Sam Dudgeon/HRW photo; 30-31(all) Karen Allen

CHAPTER 2

Page 35(cl), Robert Landau/Westlight; 35(br), F. Stuart Westmoreland/Tony Stone Images; 35(bl), 35(tc), George O. Miller; 35(cl), Arthur C. Smith III/Grant Heilman Photography; 37(c), George O. Miller/TexaStock; 37(tr), Frans Lanting/Minden Pictures; 37(cl), Lynn M. Stone; 37(tl), Larry Source/Photo Researchers, Inc.; 38(tc), Tom Brakefield/Tom Brakefield Photography; 38(cr), Y. Arthus-Bertrand/Peter Arnold, Inc.; 38(tl), Heather Angel/Biofotos; 38(tr), Beverly Joubert/National Geographic Society; 39(bl), W. Perry Conway; 39(cr), Alan Blank/Tony Stone; 39(br), Harry M. Walker; 39(bl), W. Perry Conway; 39(c), Russ Linne/Comstock; 40(c), Gary Braasch Photography; 40(bl), Greg Brant/Texas Department of Agriculture; 40(br), William H. Allen, Jr.; 40(cr), Kenneth Garrett; 41(tl), Heather Angel/Biofotos; 41(tr), Heather Angel/Biofotos; 41(inset), Runk Schoenberger/Grant Heilman Photography; 41(tl), Runk Schoenberger/Grant Heilman Photography; 42(tr), Patti Murray/Animals Animals/Earth Scenes; 42(br), Mark Stouffer/Animals Animals/Earth Scenes; 43(br), John Cancalosi/Peter Arnold, Inc.; 44(br), Kim Taylor/Bruce Coleman, Ltd.; 44(br), Kim Taylor/Bruce Coleman, Ltd.; 46(tl), Heather Angel/Biofotos; 51(tr), Sam Dudgeon/HRW photo; 51(br), David Dvorak, Jr.; 52, 53 Lincoln Brower

CHAPTER 3

Page 55(br), Philippe Giraud/Sygma; 55(cr), Fred Atwood Photography; 55(inset), Jim Brandenburg/Minden Pictures; 56(tl), NASA; 56(cl), Doug Wilson/Westlight; 56(tc), David R. Frazier Photolibrary; 56(tr), Tom & Pat Leeson/Photo Researchers, Inc.; 56(bl), Institute of Marine and Coastal Sciences, Rutgers, The State University; 57(br), Russell Dian/HRW photo; 57(cl), Hans Pfletschinger/Peter Arnold, Inc.; 57(cr), Michael Fairchild/Peter Arnold, Inc.; 57(bl), Russell Dian/HRW photo; 57(br), Courtesy Minister of the Environment, Quebec; 59(bc), David R. Frazier Photolibrary; 64(bl), Runk Schoenberger/Grant Heilman Photography; 66(Left), Tom Zimberoff/Sygma; 66(br), William E. Ferguson; 67(cr), Grant Heilman/Grant Heilman Photography; 69(tr), SuperStock; 69(bl), Vanuga Photography; 70(br), David R. Frazier Photolibrary; 74(bc), Sam Dudgeon/HRW photo; 76-77(bc), Courtesy of International Wolf Center; 77(cr), Art Wolfe, Inc.

CHAPTER 4

Page 80-81(bckgd), 80(bl), 80(br), Tom Boyden; 80 (bc), Robert and Linda Mitchell; 81(tr), 81(c), Tom Boyden; 81(tc), 81(bl), Frans Lanting/Minden Pictures; 82(bl), Merlin D. Tuttle/Bat Conservation International; 82(br), Whit Bronaugh; 83(tr), Thomas C. Boyden; 83(b), Alberto Venzago/Magnum Photos; 84(tr), Gary Braasch Photography; 85(b), Renee Lynn/Photo Researchers, Inc.; 86(bl), Mark Antman/The Image Works; 86(bc), Mark Antman/The Image Works; 86(br), Mark Antman/The Image Works; 87(tc), Carl R. Sams II/Peter Arnold, Inc.; 87(tr), John Cancalosi/Peter Arnold, Inc.; 87(cr), S.J. Kraseman/Peter Arnold, Inc.; 88(br), Ron Levy; 88(Inset), Peter K. Ziminski/Visuals Unlimited; 89(Center Right), Daniel J. Cox/DJC & Associates; 89(c), 89(cl), Art Wolfe, Inc.; 89(bl), 89(bc), S. J. Krasemann/Peter Arnold, Inc.;

91(t), Tim Laman/The Wildlife Collection/Hillstrom Stock Photo; 91(bl), 91(br), Lynn M. Stone; 91(cr), Ric Ergenbright; 92(cl), Laurence Parent; 92(bl), Joel Bennett/Peter Arnold, Inc.; 92(br), Jeff Gnass; 93(bl), Carl Kurtz; 93(cr), Thomas A. Wiewandt, Ph.D.; 94(b), Bobbi Lane/Tony Stone Images; 94(br), Ernest H. Rogers/Sea Images; 95(tr), William E. Ferguson; 96(t), Jon Mark Stewart/Biological Photo Service; 96(tl), Dan Porges/Peter Arnold, Inc.; 96(cr), Frans Lanting/Minden Pictures; 97(tl), Anthony Bannister/NHPA; 98(t), Jo Overholt/AlaskaStock Images; 98(bl), S.J. Krasemann/Peter Arnold, Inc.; 99(cl), John W. Warden/West Stock; 99(tc), George Herben/AlaskaStock Images; 101(t), Gary Braasch; 101(bl), Robert and Linda Mitchell; 101(inset), Jack Dermid/Bruce Coleman, Ltd.; 101(cr), Doug Wechsler; 101(br), Doug Wechsler/Science VU/Visuals Unlimited; 102(bl), Doug Wechsler; 103(tr), Doug Wechsler; 104(tc), Gary Braasch ; 104(tr), Gary Braasch ; 105(b), Fred Bavendam; 106(cl), Fred Bavendam/Peter Arnold, Inc.; 107(b), Norbert Wu; 108(t), Norbert Wu; 108(b), Galen Rowell/Hillstrom Stock Photo; 109(bl), Flip Nicklin/Minden Pictures; 110(tl), Neil G. McDaniel/Photo Researchers, Inc.; 110(br), Norbert Wu/Peter Arnold, Inc.; 111(tl), Visuals Unlimited; 112(t), Kim Heacox/DRK Photo; 117(br), Glen Allison/Tony Stone Images; 118(bl), Craig Hartley/FPG International; 118(tl), Johnny Johnson/AlaskaStock Images; 118-119(b), Ken Graham/Tony Stone; 119(tr), Clyde H. Smith/FPG International

CHAPTER 5

Page 121(b), SI/J.P. Nova/Nawrocki Stock Photo; 122(br), Stephen J. Krasemann/DRK Photo; 123(b), Georg Gerster/Comstock; 124(br), Jim Richardson/Westlight; 125(tr), Coskun Aral/SIPA Press; 125(br), C.C. Lockwood/DRK Photo; 127(b), Dwight B. Miller; 130(t), City of Austin Environmental & Conservation Services; 131(br), Jerry L. Ferrara/Photo Researchers, Inc.; 132(b), Jeremy Walker/Tony Stone Images; 133(tr), Sam Dudgeon/HRW photo; 135(bl), Marianne Austin-McDermon; 135(cr), W. Campbell/Sygma; 136(tl), VU/R.F./Visuals Unlimited; 137(cr), Barbara Van Cleve/Tony Stone Images; 138(tl), Leo de Wys/Leo de Wys; 140(br), Warren Bolster/Tony Stone Images; 141(bl), Jeff Schultz/AlaskaStock Images; 142(tl), Frank S. Balthis; 147(cr), Sam Dudgeon/HRW photo; 148(tr), Sam Dudgeon/HRW photo; 148(br), Courtesy Elizabeth Philip; 149(b), Bill Meeks; 149(tc), Courtesy Elizabeth Philip

CHAPTER 6

Page 150(c), Ray Pfortner/Peter Arnold, Inc.; 150(cr), Kevin Schafer/Peter Arnold, Inc.; 150(b), Helena Kolda/HRW photo; 150(bc), Russell Dian/HRW photo; 150(tl), Werner H. Muller/Peter Arnold, Inc.; 150-151(Inset), Bill & Jan Moeller/The Stock Market; 151(br), Photri; 153(br), Ken Biggs/Tony Stone Images; 154(tc), Sam Dudgeon/HRW photo; 154(bl), Tony Freeman/PhotoEdit; 156(br), Ted Spieigel/Black Star; 157(br), David R. Frazier Photolibrary; 158(br), Christopher Pillitz/Matrix International; 159(Inset), Gianni Giansanti/Sygma; 160(tl), Michael Landes Images/HRW photo; 160(br), Jim Pickerell/Tony Stone Images; 160(bc), Thomas Ives/The Stock Market; 161(bl), Buddy Mays/Travel Stock/Hillstrom Stock Photos; 162(bl), Ted Spiegel/Black Star; 163(c), David R. Frazier Photolibrary; 163(bl), Bill Weedmark/Panographics; 163(tr), Argonne National Laboratory/U.S. Department of Energy; 164(t), Simon Fraser/SPL/Photo Researchers, Inc.; 169(tr), Sam Dudgeon/HRW photo; 170(cl), Steve Winter/Black Star; 170(bl), Fred Hirschmann/Tony Stone Images; 171(tr), Michelle Bridwell/Frontera Fotos; 171(bl), Spencer Grant/Photo Researchers, Inc.

CHAPTER 7

Page 173(b), 173(c), NASA; 176(bl), Doug Wilson/Westlight; 176(br), Robert Landau/Westlight; 179(t), Wallace Kleck/Terraphotographics; 179(t), Wallace Kleck/Terraphotographics; 180(b), Randall Hyman; 182(t), Hank Morgan/Photo Researchers, Inc.; 183, Dr. Jeffrey Kiehl/National Center for Atmospheric Research; 185(b), Victoria Smith/HRW photo; 185(t), David R. Frazier Photolibrary; 187(tl), (tr), NASA-Goddard Space Flight Center; 192(c), 193(c), Sam Dudgeon/HRW photo; 194(bl), 194(br), R. Sanders/Courtesy of Susan Solomon; 195(t), Courtesy of Susan Solomon; 195(b), Louis Psihoyos/Matrix International

CHAPTER 8

Page 196(bl), Steve Allen/Peter Arnold, Inc.; 196(c), Jim Wark/Peter Arnold, Inc.; 196(br), H.R. Bramaz/Peter Arnold, Inc.; 196(cr), Yoav Levy/HRW photo; 196(t), John Kieffer/Peter Arnold, Inc.; 197(br), L. Linkhart/Visuals Unlimited; 197(bl), Scott T. Smith; 198(b), Jeff Gnass; 199(), Yoav Levy/HRW photo; 200, Peter Gridley/FPG International; 201(br), Courtesy Maryland National Park and Planning Commission; 202(b), Chromosohm/Joe Sohm/Tony Stone; 203(tl), Dennie Cody/FPG International; 203(cr), Russell Dian/HRW photo; 204(b), Jon Gnass; 205(), Bruce Forster/Tony Stone Images; 207(Center Right), William Campbell/Time Magazine; 207(bl), Jason Laure'/Laure' Communications; 209(t), J. Alcock/Visuals Unlimited; 209(b), John D. Cunningham/Visuals Unlimited; 210(c),(b), (t), E.R. Degginger/Color-Pic, Inc.; 211(t), R. Caton/FPG International; 211(bc), Rob Badger; 212(t), P. Hickman/Visuals Unlimited; 213(b), Fernando Bueno/The Image Bank; 216(tl), Gary Moon/Tony Stone Images; 216(b), Rob Badger; 217(t), Appel Color Photography; 217(b), Rob Badger; 218(), Randa Bishop/Uniphoto Picture Agency; 223(br), Dennis Fagan/HRW photo; 223(bl), Sam Dudgeon/HRW photo; 223(cr), A. Sirdofsky/HRW photo; 223(tr), Bob Glaze/ArtStreet; 224(Left), Courtesy of Otis Butler; 224(Right), Sam Abell/National Geographic Society; 225(c), Courtesy of Otis Butler

CHAPTER 9

Page 226(tl), Kim Taylor/Bruce Coleman, Inc.; 226(cr), David R. Frazier Photolibrary; 226(c), Walter H. Hodge/Peter Arnold, Inc.; 226(t), Wyman Meinzer/Peter Arnold, Inc.; 226(tr), Gary J. James/Biological Photo Service; 226(tl), David R. Frazier Photolibrary; 226(b), Walter H. Hodge/Peter Arnold, Inc.; 226(tl), John Cancalosi/Peter Arnold, Inc.; 227(br), Robb Kendrick/Aurora; 228(bl), Alain Nogues/Sygma; 230(tr), Chris Bryant/Tony Stone Images; 230(br), Chris Rainier/J.B. Pictures; 232(tl), Bernard Pierre Wolf/Photo Researchers, Inc.; 232(br), David R. Frazier Photolibrary; 235(), Robert E. Ford/Terraphotographics; 236(tl), Larry Lefever/Grant Heilman Photography; 236(br), Doug Plummer/Photo Researchers, Inc.; 237(tl), Robert J. Bennett/Photri; 237(tr), Grant Heilman Photography; 237(br), David R. Frazier Photolibrary; 238(br), Mark E. Gibson; 239(tr), Courtesy Girl Guides Association of Victoria, Australia; 239(bl), David Cavagnaro/Peter Arnold, Inc.; 239(bc), Alan Bonicatti/Liaison International; 240(bc), William E. Ferguson; 240(tl), Robert Bornemann/Photo Researchers, Inc.; 240(c), William E. Ferguson; 240(tc), Tony Stone Images; 240(br), Andrew Henley/Biofotos; 240(all), Randall Hyman; 240(bl), Tony Stone Images; 241(b), John Zoiner; 242(br), Laurie Sparham Network/Matrix International; 242(tl), Runk Schoenberger/Grant Heilman Photography; 244(tl), Grant Heilman/Grant Heilman Photography; 244(br), Gary Ellis/Ellis Nature Photography; 249(tr), Sam Dudgeon/HRW photo; 250(cl), Jim Strawser/Grant Heilman Photography; 250(bl), Rob Badger; 250-251(bc), Patrick Robert/Sygma; 251(bl), Rob Badger; 251(tr), USDA/Science Source/Photo Researchers, Inc.; 251(tl), Sidney/Monkmeyer Press